Edith Watson Schipper gradu-ated from Carleton College in 1930 and received her Ph.D. degree in philosophy from Radcliffe College in 1937, following which she taught philosophy at Elmira Col-lege and at Carleton College, and assisted at the University of Mich-igan. During the war she was in São Paulo, Brazil, where she taught English at the União Cultural Brasil-Estados Unidos. Since 1947, she has taught philosophy at the

University of Miami, where she is now Associate Professor. Professor Schipper is the author of several articles for philoso-phical periodicals and from the time she began teaching at the University of Miami has worked on developing a logic text suitable for use for beginning students. After Professor Schuh joined the philosophy faculty, he collaborated on the book and this text is the result.

Edward Schuh received his B.A. and M.A. degrees at the University of Buffalo, and his Ph.D. at Har-vard University in 1953. From 1948 to 1950 he was an Instructor in English and a Teaching Fellow in Philosophy at Harvard Univer-sity. After a year as Visiting In-structor at The Ohio State Uni-versity, he moved in 1954 to his present position with the Philoso-phy Department at the University of Miami. Beside his teaching ac-tivities, Professor Schuh has published several articles and reviews in philosophy journals. He is a member of Phi Beta Kappa, the American Philosophical Association, the Southern Society for Philosophy and Psychology, the Florida Philo-sophical Association, and the American Association of Uni-versity Professors.

EDITH WATSON SCHIPPER
and EDWARD SCHUH

UNIVERSITY OF MIAMI

A FIRST COURSE IN

MODERN

LOGIC

A HOLT-DRYDEN BOOK

HENRY HOLT AND COMPANY, INC.

NEW YORK

Copyright © 1959, by
Henry Holt and Company, Inc.
Library of Congress Catalog Card Number 59-5890

27736-0119

Printed in the United States of America

PREFACE

Two pedagogical assumptions underlie the conception of this book. First, it is assumed that many of the basic principles and techniques of modern symbolic logic can be formulated in such a way as to be understood by college students on the freshman level. And second, it is believed that symbolic logic is no less "practical" for beginning students than is the logic of Aristotle, and that the newer techniques, since much more general and rigorous, are to be preferred to the traditional methods even in an elementary course.

There is a widespread belief among teachers of logic that a student is more likely to remember and apply the principles of Aristotelian logic than those of symbolic logic. The tools of symbolic logic are admitted by these teachers to be more fundamental and precise, but the symbolism, they say, is too abstract for underclassmen, and the methods are too technical to permit practical application in everyday situations.

Yet the somewhat depressing truth of the matter seems to be that the average student, upon completing his course in logic, will no more carry away the principles of Aristotle than he will the principles of Whitehead and Russell. The value of a course or two in logic appears to stem, not from the ability of a student deliberately to apply the techniques he has learned, but rather from the semester's *practice* he has had in analyzing propositions and arguments, in grappling with the complexities of language, and in becoming habituated to more rigorous, systematic ways of thinking. The rules of the syllogism will be forgotten as promptly as will Venn diagrams or Boolean expansions. But a semester's contact with cautious, precise analysis and reasoning is an experience the benefits of which, to a conscientious student, are of a much more lasting character.

Another advantage of introducing the beginning student to modern logic, and one which is commonly overlooked, is the opportunity that is thereby given him to become reacquainted under more favorable circumstances with the rigorous symbolism of formal science. Among college students in this country there is a widespread and perhaps (when we consider the present international situation) an alarming fear of mathematics, usually induced during early school years. This phobia, to be sure, may be remedied by a good course in mathematics itself. But the study of modern logic, which possesses the formal characteristics of mathematics and yet demands no prior knowledge of formal science, seems for this purpose to be of even greater therapeutic value.

The possibility remains, it is true, that a sound, unpopularized course in symbolic logic, like courses in quantum mechanics or differential equations, inherently belongs to the junior or senior level of instruction. Elementary symbolic logic, however, is a *beginning* course in its field. It no more requires previous work in Aristotelian logic than it does in mathematics. And to those who would still object that even the fundamentals of symbolic logic cannot be taught to lowerclassmen, the authors can only reply that the present text, in several earlier versions, has been used successfully by numerous instructors for almost ten years in a large freshman course at the University of Miami. The consensus of the many thousand freshmen and sophomores who have taken this course seems to be that it was by no means the easiest study they had undertaken, but that it was no more difficult than the average freshman course in mathematics.

Still, if logic is to be meaningful to the beginning student and not merely a symbolic game of some kind, he must be shown its practical application to everyday discourse. Accordingly, a systematic presentation of modern deductive logic has been sacrificed throughout this book in favor of an analysis of ordinary language and argumentation. And in line with this approach, an attempt has been made to present only those decision procedures the underlying principles of which can easily be understood by the beginning student. The reasoning behind such techniques as the inconsistent triad or the normal forms procedures, whatever their other merits, is difficult to explain, and therefore we preferred to present Venn diagrams, truth-tables, and other techniques the applicability of which is more readily seen.

A special attempt has been made in Part II, on propositional logic, to lead the student gradually from linguistic analysis to the more formal properties and techniques. The discussion of truth-tables, for this reason, has been postponed to the very end of Part II. These chapters may either be omitted altogether, or introduced any time after the notions of implication and disjunction have been presented.

Since the included material is probably too extensive to be completed in a single semester, the parts of the book have been written so as to be fairly independent of one another. Only Part III, the Logic of Propositional Functions, requires that another part, the Logic of Propositions, be studied first. The instructor will perhaps want either to omit Part I, on meaning and the informal fallacies, or to follow up the treatment of propositional logic by the functional or by the class logic. Also, Part IV, the Logic of Classes, has been presented in such a manner that it may precede a study of the propositional logic.

An effort has been made to include no more material in each chapter than can be covered in a single class session. And to each chapter has been appended a probably more than sufficient list of exercises. As an aid to the student who is not sure he is working these exercises correctly, a limited number of solutions, indicated in the text by an asterisk, has been furnished in the appendixes.

Perhaps a reason for omitting the usual treatment of scientific method should be submitted. Serious consideration was given to this possibility, but it was finally thought to be inadvisable. First, a substantial course in modern formal logic, even on an elementary level, appeared to require at least a full semester's work. Second, a little time spent in studying college bulletins revealed that in general only the smallest schools offered less than two semesters of logic, one of formal and the other of inductive logic. For the purposes of a separate course in scientific method, we decided that nothing could be incorporated into the confines of the present book that could compare in scope or effectiveness with the treatment of induction found in numerous recent texts devoted exclusively to that subject.

With respect to the actual writing of this text, Parts II and III on propositions and propositional functions, are the work of Edith Watson Schipper, while Parts I and IV, on meaning and classes, and the chapters on truth-tables, have been contributed by Edward Schuh.

If there is anything in the text that seems both new and useful, it may probably be attributed to the authors' teachers in logic: Professors E. V. Huntington, C. I. Lewis, H. Sheffer, M. Farber, W. V. O. Quine, and W. T. Parry. Various stages of the book have been read by Professor A. G. Ramsperger, whose searching criticisms and suggestions have been extremely helpful. Gratitude must also be expressed to members of the Department of Philosophy at Miami. Professor D. T. Howard helped generously with a previous text from which the present book grew, and he has continued to furnish encouragement and sound advice. Professor Gerrit Schipper has given unsparingly of his time, and has contributed substantially to the general viewpoint from which the text was written. Other members of the department have made valuable suggestions based on their classroom experience in using mimeographed and lithographed versions of the book.

E. W. S.
E. S.

Coral Gables, Florida
February, 1958

CONTENTS

PART I

THE LOGIC OF MEANING

1. Introduction   **3**

    1.1 A Preliminary Definition, *3*
    1.2 Subfields of Logic, *4*
    1.3 Logic and Related Fields, *5*
    1.4 The Utility of Logic, *6*

2. Semantics   **7**

    2.1 Functions of Language, *8*
    2.2 The Confusion of Linguistic Functions, *9*

3. Kinds of Meaning   **12**

    3.1 Propositional Meaning, *13*
    3.2 Extensional and Intensional Meaning, *14*
    3.3 Personal and Social Intension, *15*
    3.4 Law of Inverse Ratio of Extension-Intension, *16*

4. Kinds of Definition   **18**

    4.1 Ostensive Definition, *18*
    4.2 Synonymous Definition, *19*
    4.3 Nominal Definition, *19*
    4.4 Genetic Definition, *20*
    4.5 Aristotelian Definition, *21*
    4.6 Operational Definition, *22*

5. Fallacies of Definition   24

5.1 Incongruous Definition, *24*
5.2 Circular Definition, *25*
5.3 Negative Definition, *26*
5.4 Obscure or Figurative Definition, *27*
5.5 Extraneous Definition, *28*

6. Fallacies of Relevance   30

6.1 Appeal to Force, *31*
6.2 Appeal to Pity, *31*
6.3 Appeal to Ignorance, *32*
6.4 Appeal To or Against the Man, *33*
6.5 Appeal to the Crowd, *34*
6.6 False Cause, *35*
6.7 Irrelevant Conclusion, *36*

7. Fallacies of Authority   38

7.1 Sweeping Authority, *38*
7.2 Dogmatic Authority, *39*
7.3 Misplaced Authority, *42*
7.4 Misrepresented Authority, *44*
7.5 Venerable Authority, *45*
7.6 Fixed Authority, *46*
7.7 Converse Fallacies of Authority, *46*

8. Fallacies of Ambiguity   49

8.1 Simple Equivocation, *49*
8.2 Composition, *50*
8.3 Division, *51*
8.4 Accent, *51*
8.5 Amphiboly, *52*

9. Fallacies of Presumption   55

9.1 Complex Question, *55*
9.2 Disguised Conclusion, *56*
9.3 Question-Begging Definition, *56*
9.4 Circular Reasoning, *58*

PART II

THE LOGIC OF PROPOSITIONS

10. Valid Inferences and True Conclusions 67

10.1 The Logical Form of an Inference, 67
10.2 Valid Inferences, 69
10.3 True Conclusions, 70

11. Propositions: Negative and Conjunction 73

11.1 Symbolization of Propositions, 73
11.2 Negation of Propositions, 75
11.3 Law of Double Negation, 76
11.4 Conjunction of Propositions, 76
11.5 Commutative Law, 78

12. Implication 80

12.1 Implication, 80
12.2 Counterimplication, 83

13. Inferences Based on Implication 86

13.1 Inference and Implication, 86
13.2 Inferences Based on Implication, 87
13.3 Valid Inferences, 88
13.4 Invalid Inferences, 89

14. Implication-in-Reverse 94

14.1 Only If, 94
14.2 Equivalence, 95

15. Inferences Based on Implication-in-Reverse 97

15.1 Valid Inferences, 97
15.2 Invalid Inferences, 98

16. Disjunction 101

16.1 Weak Disjunction, 101
16.2 Strong Disjunction, 103

16.3 Commutative Law, *104*
16.4 The Negative of a Disjunction, *105*

17. Inferences Based on Disjunction   **107**

17.1 The Disjunctive Forms, *107*
17.2 Applications, *108*
17.3 Inferences Based on Strong Disjunction, *110*

18. Incompatibility   **113**

18.1 Negation of a Conjunction, *113*
18.2 Incompatibility, *114*

19. Inferences Based on Incompatibility   **118**

19.1 The Four Forms, *118*
19.2 Applications, *119*

20. The Equivalents of Implication   **123**

20.1 Counterimplicative Equivalent, *123*
20.2 The Disjunctive Equivalent, *123*
20.3 The Incompatibility Equivalent, *124*
20.4 The Table of Equivalents, *124*
20.5 Equivalences Between Forms of Valid Inference, *126*

21. More Inferences Based on Implications   **128**

21.1 Valid Inferences, *128*
21.2 Invalid Inferences, *130*

22. The Implicative Series   **133**

22.1 Transitivity of Implication, *133*
22.2 Valid Inferences, *134*
22.3 Invalid Inferences, *135*

23. Variations of the Implicative Series   **139**

23.1 Series Containing Disjunctions, *139*
23.2 Series Containing Incompatibilities, *139*
23.3 Invalid Inferences, *140*

24. Contradictories, Contraries, and Subcontraries 143

24.1 Contradictories, *143*
24.2 Contraries, *144*
24.3 Subcontraries, *145*

25. The Dilemma 148

25.1 The Four Forms, *148*
25.2 Constructive Dilemmas, *149*
25.3 Destructive Dilemmas, *150*
25.4 Dilemmas with False Conclusions, *151*
25.5 The Dilemma as a Form of the Implicative Series, *152*

26. Telescoped Inferences 155

26.1 The Missing Premise, *155*
26.2 Other Telescoped Inferences, *157*

27. Truth-Table Definitions 160

27.1 Negation, *160*
27.2 Conjunction, *161*
27.3 Disjunction, *162*
27.4 Implication, *162*
27.5 Equivalence, *165*

28. Truth-Table Method 168

28.1 Testing for Validity, *168*
28.2 Testing for Invalidity, *170*
28.3 Testing for Equivalence, *171*
28.4 Testing Inferences Containing *n* Propositions, *171*
28.5 Testing for Consistency, *172*

29. Shorter Truth-Table Method 176

29.1 Invalid Inferences, *177*
29.2 Valid Inferences, *180*
29.3 Inferences Containing Compound Conclusions, *181*
29.4 Limitations of the Shorter Method, *182*

30. Review 184

PART III

THE LOGIC OF PROPOSITIONAL FUNCTIONS

31. Quantified Propositions   197

31.1 The Generality of Propositions, *197*
31.2 The Term Variable, *198*
31.3 Propositional Functions, *199*
31.4 Universal Propositions, *200*
31.5 Particular Propositions, *201*
31.6 Singular Propositions, *202*

32. Other Wordings of Quantified Propositions   204

32.1 Universal Propositions, *204*
32.2 Particular Propositions, *205*
32.3 Singular Propositions, *206*

33. Other Relations Within Quantified Propositions 208

33.1 "Only" Propositions, *208*
33.2 Disjunctive and Incompatible Propositions, *209*
33.3 Particular Propositions, *210*

34. Contradictories of Quantified Propositions   212

34.1 Contradictories of Universal Propositions, *212*
34.2 Contradictories of Particular Propositions, *214*
34.3 Contradictories of Singular Propositions, *214*

35. Inferences Containing Existential Propositions   217

35.1 An Application of a Universal Proposition
to a Special Instance, *217*
35.2 A Form for Valid Inferences, *218*
35.3 Invalid Inferences, *219*

36. Other Inferences Containing Existential Propositions   224

36.1 Another Qualification, *224*
36.2 Invalid Inferences, *226*

37. Inferences Composed of Universal Propositions 229

37.1 Valid Inferences, *229*
37.2 Invalid Inferences, *230*

38. Other Inferences 234

38.1 Inferences Based on Implication-in-Reverse, *234*
38.2 Inferences Based on Disjunction, *235*
38.3 Inferences Based on Incompatibility, *235*

39. Telescoped Inferences 238

39.1 The Missing Generalization, *238*
39.2 Telescoped Inferences with
Universal Conclusions, *240*

40. Review 243

PART IV

LOGIC OF CLASSES

41. Symbolization of Classes 255

41.1 Class Variables, *256*
41.2 Class Abbreviations, *256*
41.3 Singular Variables and Abbreviations, *257*
41.4 Complementary Classes, *257*

42. Class Products and Sums 259

42.1 Class Products, *259*
42.2 Class Sums, *262*

43. Class Propositions 265

43.1 Class Identity, *265*
43.2 Class Nonidentity, *266*
43.3 Singular Membership, *268*

44. The Universe Class and the Null Class   270

44.1 The Universe Class, *270*
44.2 The Null Class, *273*
44.3 Interchangeability of Null and
Universe Classes, *274*

45. Some Elementary Laws   276

45.1 Validity and Truth, *276*
45.2 Laws of the Class Logic, *277*
45.3 Law of Double Negation, *278*
45.4 Laws of Commutation, *278*
45.5 Laws of Association, *279*
45.6 DeMorgan's Laws, *279*
45.7 Laws of Distribution, *280*
45.8 Rule of Replacement, *280*

46. Classification of Propositions   282

46.1 Complexity: Simple, Compound,
and Conjunctive Propositions, *282*
46.2 Quantity: Universal, Particular,
and Singular Propositions, *283*
46.3 Quality: Affirmative and
Negative Propositions, *284*

47. Universal Propositions   286

47.1 Universal Affirmative Propositions, *286*
47.2 Universal Negative Propositions, *288*
47.3 Exclusive Propositions, *289*

48. Particular and Singular Propositions   292

48.1 Particular Affirmative Propositions, *292*
48.2 Particular Negative Propositions, *294*
48.3 Singular Propositions, *295*

49. Pure Conjunctive Propositions   298

49.1 Conjunctive Particular Propositions, *298*
49.2 Coextensive-Class Propositions, *300*
49.3 Exceptive Propositions, *301*

50. Mixed Conjunctive Propositions   304

50.1 Existential Affirmative Propositions, *304*
50.2 Existential Negative Propositions, *306*
50.3 Summary Classification of Propositions, *307*

51. Inference in General   310

51.1 Symbolization of Inferences, *310*
51.2 Reciprocal Inference: Equivalence, *311*
51.3 Diagrammatic Test of an Inference, *312*
51.4 Detecting the Form of an Inference, *314*

52. Simple Inferences Based on Double Negation   316

52.1 Obversion of Universal Propositions, *316*
52.2 Obversion of Particular Propositions, *317*
52.3 Obversion of Singular Propositions, *318*

53. Simple Inferences Based on Commutation   320

53.1 Conversion, *320*
53.2 Contraposition, *321*

54. Inferences Based on Opposition   323

54.1 Contradiction, *324*
54.2 Contrariety, *326*
54.3 Subcontraiety, *327*
54.4 Subalternation, *328*

55. Pure Compound Inferences   331

55.1 Valid Inferences, *332*
55.2 Invalid Inferences, *335*

56. Mixed Compound Inferences   337

56.1 Inferences Containing
Singular Propositions, *337*
56.2 Inferences Containing
Particular Propositions, *340*

57. Pure Telescoped Inferences   344

57.1 Telescoped Inferences in General, *344*
57.2 Requirements of a Suppressed Premise, *345*
57.3 Diagrammatic Discovery of
a Suppressed Premise, *346*
57.4 Invalid Telescoped Inferences, *348*

58. Mixed Telescoped Inferences   350

58.1 Pure and Mixed Telescoped Inferences, *350*
58.2 Telescoped Inferences With
Particular Conclusions, *350*
58.3 Telescoped Inferences With
Singular Conclusions, *353*

59. The Symbolic Expansion Test   356

59.1 Pure Inferences, *356*
59.2 Mixed Inferences, *359*

60. The Shorter Symbolic Expansion Test   361

60.1 Pure Inferences, *362*
60.2 Mixed Inferences, *363*

61. A Look Ahead   368

APPENDIXES

A. Summary of Basic Laws and Inferences, *375*
B. Answers to Selected Exercises, *379*
Index, *391*

PART I

THE LOGIC OF MEANING

1 INTRODUCTION

The least one might reasonably expect of a logic textbook is that it be presented in a logical manner. This text, therefore, ought to begin with a definition of the term "logic." However, it happens that few definitions of "logic" are as easily and widely understood as the term itself. Every beginning student in logic has for years applied many of the principles of logic in his daily activities, has learned to know when his friends are being logical and when illogical, and has learned to detect numerous elementary errors in logic.

Still, before plunging into the subject, some attempt should be made to explain "logic," as that term is used by professional logicians. A simple definition will therefore be offered and expanded upon in this chapter, with the warning that a truly precise definition cannot be formulated until a systematic study is made of the subject matter itself.

1.1 A Preliminary Definition

Logic, in its traditional sense, is the *science of reasoning*. The logician is concerned primarily with a classification and evaluation of the *rational* ways in which men seek to establish their assertions. Some of these ways are sound and some are unsound. But all must be rational, in the sense that they must involve an attempt to produce *reasons* for what is asserted.

The reasons we offer in support of an assertion are called *premises* by the logician, while the assertion being proved is known as a *conclusion*. When taken together as a unit, premises and conclusion make up an *inference* or (if we are careful not to confuse the logician's usage with the more common meaning of the term) an *argument*. Our definition may be refined somewhat, therefore, by considering logic as the field in which we carefully and systematically examine methods of inference or the ways in which men have attempted to solve problems by arguing from premises to conclusions.

As a systematic science, logic probably begins in the 4th century B.C. with the Greek philosopher, Aristotle. But even before the time of Aristotle, some of the elementary forms of reasoning were being investigated. Through the centuries following, logic has continued to occupy a prominent place among the intellectual disciplines. During the Middle Ages, especially, logic was considered the university study *par excellence*— so much so, that "logic-chopping," or an over emphasis upon and delight in formal logical manipulation, became an object of ridicule for later ages.

1.2 Subfields of Logic

The subject matter of logic is now often organized into three subfields: induction, deduction, and semantics. The purpose of reasoning, first, may be to draw generalized assertions from observations of particular events, thereby permitting us to explain, control, or predict such events. This kind of reasoning or inference is called *inductive,* and its systematic study is known as *inductive logic* or *scientific methodology*. Among the topics falling under inductive logic are methods of collecting data (premises), experimentation, sampling, statistical procedures, and in general, the evaluation and verification of hypotheses.

Induction, however, is a highly complex study and therefore is better postponed to a later course in logic. The present book, as an introductory text, will concern itself mainly with *deductive* or *formal logic*. This is not to say that deductive reasoning is divorced from induction. On the contrary, deduction is inextricably bound up with induction, and it is thoroughly misleading to maintain, as is often done, that the two are opposite modes of inference. The essential difference between them is *not* that induction is reasoning from particulars to generals and deduction is reasoning from generals to particulars, but that induction is *probable* reasoning based on sense-observation of factual phenomena, while deduction is *necessary* reasoning based upon the *meaning* of the language involved. However, this difference between induction and deduction will probably not be grasped fully by the student until some of the specific methods of deductive reasoning are examined in Parts Two, Three, or Four of this textbook.

If deductive reasoning depends upon the meanings of the words involved, it becomes necessary for the student of logic to investigate the structure and functioning of language. Such investigation has been conducted by logicians ever since Aristotle and even before, although, under the title of *semantics,* the study of meaning has been pushed with particular vigor during recent decades. Part One of the present text will deal with some elementary semantical matters: the functions of language, modes of meaning, definition, and a classification of informal fallacies, that is, errors in reasoning due, not to the form of an argument, but to the ambiguities and other misleading features of language.

1.3 Logic and Related Fields

Logic must be carefully distinguished from three closely related disciplines: psychology, rhetoric, and mathematics. *Psychology* is concerned, in part, with the study of thinking or cognition. And of course reasoning is a type of thinking. However, the psychologist is interested in thinking as an empirical or factual phenomenon, whereas the logician seeks to establish the norms or standards of sound thinking. In short, the difference between the psychology and logic of thinking is simply this: psychology describes how people do think, while logic establishes how people *ought* to think.

A distinction must also be made between logic and *rhetoric.* There is a superficial likeness between the two studies in that both are concerned with the form of arguments and proofs. But the rhetorician studies ways in which arguments may be presented most convincingly, while the logician inquires into the actual validity of arguments. A study of rhetoric will enable one to argue more plausibly. And although the same ability might perhaps be gained from studying logic, it is merely a by-product of such learning.

Rather, the study of logic is designed primarily to teach one how to follow up the implications of his ideas or to arrive at a reasonable solution of his problems, no matter how distasteful or unconvincing these implications or solutions might seem.

The distinction between logic and *mathematics* is not so easily drawn. Since the turn of the century, it has been discovered that mathematics may be taken either as following from logic, or as a subfield of logic. Alfred North Whitehead and Bertrand Russell, in an epoch-making book, the *Principia Mathematica,* demonstrated that logic and mathematics together constitute the body of formal or nonempirical science, and that mathematics, with the addition of a few assumptions, may be deduced from logic. In view of this close relationship, it is probably best to distinguish between the two fields simply by calling mathematics the science of *quantitative* reasoning, and logic the science, for the most part, of nonquantitative reasoning. The boundary line, however, between the two studies is so indefinite that the student should understand that, while mathematics presupposes logic, the reverse does not hold true. The study of logic requires no mathematical background whatsoever.

1.4 The Utility of Logic

One is perfectly justified, before embarking upon a study such as this, in asking: What is the use of learning logic? A facetious answer might be that one is better enabled thereby to outargue his fellow students or wife, or that a command of logical principles will permit one to raise his score (spuriously, of course) on an I.Q. test. And these answers illustrate the more general and serious use of logic: that it helps one to think a little more clearly and accurately.

Logic, needless to say, is no cure-all for muddled thinking. The most a student of logic can hope to gain from a semester's work in the field is a more systematic and cautious approach to language and to the problems with which he is everywhere confronted. It must indeed be admitted that the ordinary student, after his final examination in logic, manages with amazing dispatch to forget almost every one of the technical principles and methods he has so laboriously learned. This, however, is not so unfortunate as it might seem. For the experience of students over many centuries has demonstrated that the *habits* of clearer, more rigorous thinking are not so easily dismissed and are such that they continue to operate long after the technicalities of logic are forgotten.

2 SEMANTICS

As early as the fifth century B.C., the Greek thinker, Socrates, spent a lifetime in wrestling with problems of language. In the process of examining meanings and implications of important but highly abstract words—justice, piety, truth, beauty, goodness—he (or his disciple, Plato) found it necessary to formulate a theory of the meaning and function of language. This theory may be considered one of the first in a long history of systematic treatments of semantics.

It was not until the present century, however, that semanticists began to apply empirical techniques and the apparatus of modern symbolic logic to problems of meaning. Only then did investigators become fully aware of the enormous complexity of language, and of its profound influence on men's thinking and behavior. We may now truthfully say that the use and misuse of language has been a fundamental factor in the shaping of human history.

So much progress has been made recently in semantical inquiry, that by now a beginning student in the field is confronted by a formidable—one is tempted to say a fearsome—body of technical knowledge. To be sure, attempts have been made to popularize the problems of semantics. Under the title, especially, of "general semantics," some fairly nontechnical literature has been produced. Such attempts, however, are subject to the failings of any popularization of a highly complex subject: those of oversimplification and often of melodramatic distortion. Indeed, there are semanticists who feel that the popularity of general semantics stems mainly from its appeal to persons who are fond of using a scientific sounding jargon, but who are unwilling to undertake the strenuous and exacting study required to master a true science.

In any event, the bristling technicalities of logical semantics render impossible a systematic treatment of the field in an elementary logic text. We must content ourselves here with examining a few of the more important and relevant semantical distinctions and drawing some consequences pertinent to clear thinking.

2.1 Functions of Language

It is important to observe, first, that language is used for several different purposes. Three functions of language are especially worthy of note: (i) its *directive* function, in virtue of which we command or exhort or suggest that something be done or believed; (ii) its *emotive* function, in which we express our feelings or attitudes; and (iii) its *descriptive* function, by which we communicate beliefs or opinions or even falsehoods about the world.

At first glance, it may seem that the directive, emotive, and descriptive functions of language might be identified with the three modes of sentences we were all forced to learn in elementary school: imperative, exclamatory, and declarative sentences. This identification cannot be made, however, because one sentence will often *function* in two or three different ways at the same time. For example the imperative sentence, "Open the window," can function directively, as a command to perform the operation in question. And at the same time, it may function expressively, as when a person evinces his discomfort in an overheated room, or when he expresses idiomatically his disdain of the utterances of an intimate friend. The same imperative sentence may even function descriptively in the sense that a command to open the window might be intended in part to inform another that the window now is closed, or that fresh air is required.

Similar considerations apply to exclamatory and declarative sentences. The latter, especially, are commonly found to serve more than merely a descriptive function. The declarative sentence, "It's hot in here," for example, describes the temperature, expresses one's discomfort, and suggests that something ought to be done about it. Again, the declarative sentence: "We are in a state of cold war," describes an international condition, but it might also evince the speaker's patriotism and exhort his listeners to stop complaining about their federal tax burden.

2.2 The Confusion of Linguistic Functions

In examining the functions of language, then, we have already encountered one of the factors which render semantics so complicated a discipline. The same sentence may be used in a single assertion to serve two or three purposes at the same time. The grammatical mode of the sentence is not at all a clear indication of its purpose or function.

As a result, language, unless used very carefully, becomes a ready vehicle for all sorts of bad communication and muddled thinking. For example, a declarative sentence, used ostensibly in its descriptive function, may be intended also by the speaker to express an emotion, and may be interpreted by a listener as functioning directively. A young man might innocently remark to his girl: "You know, I really would like to get married," intending not only to *describe* his feelings in the matter, but also to *express* his disinclination at present to take so drastic a step. And if the girl interprets this naive young man's remark as an exhortation—that is, *directively*—one can only shudder at the consequences.

Of particular importance to the person intent upon thinking clearly, is the possibility of confusion between the descriptive and emotive functions of language. This confusion is the cause of much that is disreputable about propaganda. It is easy for the skillful propagandist to describe truthfully a given state of affairs, and still, by a clever use of emotionally charged language, to sway almost at will the attitudes of audience or reader. The shifting back and forth of this country's attitude toward Finland during World War II will perhaps become a classic example of the power of clever propaganda. And people now are painfully beginning to realize that, during time of war, our heroic bomber crews blaze their way through swarms of fanatical enemy fighter pilots to drop their bomb loads unerringly on a military target, while the sadistic enemy sends its vulture-like bombers over helpless, culture-laden cities—descriptions of the same general situation, but designed to express and arouse decidely different emotions.

This is not to say that the emotive function of language is misleading and therefore to be avoided. The poet, for example, is usually more concerned with expression than with description. To eliminate the emotive function of poetic language (if that were possible) would be to lose some of the most sensitive and treasured expressions of the human spirit. And even in areas where descriptive language would appear to be of prime importance, such as the giving of information during time of war, it seems clearly, though unfortunately, true that no modern nation can be aroused to a sufficiently feverish wartime pitch without the use of emotionally distorted propaganda.

Even if we grant (as some intelligent people refuse to do) that information must sometimes be communicated in an emotively misleading fashion, it still is essential that we learn to distinguish between expression and real information. Even during time of war, at least some individuals—generals, diplomats, intelligence personnel, and so on—must remain calm and unbiased enough to sort out neutral information from superadded expression. And for the rest of us, when confronted by situations demanding clear thinking, an awareness of the difference between descriptive and emotive language will often permit us to arrive individually at reasonable beliefs, attitudes, and decisions, instead of being herded from one belief to another by self-appointed shepherds of public opinion.

This means that when we are interested in acquiring facts rather than in giving vent to our emotions, we must learn to discount automatically everything but sheer information. When we read that Tusk-white toothpaste is guaranteed to kill mouth bacteria, stop tooth decay, strengthen gums, correct vitamin C deficiency, and make food taste better, we must infer only that Tusk-white will clean our teeth probably as well as most other dentifrices on the market. When a candidate for political office accuses his rival of a despicable violation of the sacred trust placed in him by honest American citizens, we must take his accusation, in the absence of anything more concrete, to mean that he is not particularly fond of the rival politician, and prefers to win the election himself. When a newspaper columnist mentions a union gang leaders' meeting in Detroit for the purpose of devising new schemes to enrich them-selves and debase the American way of life, we are actually informed only of a union meeting in Detroit and of the columnist's aversion to organized labor.

EXERCISES

A. Identify the ostensible or most obvious function of each of the following sentences:

1. Women are all frivolous.
2. Russia is our implacable enemy.
3. Take a letter.
4. All the aims and principles of our country's founders have crystallized in the Republican Party.
5. Why don't you sit down?
6. Capital is built upon the exploitation of labor.
7. This is one of the best movies I've ever seen.
8. Vote for Senator Smith.

B. Show how each of the above sentences may be interpreted as serving more than one function. Rephrase the sentences to make apparent these other functions.

C. The following two passages consist of the closing lines of Plato's *Republic* and of the *Communist Manifesto*. Rewrite each passage, eliminating as much as possible the directive and expressive functions, and retaining only the informative content:

"And thus, Glaucon, . . . we shall pass safely over the river of Forgetfulness and our soul will not be defiled. Wherefore my counsel is that we hold fast ever to the heavenly way and follow after justice and virtue always, considering that the soul is immortal and able to endure every sort of good and every sort of evil. Thus, we shall live dear to one another and to the gods, both while remaining here and when, like conquerors in the games who go around to gather gifts, we receive our reward. And it shall be well with us both in this life and in the pilgrimage of a thousand years which we have been describing."

"The Communists disdain to conceal their views and aims. They openly declare that their ends can be attained only by the forcible overthrow of all existing social conditions. Let the ruling classes tremble at a Communistic revolution. The proletarians have nothing to lose but their chains. They have a world to win.

"Working men of all countries, unite!"

3 KINDS OF MEANING

In examining some of the basic functions of language, we have already come to grips with the central problem of semantics: the problem of meaning. Each of the three lingustic functions we have discussed may be interpreted as a kind of meaning. For example, the meaning or significance of a sentence in its directive function is its directive or imperative meaning.

Logicians, however, until the present century, were concerned almost entirely with language in its descriptive function. And since this is the function used for reasoning, at least in the ordinary sense, let us turn to a closer examination of descriptive meaning.

3.1 Propositional Meaning

The meaning of a sentence in its descriptive function may be called a *proposition*. We must be careful not to confuse a proposition with the sentence of which it is the meaning. The sentence itself is only a series of written characters or spoken sounds. But a proposition is the descriptive meaning or information conveyed by this series of characters or sounds.

That a sentence is different from the proposition it asserts may easily be seen when we consider that the sentences: "I am studying logic," and "J'étudie la logique," and "Ich studiere Logik," all assert the same proposition. Again, when we say: "It is quarter of nine," or "It is fifteen minutes before nine," or "It is eight forty-five o'clock," we use different sentences but assert once more the same proposition.

It will further be observed that a proposition is always characterized by its truth or falsity. The descriptive sentences: "I am studying logic," "I went to the movies last night," "I am going to a dance tomorrow night," are all statements which are true or false. Sentences, on the other hand, such as: "Come to the movies with me," or "Oh! what a beautiful girl!" have mainly directive or emotive meaning, and cannot be considered true or false—cannot, that is, unless descriptive meaning is read into them, thereby interpreting them, for example, as: "You will enjoy yourself if you come to the movies with me," or "There goes what I take to be a beautiful girl."

In this introductory treatment of logic, we will be concerned mainly with sentences only insofar as they convey descriptive meaning, that is, insofar as they assert propositions. The validity of arguments or inferences, we shall find, will depend upon the relationship holding between those two types of proposition we have called premise and conclusion. And the ability to recognize the same proposition when expressed by different sentences, thereby enabling us to determine whether a conclusion does or does not follow from its premises, will prove one of the most difficult but important accomplishments in the study of logic.

3.2 Extensional and Intensional Meaning

Not only are arguments composed of propositions, but sentences asserting propositions may themselves be broken down into words or, as we shall call them, *terms*. As components of propositions, terms by definition have only descriptive meaning. However, it is rather difficult to find terms, as they appear in specific sentences, that have emotively neutral meaning. The terms: "attorney," "lawyer," and "shyster," all have broadly the same descriptive meaning. But even the apparently neutral term, "lawyer," when used in ordinary contexts, will carry with it either a little of the comfortable, professional sound of "attorney," or the greedy, dishonorable tone of "shyster," or perhaps both emotive distortions at the same time.

Logic, we said, has traditionally been concerned with only the descriptive meaning of sentences. Similarly in the case of terms, we will be interested only in their descriptive, informational function. Once more, however, it becomes necessary for us to be on the alert that we are not misled by the emotive or directive overtones of terms. Clear thinking about factual problems requires knowledge of what actually is the case, not what some informant feels or wants done about it.

In dealing with terms, a further distinction must be made between two kinds of descriptive meaning. There are other kinds, but they will not concern us here. The two kinds of meaning we need to know are called *extensional* and *intensional meaning*. The *extension* of a term, sometimes referred to as *denotation,* is its semantical property of designating or pointing out some object or event or class of objects or events. For example, the extension of the term "lawyer" is the class of all persons who have a law degree or who practice before the bar. The singular term, "Abraham Lincoln," has for its extension an individual lawyer from Illinois who became the sixteenth President of the United States. What the term "lawyer" *means,* in one sense of "meaning," is all actual members of a specified professional group. And what the term "Abraham Lincoln" *means* is one specified member of that group.

Intensional or *connotative* meaning, on the other hand, refers to the qualities or properties that serve to distinguish the extension of a term from anything else. The intension or connotation of "lawyer" is: "person permitted to plead cases in court," or "graduate of a recognized law school." Intension therefore is basically different from extension. "Lawyer" denotes (has for its extension) the body of presently or formerly or prospectively existent lawyers, while the same term connotes (has for its intension) those qualities or characteristics of lawyers which serve to distinguish them from doctors, dentists, bricklayers, and so on.

3.3 Personal and Social Intension

The intension of a term, of course, varies according to the person using it. For instance, the term "communist," when used by Americans nowadays, seems to connote a multitude of different things, all the way from "dialectical materialist" to "somebody I don't like." Nevertheless we manage for the most part to communicate meanings, and hence must distinguish two types of intension: *personal intension,* or the connotation of a term as used by a given individual, and *social intension,* or the meaning of a term common to a group of people, in virtue of which they are able to communicate among themselves.

Personal intension may be more or less specific than social intension, since individuals use language with greater or less precision. However (as disheartening as it sometimes appears to those who have laboriously acquired an extensive and precise command of the language), the *utility* of a person's vocabulary depends upon how closely the personal intension of his language approximates the social intension of language as used by friends, associates, writers, and others with whom he comes in contact. The practical confession story writer or local politician will carefully avoid becoming involved in any of the perennial "improve-your-vocabulary" plans.

3.4 Law of Inverse Ratio of Extension-Intension

Our understanding of the difference between extensional and intensional meaning will be augmented by an examination of the so-called "law of inverse ratio" holding between these two types of meaning. This law states that as the intension of a term increases, the extension decreases, and vice versa. For example, as we increase the intension of "lawyer," say by adding the specification "criminal," we decrease the extension, since there are, of course, fewer criminal lawyers than lawyers in general. If we increase the intension still further, for instance by speaking of "*good* criminal lawyers," we further decrease the extension. On the other hand, if we *decrease* the intension of "lawyer," that is, make it less specific, by referring only to a "professional man," the extension of the term obviously increases.

But the term "law" seems a little too honorific for the inverse ratio we are discussing. For one, the ratio is clearly not quantitative or mathematical. And secondly, the alleged ratio sometimes appears not to hold, as when, for example, we increase the intension of "lawyer" to "trained lawyer." All we can safely say is that, in general, it does seem that an increase of intension is accompained by a decrease, more or less, of extension, and *vice versa*.

Broadly speaking, then, the more specific we become about the connotation of a term, the more narrow or delimited is the class of things denoted by that term. This suggests that a statement of the intension of a word might be interpreted as a *definition*. For if we state what distinguishes the meaning of a given term from that of any other term, we are in effect defining the term in question. Let us follow up this suggestion by examining, in the next chapter, the very important notion of definition.

EXERCISES

A. Which of the following sentences assert the same proposition?

1. No social climbers are genuine.
2. All social climbers are phonies.
3. Persons wishing to enter polite society are to be commended.
4. I detest social climbers.
5. Anyone who is conscious of his own worth will refrain from attempting to enter polite society.
6. The idea of striving to find a place in the social register is repugnant to me.
7. Were it not for social climbers, high society would lose its rightful prestige.

B. Arrange each of the following sets of terms according to *increasing intension,* noting what happens to the degree of extension:

1. automobile, Buick sedan, motor vehicle, General Motors automobile, means of transportation, Buick, green Buick sedan.
2. white shirt, garment, new white dress shirt, new white dress shirt size 16–33, man's garment, shirt, white dress shirt.
3. natural science, mechanics of liquids, physical science, physics, science, mechanics.
4. red, secondary quality, color, crimson, property.
5. mammal, organism, man, animal, primate, vertebrate.

4 KINDS OF DEFINITION

A statement of the intension or connotation of a term, as we have seen, can be considered a definition of that term. However, not all kinds of definition are intensional. And even when a definition is intensional, it may vary according to the function it is supposed to serve. *All* definitions are designed in some way to explain the meanings of terms. But this purpose may be fulfilled in a number of different ways. When, in the middle of a discussion, one is asked that popular (or unpopular) question: "What exactly do you mean?" or "Would you mind defining your terms?" an answer does not always eliminate vagueness or ambiguity of expression. For the counterquestion must often be asked: "What *kind* of definition do you want?"

That being true, some of the more important kinds of definition, distinguished according to the function or purpose each serves, must now be examined.

4.1 Ostensive Definition

The only truly *extensional* definition consists in literally pointing out or indicating in some other behavioral way the extension of the term being defined. An ostensive definition, as it is called, of a proper name, say "the Empire State Building," is given by actually pointing at the building (if one is in New York City) or otherwise by showing a photograph of it. An optimistic father points at his chest and repeats to his six-month-old son: "Da-da!" Or, if the term being defined is a general or abstract term, for example "skyscraper" or "father" or "blue," it is defined ostensively by pointing out one or more members of the appropriate class, or illustrations of the property or abstraction in question.

While ostensive definitions in many situations are very convenient and even necessary, as will be attested by any person who has traveled much in foreign countries, still such definitions have an obvious shortcoming. A father's faith in his baby's scholarly stature is likely to waver momentarily when the infant begins using "da-da" to indicate neckties, sport shirts, pajama tops, buttons, chests, or men in general.

4.2 Synonymous Definition

As its name indicates, a synonymous definition is composed of a term or terms with the same meaning as the term being defined. One may define "bug" as an "insect," or "book" as a "tome," or "bed" as a "couch." This type of definition is often quite useful, for example in pocket dictionaries, where space is at a premium, or in foreign language dictionaries, or when defining a rare word by a synonym that is more common.

However, for the many other occasions requiring a definition, the synonymous definition has a serious drawback. Rather than explaining the nature of that which is designated by a term, or explaining its usage, the synonymous definition substitutes another word or words, the meaning of which is supposed to be clearer. But very few words, perhaps no words, have exactly the same meaning in any well-developed modern language. We study about "insects," but we use a spray-gun on "bugs." The same person who delights in reading a "book" will religiously avoid contact with a "tome." And a "bed," to most people, is something to sleep on at night, while a "couch" is something on which to steal an afternoon's nap.

4.3 Nominal Definition

This is sometimes called a "stipulative" definition, because it stipulates what the meaning of an as-yet-undefined term is to be. When a scientist, for instance, discovers a new phenomenon or makes a new distinction, or wishes to abbreviate a cumbersome expression, he must use a new word or symbol, or else redefine an old word or symbol. And for this new term, or old term with a new meaning, he will offer a nominal definition.

To illustrate a nominal definition, we might anticipate a notion to be dealt with at length in the second part of this book—the notion of "material implication." This expression was first used in 1910 by Bertrand Russell who, in attempting to treat systematically statements of the general type: "If a proposition p is true, then another proposition q is true," found that he had to specify a kind of implication never before explicitly distinguished by logicians. He thereupon coined the term "material implication," abbreviated it by a reclining horseshoe symbol ($p \supset q$), and nominally defined it as meaning: "It is false that the proposition p is true and the proposition q is false."

In the interest of good communication, one should be very careful in the use of nominal definitions. It must be admitted, of course, that so long as a person clearly indicates his usage, he may define any term whatsoever in any way he chooses. If someone tells us he is nominally defining the term "red" as meaning blue, and if we remain alert to his odd usage, we will still be able to understand everything he says about colors. But nominal redefinitions of already established terms are clearly not conducive to making oneself understood. And communication, after all, is the ruling purpose of language. It follows that nominal definitions ordinarily ought not to be used unless a situation demands that new words or symbols be invented and therefore defined.

4.4 Genetic Definition

Sometimes a term is best defined by giving the *origin* or *development* of whatever is designated by the term, that is, by using a genetic definition. The historian is particularly concerned with genetic definitions, since he wants to know the origins and historical development of nations, dynasties, wars, institutions, and so on. And when a child asks the meaning of "lumber," or a student the meaning of "Relativity Theory," he also wishes to learn, in part, about the origins of lumber in the forest and activities of the lumberjack, or the development of Relativity Theory through Einstein's modification of Newtonian physics.

Once more, however, there is a pitfall in the incautious use of this kind of definition. For something may easily be "explained away" by assuming that its origin and development constitute its entire nature. Ordinarily there is more to the extension of a term than its history, and therefore it is fallacious to suppose that something is entirely explained by a genetic definition. So widespread has this fallacy been, however, that it has been given a name by logicians and philosophers: the *genetic fallacy*.

It is not required of a good definition, to be sure, that it exhaust the significance of the term being defined. Different kinds of definition serve different purposes, and even if we brought them all together in an attempt to define a given term as comprehensively as possible, we still would not have stated everything that is connoted by that term.

Nevertheless it is well to remember that a genetic definition, especially, is an explication of only one aspect of a term's meaning. To neglect this is to commit the genetic fallacy. Sometimes the consequences of such neglect are quite tragic, as when all sorts of otherwise intelligent people during the latter half of the last century interpreted Darwin's evolutionary theory as a complete, rather than a genetic, definition of "man," forgetting that proof of man's animal origins does not necessarily threaten the significance of his present-day stature or his aspirations and ideals.

4.5 Aristotelian Definition

The type of definition originally formulated by Aristotle is still the appropriate definition for most ordinary situations, and is the kind of definition generally used in good dictionaries. It consists in giving the subsuming class or *genus* of a term, along with the *distinguishing characteristics* of that which is designated. In other words, an Aristotelian definition includes both the class or group of things in which the extension of a term is contained, and the characteristics or properties which distinguish that extension from any other within the given class.

A "father," defined in this manner, is a "male parent"—"parent" being the genus or encompassing class in which fathers are contained, and "male" the characteristic or attribute that distinguishes fathers from other members of the genus, namely, mothers. In like manner, a "book" is a printed and bound means of communication, a "chair" is a piece of furniture used for sitting, "fear" is a type of animal emotion characterized by withdrawal or aggressive behavior and certain concomitant physiological manifestations, and "yellow" is a color the wavelength of which lies between 0.55 and 0.59 microns.

There are a number of ways in which Aristotelian definition can be abused. However, since this type of definition is so common and useful in ordinary discourse, a discussion of its peculiar fallacies will be given a separate treatment in the following chapter.

4.6 Operational Definition

Probably the most precise kind of definition one can formulate consists in a list of the operations or experiments that should be performed if one is to know that he is using the term correctly. The operational definition of a term designating a chemical substance is expressed by a description of the tests one must perform in order to determine whether or not the term is applicable to the substance in question. The zoological term "amoeba" is defined operationally by a list of the microscopic observations that should be made and verified if one is to apply that term to the proper organism.

Operational definitions clearly are too laborious to be used in ordinary, nontechnical situations calling for definition. They are designed primarily for the scientist or scholar who wishes his key terms to be understood in the most precise way possible by fellow workers in his field. Nevertheless, there is no intrinsic reason why operational definitions should not with great profit be applied to troublesome and ambiguous terms in our everyday language. Who can calculate the social turmoil and grief that might have been avoided during recent years if prominent persons had been required to furnish operational definitions along with their frequent use of such terms as "communist," "fellow-traveler," "free enterprise," "the American Way," "democracy," and so on?

EXERCISES

Identify the kind of definition used for each of the following terms, and explain how each definition might be improved by supplementing it with one or more different kinds of definition:

1. A "simian" is a monkey or ape.
2. "Famine" is a social condition in which there is a scarcity of food.
3. A "table" is this object right here.
4. The "atomic bomb" is a result, in part, of Einstein's finding that mass is equivalent to energy.
5. "Mortal" means perishable.
6. "Length" means the reading that is obtained when a measuring gauge is laid along a straight line.
7. A "Democrat" is someone who is in favor of a welfare state.
8. A "book" is what you are holding in your hand.
9. "Homicide" is the act of killing another human being.
10. "Ego" will be taken to designate an organism considered as the central point of reference in an interaction situation.
11. "Sincerity" means honesty.
12. "Intelligence" is a capacity of the organism which develops as a function of the nervous system.
13. "Pleasure" is felt satisfaction or the experience of hedonic tone.
14. "Pleasure" is what that person there is experiencing.
15. "Pleasure" is enjoyment.
16. "Pleasure" is that which results from the gratification of desire.

17. "Pleasure" is the good of man.
18. "Pleasure" is a physiological reaction of a more complex organism to its environment, and is identified in general by the observation of behavior designed to maintain a given situation or state of affairs.

5 FALLACIES OF DEFINITION

Strictly speaking, the term "fallacy" designates an unacceptable mode of reasoning. However, the term is usually extended to include types of improper definition. In this chapter we will examine five common fallacies of definition. These fallacies are most often discussed in connection with Aristotelian definition, but there is no reason why an awareness of them should not be helpful in evaluating other types of definition as well.

5.1 Incongruous Definition

One of the most obvious fallacies of definition is committed when the definition is extensionally *too broad* or *too narrow* to distinguish the word being defined. If the definition encompasses more or less than the word defined—if the former does not fit or properly delineate the latter—then the fallacy of incongruous definition has been committed.

To define "coed" as a "college student" is fallacious, because the definition includes male as well as female college students, and therefore is too broad. To define "coed," on the other hand, as a "young female college student" is too narrow a definition, because coeducational colleges are not restricted to *young* female students.

Similarly, the term "star," in the astronomical sense, cannot properly be defined as a "heavenly body," because the definition includes not only stars but planets, satellites of planets, comets, and so on. Thus the definition is too broad. But neither can "star" be defined as a "stellar body seen most clearly at night," since this would exclude our own sun, thereby rendering the definition too narrow.

5.2 Circular Definition

When the word being defined, or a synonym, is used in a definition, the fallacy of circular definition has been committeed. Such a definition is called "circular," because in order to understand the word being defined, one must presumably understand the definition; but in order to understand the definition, if it contains the same word or a synonym, one must already understand the word being defined.

It follows that a synonymous definition always is guilty of circularity. But we have already seen that the synonymous type of definition is subject to criticism on the grounds that a synonym may be as unfamiliar as the word being defined. When one has at his disposal the means for a better, more exact definition, the use of a synonym is ill-advised. The Aristotelian is a better definition, and hence the inclusion of a synonym, under these circumstances, is fallacious.

Sometimes, as already mentioned, a term is circularly defined in a more obvious way, that is, by a frank use of the word being defined. If "logic" is defined as the "science of logical thinking," the definition is clearly circular. For if one does not understand what "logic" means, he will no more understand what "logical thinking" means. In like manner, if that much-abused term "love" is defined as "a mode of behavior in which an affectionate or loving attitude is displayed by one person toward another," the definition again should be rejected as circular.

When an Aristotelian definition contains a synonym, however, the circularity is not so easily detected. One is likely, for example, to overlook the weakness of a definition of "logic" as the "science of rational thinking." But the term "rational," in this context, appears to be a synonym of "logical," and the definition consequently is circular—indeed, the same weakness might be charged against our preliminary definition of logic in Chapter I as the "science of reasoning." Nor can we accept a definition of "love" as a "fondness or amorous attitude of one person with respect to another person or object," since "love" seems, at least in its more serene manifestations, roughly to be synonymous with "fondness or amorous attitude."

5.3 Negative Definition

A definition can state what something is, or what it is not, that is, can be affirmative or negative. However, for a very good reason, an affirmative definition is ordinarily preferable to one that is negative. For after enumerating the things that a term does *not* designate, in order to isolate that which it does, one seldom knows whether or not he has exhausted all the possible negative instances.

Thus, in defining "red" as "the color which is not green, blue, yellow, purple, and so on," the definition might eventually become congruous with "red," but how is one to know this? Should this enumeration, for example, be restricted to the basic color wheel, or should it continue to include the buffs, lavenders, greenish yellows, and midnight blues? This whole procedure, clearly, is not a satisfactory approach to definition.

Fallacies of negative definition may be more subtle than our previous examples. If one defines "anger" as "a lack of restraint," or "evil" as the "privation of good," he is guilty of negative definition. For such terms as "anger" and "evil," to most people, designate very positive phenomena, and thus would better be defined affirmatively.

The problem of whether to define a term affirmatively or negatively is complicated somewhat by a kind of term that seems inherently negative—*privative* terms, they are called. Examples of privative terms are: "infinity," "bachelor," "baldness," or any other term the very connotation of which seems to be negative. "Infinity" (in many contexts) means the *absence* of any limit, a "bachelor" is a man of a certain age who is *not* married, and "baldness" is the condition of a head *without* any hair. But even here, when defining privative terms, we may interpret our definitions as *affirmative* definitions of negative words—affirmative, in the sense that a connoted privation is affirmatively expressed.

5.4 Obscure or Figurative Definition

The shortcomings of a definition that is obscure or figurative or intended humorously are easily seen. If the purpose of definition is the clarification of meaning, it is fallacious to define a word in ambiguous or abstruse language, or to express the definition metaphorically or humorously or in an otherwise nonliteral way.

Since obscurity is often relative to an individual's own experience, technical definitions, in their proper place, must be excepted from this requirement. When a psychologist defines "adaptation" as the "decrement in a response which is a consequence of its repeated elicitation," he is not to be condemned on the grounds that his definition is obscure. On the contrary, such a definition is much more precise and clear to one with a proper background than would be a definition of the same word, say, as "the process of getting used to something." The latter definition might indeed be more appropriate under certain circumstances, as when explaining the word to a person with limited vocabulary. But this consideration does not render the psychologist's definition obscure to persons for whom it is intended.

The definition of "evolution" formulated by Herbert Spencer, on the other hand, is one well-known example of an obscure definition: "A continuous change from indefinite, incoherent homogeneity to definite, coherent heterogeneity of structure and function, through successive differentiations and integrations." Obscure definitions are not always ponderously expressed however. Plato's definition of "justice" as the "health of the soul," and of "time" as the "moving image of eternity," strike many people as highly interesting, but no less obscure than Spencer's definition of "evolution."

Similar considerations hold for figurative or poetic definitions. Some of these are very suggestive, even enlightening, but as clarifications of the literal meanings of terms, they must be condemned as misleading and fallacious. When "architecture" is defined as "frozen music," we may gain insight into the nature of architecture, but only if we already know the literal meaning of the term. We learn that Samuel Johnson had little admiration for Scotchmen when we are presented with his definition of "oats" as a "grain which in England is generally given to horses, but in Scotland supports the people." We learn almost nothing, however, about oats.

5.5 Extraneous Definition

There are definitions which are examples of none of the preceding fallacies but in which the definition still must be condemned because of needless complexity or the attribution of properties that are extraneous to an understanding of the term being defined. This fallacy is difficult to explain, and its identification is doubtful. But a few examples will perhaps suffice to show what is meant.

If a "triangle" is *defined* as a "plane figure the sum of the angles of which are equal to 180 degrees," none of the first four fallacies are pertinent. The definition is neither too broad nor too narrow, but is exactly congruous with the term defined. Neither is the definition circular, negative, obscure, or figurative. Yet we must say it is not a good definition, since a much simpler definition of "triangle," and one which states the truly essential attributes of that figure, is easily formulatable: for example, "a 3-sided closed plane figure" or "plane closed figure consisting of 3 points joined by straight lines." From either of these definitions, with the addition of a few axioms, the definition first mentioned can of course be deduced. But the number of degrees in the sum of its angles is a more complex property of a triangle, and certainly not designed to acquaint someone for the first time with the notion of triangularity.

It must be noted that the "essential" attributes required of a good definition are those relative to the purpose for which a definition is being offered. The ingredients of a good definition can no longer be interpreted as essential in the sense of stating what used to be called the "essence" of a thing, for *all* properties of any individual or class are usually considered now to be equally essential. But if the purpose of an Aristotelian definition is to clarify meanings, then we may still demand that a definition state the attributes that are essential primarily for an understanding of a term's meaning.

EXERCISES

Identify the fallacy of Aristotelian definition most obviously committed in each of the following definitions:

1. "Novels" are literary works that are longer than short stories.
2. A "hedonist" is a moral philosopher who does not accept the Ten Commandments as the basis of obligation.
3. "Virtue" is knowledge.
4. A "college student" is one who attends lectures at an institution of higher learning.
5. A "football" may be defined as a pigskin used in a football game.
6. A "satellite" is a country dominated by Russia or in the sphere of Soviet Union influence.
7. A "superior student" is one who is not average or below average.
8. "Brevity" is the soul of wit.
9. A "murderer" is a person who has killed another human being.
10. "Sympathetic persons" are those who are not selfish and egotistical.

11. "Beauty" is the property of things sought by an artist.
12. "Man" is the rational animal.
13. "Man" is the animal who shaves his beard and wears hats.
14. "Youth" is the absence of age.
15. A "circle" is a plane figure the tangents of which, from any given outside point, are equal.
16. "Life" is the vital functioning of a body.
17. "God" is Love.
18. "Business" is business.
19. "Up" means the opposite of down.
20. The "world" is my idea.
21. The word "illness" can be defined as the absence of health.
22. "Hydrogen" is an element which, if mixed atomically with oxygen in a proportion of 2 to 1, results in water.
23. "Evil" is that which is not pleasant.
24. "Truth" is the characteristic of a proposition that is not false.
25. "Truth" is a property of a true proposition.
26. "Truth" is that which is discovered by a scientist.
27. "Truth" is goodness and beauty.
28. "Truth" is an attribute of a proposition.
29. "Truth" is that which is fated ultimately to be agreed upon by all the experts.
30. "Truth" is the property of a proposition that has been verified.

6 FALLACIES OF RELEVANCE

The fallacies discussed in this and the following three chapters are called *informal* fallacies, because in order to detect and identify them, one cannot simply examine the form of an inference, but must know the content, that is, the meaning of the premises and con-clusion. Formal fallacies, or errors in reasoning based entirely on the form or structure of arguments, will be treated in subsequent parts of this book.

Fallacies of *relevance,* to which the present chapter will be devoted, are illicit modes of reasoning in which the premises, in some way or other, are not relevant to the conclusion. This is to say, the premises are beside the point, and will not logically yield the intended conclusion.

6.1 Appeal to Force (Argumentum ad baculum)

It requires no great logical acumen to see that premises con-sisting of a threat of physical violence are completely irrelevant to the *truth* of any conclusion—unless that conclusion be that the person threatened had better take care. But the fallacy of appeal to force may often appear in a more subtle, nonphysical manner. Suppose, for example, that a man who buys a great deal of adver-tising space in a newspaper writes to the editor of that paper, in-forming him that a certain little nocturnal escapade of his, the adver-tiser's, son has no real news value. And suppose he offers as a reason (premise) for this contention a reference to the amount of adver-tising he does. This premise, although of great concern to a badgered editor, is clearly irrelevant to the conclusion, and the argument is based upon an illicit appeal to force.

The same fallacy is committed if a union president informs his senator that a certain legislative measure is worthy of the latter's support in Congress (conclusion), because a thousand union mem-bers are eager to know for whom to vote in the coming election (premise). Equally fallacious is the case in which an industrialist lets his employees know that unionization is the bane of American civilization, because he is seriously thinking of shutting down his factory.

6.2 Appeal to Pity (Argumentum ad misericordiam)

Sometimes the premises of an argument direct their appeal to the listener's feelings of sympathy, rather than fear. And most of us might be inclined to look more favorably upon such an argument. But whatever the virtues of mercifulness, an appeal to pity is no more relevant logically to the truth of a conclusion than is a threat of force.

Appeals to pity are very common in the courtroom, especially when the defense attorney is unable to offer any good reasons why his client should be found not guilty. One may feel the utmost compassion for a pretty female defendant in a jury trial—tear-stained face, mourning attire, fluttering little hanky, and all that. But if she is accused of murdering her husband, it seems quite irrelevant to plead for her acquittal on grounds that she is a widow.

6.3 Appeal to Ignorance (Argumentum ad ignorantiam)

Another fallacy of relevance is committed when a lack of knowledge in some respect is taken as evidence for a positive assertion. This fallacy usually falls into one of two categories: (1) Arguing from the absence of proof to the presence of disproof, or the converse fallacy, (2) Arguing from the absence of disproof to the presence of proof.

Arguments involving the appeal to ignorance are often found in philosophic or theological contexts. An atheist might argue, for instance, that there is utterly no evidence for the existence of a supernatural being, and therefore that such a being does not exist. Or a theist might argue conversely, and with equal fallaciousness, that no disproof of a deity has ever been offered and hence we must accept the existence of such a being. To point out that these are fallacies is not to say, of course, that the theist or atheist has no sound arguments. But if either is to prove his contention, he must find better premises than those which appeal only to our present ignorance.

Of more urgent importance, to some people, is an argument appearing regularly in many newspapers from the beginning of the "cold war" between Russia and the United States. It runs something like this: Russia has never demonstrated any real willingness to cooperate with the Western Powers, and consequently this or that current Russian proposal to cooperate now must be insincere. An argument such as this seems plausible to many people, because the premise might conceivably be true. But to draw the given conclusion is to preclude irrevocably any future settlement short of war between the nations in question, and thus constitutes a peculiarly dangerous illogicality.

6.4 Appeal To or Against the Man (Argumentum ad hominem)

A very popular fallacy, usually called by its abbreviated Latin name: *ad hominem,* consists in an irrelevant appeal to the person being addressed, or against a third person, instead of an appeal to the matter at issue. The first type of *ad hominem* usually occurs when a man's special circumstances are taken as a reason for his accepting the truth of some belief, while the second type is ordinarily committed when one person attempts to refute another's argument or contention on the grounds that there is something disreputable about the character or background of the man who is proposing the argument. The first type of fallacy may therefore be called a *constructive ad hominem,* while the second type, since it attempts by irrelevant means to overthrow an argument or proposal, is a *destructive ad hominem.*

As an example of the constructive type of fallacy, one might be told that he ought to believe in the rightness of high corporation taxes, because he is poor and owns no stock; or that he should accept the principle of low corporation taxes, because he is a wealthy stockholder. Again, the premise of a constructive *ad hominem* might be that the person to whom the argument is addressed is a Presbyterian, and the conclusion that he ought to believe that all events are predetermined by God. Or he is an American and thus should believe that Americans make the finest soldiers in the world. Or he is a doctor of medicine and therefore should condemn the profession of chiropractic.

We must carefully note, of each of these arguments, that the conclusion might possibly be proved by sound reasoning. The argument in each case is fallacious, not because the conclusion is false, but because the reasons given are irrelevant appeals to a man's personal circumstances.

The *destructive ad hominem* is a similar kind of fallacy, since it also consists of an appeal to a man's circumstances. But it differs in that these circumstances involve something in the man's character or motivation that is open to suspicion, thus giving reason to reject something he proposes or for which he argues. To illustrate this fallacy, the contentions and arguments of the German philosopher, Friedrich Nietzsche, have often been considered unsound because their author spent his last years in a state of insanity. But this evaluation of Nietzsche's philosophy is unwarranted, because there is no intrinsic reason why a madman should not assert the truth and argue logically—indeed, certain types of paranoid personality are characterized by their ability to offer exceedingly complicated and logically rigorous arguments (though usually in support of fantastic conclusions). Nietzsche's arguments and assertions, in short, must be examined on their own merits, without regard to the abnormality of their author.

Similar considerations hold for the arguments offered by persons of unsavory reputation, or by persons of whose motivation we are suspicious. We may condemn Adolph Hitler as excessively evil and as a large-scale criminal, but the arguments and contentions of *Mein Kampf* must be refuted on other grounds. We might fear and dislike certain senatorial demagogues, but the individual proposals of these men in Congress are logically distinct from the motives which prompted them, and hence must be evaluated by impersonal logical criteria.

6.5 Appeal to the Crowd (Argumentum ad populum)

When the premises of an argument contain an appeal to popular attitudes or feelings in order to support the truth of some unrelated conclusion, that argument is said to commit the fallacy of "appeal to the crowd." One of the very common forms of this fallacy has already been described in Chapter 2; perhaps the easiest way of arousing popular enthusiasms or prejudices is by the propagandist's device of using emotionally toned words. Clearly the expressive connotation of language used in an argument is irrelevant to its informational content, and therefore to attempt a proof of some statement in this way is fallacious.

An appeal to the crowd, however, need not contain emotionally toned words. Advertising, for example—a pretty girl standing beside a shiny new car, a major league ball player shaving with a certain kind of razor, or a box of cornflakes picturing the smiling faces of a cowboy favorite and his horse—may be interpreted as a form of argument in which the conclusion is a statement, explicit or implied, of the superior quality of a given product, and the premises are graphic but irrelevant appeals to different kinds of crowds.

6.6 False Cause (Non causa pro causa)

Any argument in which the premises are insufficient or irrelevant grounds for a conclusion asserting a causal connection is said to commit the fallacy of false cause. In practice, however, the false-cause fallacy has come to mean a more specific kind of illicit argument, that is, one which involves an inference from a merely temporal sequence of events to a causal sequence. The Latin expression for this fallacy precisely describes its nature: *post hoc, ergo propter hoc*— after this, therefore because of this.

It may easily be seen that this confusion of a temporal with a causal sequence lies at the root of most superstitions. A black cat crosses a man's path and shortly afterward he trips and breaks his leg. If he then infers a causal connection from this coincidental temporal sequence, he is guilty of the false-cause fallacy. Another man begins carrying a rabbit's foot on his key chain, and thereupon receives a five-dollar-a-week increase in salary. If he reasons that the rabbit's foot is the cause of this good fortune, the false-cause fallacy has again been committed.

It must not be overlooked that a temporal sequence is often a *sign* of a causal connection among events. But while a temporal relation is a *necessary condition* of the causal relation, it clearly is not a *sufficient condition*. After the sequence in time is noted, more proof must be obtained before beginning to speak of cause and effect. And the vast majority of temporal sequences in the world, it is evident, are not causal, but only coincidental.

6.7 Irrelevant Conclusion (Ignoratio Elenchi)

Many arguments in which the premises are irrelevant to the conclusion cannot be classified properly under any of the foregoing headings. It will prove convenient, therefore, simply to call these fallacies of *irrelevant conclusion,* using this as the title of a miscellaneous or catchall category of fallacies of relevance.

Thus, for instance, when premises showing the dangers of socialized medicine are used to denounce federal health insurance plans quite unlike the socialized medicine programs, say, of Great Britain or Sweden, we may speak of such arguments as guilty of irrelevant conclusion. Or if someone attempts to prove that all American applicants should be admitted into our institutions of higher learning because the Constitution guarantees equal opportunity to all, his argument, though committing a fallacy of relevance, seems not to fall into any more specific category, and may therefore be called an irrelevant conclusion.

EXERCISES

Identify the fallacy of relevance most clearly committed in each of the following arguments:

1. No evidence whatever has been offered for the existence of flying saucers. It follows that flying saucers are merely figments of the imagination.

2. No sooner did they start to fluorinate the water but my friends began dying of heart disease. It just doesn't pay to tamper with nature.

3. Socrates should be considered a greater thinker than he now generally is. After all, he was persecuted continuously, first by his wife and then by the Athenian people. He died a martyr to his convictions.

4. You had better detect the fallacy in this argument. For, if you don't, you'll probably flunk the course.

5. The defendant must be guilty, for his lawyer is a man with utterly no professional scruples.

6. Has anybody ever proved that John L. Lewis is not a communist? The inference is obvious.

7. This shotgun is the reason you are morally obligated to marry my daughter.

8. You are a woman, and consequently must accept the fact that women are no less intelligent than men.

9. Shortly after they began experimenting with the atomic bomb, the weather began acting queerly. I say stop playing with the atom and you'll bring back good old-fashioned weather again.

10. The existence of a spirit world has never been disproved. A wise person, therefore, will consult his local spirit medium at the first opportunity.

11. He's a veteran and therefore ought to support the new veterans' bonus plan.

12. A husband-beater should always be treated more leniently than a wife-beater, because women are physically weaker than men.

13. More Sweet-Kleen washers are sold than any other washing machine on the market. They must be good.

14. During the last war there was a revival of religious interest followed immediately by a national lowering of moral standards. Thus, in order to encourage morality, we must do away with religion.

15. My legal work is handled by the firm of Rosenkrantz and Guildenstern. I think, therefore, that you really ought to pay me what you owe me.

16. His arguments for the new veterans' bonus plan must be rejected, because he, as a veteran himself, stands to profit by such a plan.

17. The money which should be going into your pay envelope is instead being given to a pack of lazy, ungrateful foreigners.
18. The Dutch biologist, De Vries, proved that Darwin was mistaken about the time required for a new species to develop. Hence we may rest assured that the evolutionary theory is untenable.
19. Lucretius has in substance been proved correct in his arguments for the atom, and therefore he must be correct in his arguments against the immortality of the soul.
20. We must take Schopenhauer's famous essay denouncing and belittling women with a grain of salt. Any psychiatrist would at once explain this essay by reference to the strained relationship between Schopenhauer and his mother.

7 FALLACIES OF AUTHORITY

Arguments very often contain a premise calling improperly upon some authority as grounds for their conclusions. This kind of fallacy, like those treated in the previous chapter, is a fallacy of relevance, since an illicit appeal to authority is simply not relevant to the truth of a conclusion. However, fallacies of authority appear in so many different contexts, and are so varied in nature, that it seems best to examine them separately.

7.1 Sweeping Authority

Often the appeal to authority in an argument is not specific enough to warrant drawing the intended conclusion. Why is smoking harmful (or not harmful) to one's health? Because "doctors" or "psychologists" or "cancer specialists" say so. And what is your reason for claiming that wrestling matches are fixed? Why, "everyone," or at least "every well-informed person," knows that wrestling is not an honest sport.

Even if we are kind enough to overlook the fact that "everyone," or even "every well-informed person," has, during several stages in the history of thought, been wrong, it still remains apparent that to use such vague and general designations of authority, for all practical purposes, is of no evidential value whatever, and that therefore the fallacy of sweeping or unnamed authority has been committed.

It is true that sometimes a person who uses such empty premises as "Science says so-and-so" or "Humanity denounces this or that" is able, when pressed, to furnish some specific authorities for his conclusions. And under these circumstances no fallacy has been committed. But it seems more often that the man who appeals to an indefinite authority is only incensed or embarrassed or seemingly amused by a request for some more specific reference. And then we must chalk his argument up as a statement for which he would like to have some definite authority, but does not, since he is unable to name who or what it is.

7.2 Dogmatic Authority

An appeal can be made to a specifically named authority, and still be fallacious, if the authority is dogmatic rather than expert. Of course, the words "dogmatic" and "expert" are used in a number of different ways. In the present context, however, the term *dogmatic* characterizes an authority beyond which there is no appeal—a final, ultimate, infallible authority, neither requiring nor offering any reasons or evidence for his specific pronouncements. An *expert* authority, on the other hand, is one whose prestige in some field is based, not so much on title or rank or number of academic degrees, as on special training and the ability, if questioned, to support his pronouncements with reasons or evidence that is open to public scrutiny.

We must be careful, however, not to confuse the *appeal* to dogmatic authority with the *assertion* of such authority. It is not a fallacy to assert or claim to be a final, irrefutable authority in any or even all fields. For this assertion is not an argument and thus, while it might be false, cannot be fallacious. Only when the attempt is made to *prove* a statement by calling upon some incontestable authority may we speak of the *fallacy* of dogmatic authority.

If, for example, Emily Post or Amy Vanderbilt were to claim infallibility in the field of table manners and general social decorum, this in itself would not constitute a fallacy. But when (as often happens) we appeal to these ladies as *final* authorities on which way to tip the soup plate or how to bend the little finger, then the fallacy of dogmatic authority has been committed—by us, not by them. On the other hand, if we appeal to the author of one of the standard bibles of etiquette, not as an ultimate authority, but as a person who has made a lifetime study of the reasons for, and consequences of, certain norms of social behavior, then we have appealed to an expert authority. We should expect, under these circumstances, that the expert on table manners could, if questioned, tell us *why* we ought to tip the soup plate away from us or crook the little finger in a certain way—for instance, that if we tip the plate toward us, we risk spilling hot soup on our laps, and that a finger projected outward from a coffee cup is a physical hazard to the person sitting next to us. These reasons perhaps are not so coercive as we might desire, but the authority to whom we appeal must be able to give *some* reason for each of his pronouncements, or else he is not even a poor expert, but instead a dogmatic authority.

What about the authority who claims infallibility with respect to *specific* pronouncements, but who offers a *general* argument in support of such claim? His general argument, however, will consist either in a further appeal to dogmatic authority, or else in an appeal to some more direct evidence. If the former, then a resolution of the issue has simply been postponed, and no claim of infallibility can be established until the authority to which the appeal is made has been validated. If, on the other hand, the general argument is not a further appeal to authority, but is based on other evidence, this evidence will either be private or else be open to public inspection. If it is private and not capable of public verification, it would seem that nothing at all has been accomplished in the way of proving infallibility and indeed the argument reduces to something like this: "I am infallible because there is evidence for my infallibility, although this evidence is available only to me." But only one possibility remains, that the argument in support of dogmatic authority in some area be an appeal to publicly testable evidence. The only difficulty now is in conceiving what such evidence would be like. Even a miracle-maker would have trouble in establishing the relevance of the premise: "I can perform miracles" to the conclusion: "I am therefore infallible in certain of my pronouncements."

Suppose that the chief medium of a group of spiritualists claims to be an ultimate authority on certain matters and, realizing that the mere assertion of this authority will be repugnant to the more thoughtful of his prospective followers, he attempts to devise a general argument in support of his infallibility. Now he cannot appeal in this argument to another final authority, say to the apocryphal *Book of Esdras,* because this only shifts the burden of proof from his own shoulders to those of the author of *Esdras.* Nor can he appeal to evidence that cannot be verified by others, for example, to divine inspiration, since anybody at all can claim to be divinely inspired, and such a contention could neither be proved nor disproved by any ordinarily acceptable means.

At this point our medium, following the lead of many other dogmatic authorities, will be tempted to call upon evidence that seems to be public, but actually is private. That is, he might claim that evidence for his authority cannot be perceived by anyone who does not already accept the existence of such evidence. He might tell us, for example, that his authority is based on spirit voices and apparitions that become visible at his bidding, but that we ourselves will neither hear the voices nor see the apparitions until our attitude of skepticism gives way to faith and trusting belief.

This, however, is still an appeal to private evidence. For we do not require "faith" in the existence of objects that are commonly accepted as real. Such objects of sense-experience thrust themselves upon us whether we like it or not, and indeed to deny these objects or to conjure up new ones is often a sufficient reason for being committed to an asylum. Furthermore, it is now a generally accepted fact of human behavior that we can come to have a staunch belief in anything whatever, real or unreal, if we permit faith to precede belief based on inquiry and if our faith is sufficiently strong. But all this, when we stop to consider it, is unnecessary in replying to our medium. For we have merely to point out to him that faith in spirit voices and forms is entirely superfluous if their purpose is to furnish evidence of his dogmatic authority. We might as well have faith directly in his authority, and dispense with all this useless logic-mongering.

Let us not underestimate our medium, however. Perhaps, without resorting to any subterfuge, he will be able to produce concrete, public evidence in his favor. Perhaps he will be able, in the presence of a skeptical audience, to fill the room with dancing blue lights and speaking trumpets, eloquent Ouija boards, and the visible and audible spirits of our beloved great-grandparents. In a case such as this, we would have to turn to the medium with greatly increased respect. "Sir," we would have to say, "By this remarkable display, you have shaken to their very roots our skeptical doubts concerning spiritualism. But now, if you will forgive our impatience, we should like you to fulfill what you promised in the way of evidence in support of your infallibility."

In short, the appeal to dogmatic authority is fallacious because there is always the possibility that the assertion of such authority is false. Until it can be shown conclusively that the pronouncements of a supposedly final authority are indubitable in some area, we must satisfy ourselves with a more prosaic appeal to expert authority—an appeal which, in truth, is a roundabout way of referring to the evidence that an expert is able to produce.

7.3 Misplaced Authority

Granting, however, that we admit the fallaciousness of an appeal to sweeping or dogmatic authority, and that we are careful always to call only upon specifically named experts, there are still other pitfalls that await us when our reasoning is based upon authority. One very widespread and insidious fallacy occurs if a man who admittedly is an expert authority in one field is taken as an authority in some other, comparatively unrelated field. This fallacy is difficult to avoid, and difficult even to expose, because some men achieve so great a stature in their own field that their prestige overflows into other areas.

When, for example, such eminent physicists as Einstein, Jeans, Eddington, or Millikan write on philosophic or political matters, as they have done, they should be given the attention and respect due any intelligent layman's opinions and arguments. But no more. For not only intelligence, but experience and long years of hard work and study in a special field, are required to make a man an expert authority. The almost unavoidable naiveté of an expert working outside his own field may not be apparent to the general public, but it is usually at once discernible by real authorities in the field.

The fallacy of misplaced authority has been committed, then, when retired generals are taken as authorities on politics, or politicians as authorities on theology, or theologians as authorities on movie-making, or Hollywood stars as authorities on soap and toothpaste. Indeed advertisers, when giving reasons for buying—and purporting to give arguments in favor of—their products, are among the worst offenders in the use of misplaced authority. That Marilyn Monroe is an authority on acting may perhaps be admitted—or if this is denied, at least she is an authority on seductive behavior of females, and amazingly expert in her own field. Presumably however it is not Marilyn but an oral hygienist who is an authority on toothpaste, or a dermatologist who is an authority on the use of soap. Marilyn's authority has been misplaced in the fields of oral hygiene and dermatology, and that her authority in these fields seems generally to be preferred to that of the real experts is simply indicative, not only of the fact that she is unquestionably more exciting than the ordinary dermatologist, but also of the average person's ineptitude at logic.

7.4 Misrepresented Authority

Even when the authority to whom we appeal is clearly identified, is an expert, and is properly placed in his own field of competence, it still may happen that his pronouncements are misrepresented in some way. This occurs especially when an authority's statements, due to their being lifted from the original context, are substantially changed in meaning. Such change may be deliberate or it may be unintentional, but in either case the authority in question has been represented wrongly, and the appeal is spurious and without logical cogency.

A peculiarly negative form of the fallacy of misrepresented authority has been prominently aired during recent years, in order that the tactics of a few unscrupulous individuals who make a profession of unjust political accusations might be exposed. For no more expert an authority on a man's political heresies and imprudent activities can be found than that man himself, as represented by his own writings and public addresses. The fact of the matter seems to be that we may take almost any important book or speech on political matters, and by a sufficiently clever quoting of sentences and passages out of context, prove in a conclusive way that the author is a socialist, communist, nihilist, a homosexual in public office, or what-have-you.

But of course the fallacy of misrepresented authority is not restricted to the political arena and to calculated defamation of character. Consider the Hebrew or Christian Scripture, for example. It is hard to determine which of the clashing religious sects have correctly represented the pronouncements of scriptural authorities, but it is not at all difficult to see, if there really is a correct interpretation of the Bible, that a great many learned and pious men have been guilty of misrepresentation in this field. Or consider the rather sad plight of graduate students in one of the arts or sciences. Each is told that in order to earn his degree, he must submit in written form a "substantial contribution to the sum of human knowledge." But for some the temptation to quote authorities out of context in order to strengthen his thesis is almost overpowering.

The number of odd dissertations in the archives of almost any large university library is evidence that this temptation is not always resisted.

7.5 Venerable Authority

Very often an argument based on authority must be rejected, not because the appeal is to an inexpert authority, but because the forcefulness of the argument can be traced to the respect and veneration we accord the pronouncements of past generations. This fallacy, identified by Jeremy Bentham in his *Book of Fallacies* as an appeal to the "Wisdom of the Ages," usually consists in calling upon the authority of ancient people simply because they are ancients, and therefore presumably wiser than living authorities.

When men prefer older medical remedies to modern, or when they measure up the dimensions of the Pyramids in order to solve present-day economic problems or to predict international events, or when they practice the rites of many pseudo-metaphysical or scientific personality cults of the day (one of which advertises extensively under the banner: "Wisdom of the Ages Revealed"), they are guilty of expressing or assuming arguments in which is committed this fallacy of appealing to venerable authority.

Two factors appear to lie at the root of this widespread fallacy: one psychological and the other logical. In a psychological sense, people seem naturally to be attracted to viewpoints of past generations. A mysterious glamour especially surrounds the distant, little-known past, and perhaps the same basic psychological mechanism operates when an appeal is made to venerable authority as when we are agreeably mystified or pleasantly disturbed by stories of the supernatural.

But a logical factor appears also to be present. This involves a confusion between the lifespan of the human individual and that of the race. It is true that we usually turn to older people for wise advice, and we set minimum age limits on many important public offices. We do this because we think that older people have had more time to gain experience and to learn judicious solutions of problems.

But when we apply this same principle to generations of the human race, we find that the term "ancients" is a misnomer for the early peoples of human history. Rather, this present generation is historically the most ancient. We today, with our fund of the knowledge and experience of past and present generations, should be best equipped to pronounce upon problems and furnish authoritative knowledge. By the same principle that led us to rely upon the experience of older living men, we should rely upon the advice of present-day authorities, and look rather skeptically upon pronouncements of the ancient, or better, the infant generations of the race.

7.6 Fixed Authority

A similar fallacy, also treated by Bentham, occurs when an appeal is made to the authority implied by a fixed precedent of some sort. Bentham refers to this as the "no precedent" fallacy and describes it as an argument designed to overthrow some new measure or proposal, not because of the proposal's inherent weaknesses, but because it has never before been tried.

The appeal to fixed authority seems to be the last resort of extremely conservative legislators, businessmen, moralists, and others who are unable in any more legitimate way to find a flaw in some new proposal or idea. However, that this type of argument is fallacious is seen immediately when we consider that every really great social or scientific innovation, indeed every step of human progress, must have been initiated by men daring enough to proceed without the sanction of precedent. One may only wonder what the present state of human civilization would be if every man had required a precedent for each of his actions.

7.7 Converse Fallacies of Authority

It is important at this point to realize that many of the informal fallacies, and in particular the fallacies of authority, in application may be pushed to undesirable extremes. The *converse fallacy of fixed authority,* for example, is exemplified by the radical's tendency never to rely upon precedent, and the converse fallacy of *venerable authority* consists in a refusal even to consider the beliefs and arguments of past generations. When we have a precedent for our contemplated actions, we may proceed with that much more assurance as to the consequences and implications of such actions. And if, in attempting to avoid an appeal to venerable authority, we deny even a hearing to men of past ages, we are guilty of arguing *ad hominem,* instead of examining opinions and arguments on their own merits.

Similarly, each of the other fallacies of authority may so impress us that we are driven to commit a converse fallacy. In our anxiety to avoid the fallacy of *misplaced authority,* we might forget that the opinions of an expert who is speaking outside his field, while not available as authoritative premises, are nevertheless well worth our close attention and respect. Or we might overlook the possibility that what seems like the fallacy of *sweeping authority* is actually an economical generalization on the part of a man who is able upon request to furnish more specific references. Awareness even of the fallacy of *misrepresented authority* can be carried to an excess. It is clear that no written or spoken passage can be removed from its context without effecting at least a slight change in meaning. And therefore to demand that a quotation retain its entire original meaning would be to eliminate the quoting of authorities altogether.

EXERCISES

Identify the fallacy of authority most clearly committed in each of the following inferences:

1. Nobody likes war, and hence there is no reason why war should not be abolished.
2. The institution of marriage is as old as human history and thus must be considered sacred.
3. Professor X, a world renowned authority on Restoration drama, maintains that a course in logic is unnecessary for the student who has studied general semantics.

4. Never in the august history of these solemn legislative halls has such a proposal been made.

5. Dental experts heartily endorse chlorophyll for the teeth.

6. Scripture tells us that Lot's wife, for being overly curious, was transformed into a pillar of salt. Biblical historians, thus, are risking their very souls by prying so deeply into religious matters.

7. Unions have never before possessed such a tremendous amount of power. Further controls must therefore be devised.

8. It's the old time religion, and so it's good enough for me.

9. Leading business men say that the history taught in grammar and high school should be American rather than world history.

10. You must believe in me, and accept what I say as true. You must have faith, for the road to hell is paved with skeptics.

11. I'm in favor of electing a woman as the nation's president. The only way to ensure progress is by continual, fearless experimentation.

12. The witch-hunters of Colonial New England are to be commended for their zeal in ferreting out and prosecuting witches, for we are told in Scripture that "Thou shalt not suffer a witch to live."

13. Plato's theory of justice, since it was formulated over two thousand years ago, is no longer tenable.

14. Professor X has stated in the classroom that certain arguments from Marx's *Capital* have been incorporated into modern economic theory. We must try at once to remove him from the faculty.

15. The great founders of our nation were in favor of maintaining a barrier between the Eastern and Western Hemispheres. We are desecrating their memory and courting disaster by meddling now in the affairs of Europe.

16. The sacred tablets discovered, translated, and then returned to an angel messenger by Joseph Smith, were divinely inspired. Hence we must accept whatever was said in these tablets, including the doctrine of polygamous marriage.

8 FALLACIES OF AMBIGUITY

The fallacies to be discussed in this Chapter are different from fallacies of relevance in that the illegitimacy of the argument stems primarily from an equivocal or ambiguous use of language. It will be recalled from previous chapters that the same words or statements often, or rather, usually have more than one informative connotation. When this plurality of meanings is used as a means of drawing an unwarranted conclusion, one of the fallacies of ambiguity has been committed.

8.1 Simple Equivocation

The simplest way in which a fallacy of ambiguity can be committed is by using different meanings of the same word or expression in the premises of an argument, thereby permitting an unjustified inference to be made.

This fallacy is perhaps best pointed out by one of the many ridiculous examples that can be devised. It might be argued, for instance, that some given individual is mad at his wife, and since all persons who are mad ought to be placed in an asylum, it follows that this individual should be placed in an asylum. If the term "mad" had the same meaning in both premises of this argument, the conclusion would logically follow. But the term in question is used equivocally, and so, fortunately for irritable husbands, the argument is unsound.

To give another example of simple equivocation, one might argue that the enforced payment of income taxes is a deprivation of freedom, and since to be deprived of freedom is to become a slave, it follows that anyone compelled to pay income taxes is a slave. Here the expression "deprivation of freedom," is equivocal. In the first premise, to be deprived of freedom means a necessary imposition for the interest of the nation. But in the second premise, it means a total or near total deprivation of liberty. If these meanings are substituted for the original expression, the argument runs like this: "The enforced payment of income taxes is a necessary imposition for the interest of the nation, and since to be totally deprived of liberty is to become a slave, it follows that anyone compelled to pay income taxes is a slave"—an argument the fallaciousness of which is much more easily detected.

8.2 Composition

Names of collections or wholes are often used equivocally, in that such names, and their modifying adjectives, may refer to *each* of the members or parts of a class, or to the class as a *whole*. When an inference is made from properties of the parts of a whole, considered individually, to properties of the whole, considered organically or collectively, it is said that the fallacy of *composition* has been committed. For what is true of each of the parts may not hold true at all for the whole.

A simple example of this fallacy occurs when one reasons that each member of a football team is a good player, and that therefore the team as a whole is a good team. This is faulty reasoning because a good team must possess qualities which are not applicable to good individual players—qualities which render the team a smoothly functioning, organic unit and in virtue of which it is said to have an intangible *esprit de corps* or team spirit. That a team consisting of all good players need not be a good team is obvious when we consider that all-star teams, composed presumably of the best individual college players, perhaps are seldom the best college teams in the nation.

Similar considerations apply to any argument purporting to infer properties of a whole from those of its parts. A collection of good individual soldiers need not make a good company of troops, for, like a newly formed unit of the French Foreign Legion, they might have been thrown together without knowledge even of a common language. Arguments such as this have no more basis than if we were to reason from the invisibility of each of the molecules composing a substance to the invisibility of the substance itself.

8.3 Division

The converse fallacy of composition is called the fallacy of *division*. It consists in reasoning from properties of a whole to properties of each of the parts, and is fallacious for the same basic reason that composition is fallacious: The parts of a whole need not have properties attributed to the organically · unified whole itself.

To use the same example as before, one cannot reason that since a given football team is a good team, each of its players must therefore be good. The football coach has never lived, perhaps, who would not privately complain about holes in his line or weaknesses in his backfield. Nor may the efficiency of each soldier be inferred from the efficiency of his company, or the visibility of each element of a substance be inferred from the visibility of the whole.

Numerous illustrations of the fallacies both of composition and division can be found in arguments concerning the interests of the nation and of its parts. Many persons reason wrongly that what is for the best interest of themselves, or their corporations, or their states, must be for the best interest of the country, thus committing the fallacy of composition. Others commit the converse fallacy by arguing that what is best for the nation must necessarily be advantageous for each state, person, or other national element. We cannot logically even say that what is for the best interest of every individual American is for the best interest of the nation. It would be beneficial for all of us, for example, to denude our forests, thus lowering the cost of housing, furniture, and so on. But this certainly would not be to the advantage of generations still unborn, whose interests are still comprehended under those of the nation.

8.4 Accent

The fallacy of accent is committed when the meaning of a statement or set of statements is changed by wrongfully stressing words or other elements of these statements. The accent in question may be oral, or it may consist in the use of italics, underlining, upper-case letters, or other devices for accenting language.

It will readily be seen that this fallacy overlaps the fallacy of misrepresented authority, since the text of an authority can be mis-quoted by improper use of italics or other means of accenting. When this is done, the fallacy may indifferently be called one of relevance or ambiguity. But of course there are other fallacies of accent which are not fallacies of misrepresented authority.

One might assert, for example, that "All men are born with equality of opportunity," not intending an appeal to authority, but only a commonly accepted moral principle or democratic statement of fact. Now if the word "men" is somehow accented, this assertion becomes the premise of an argument, the implied conclusion of which might mean that *women* should *not* be accorded an equality of opportunity. Or suppose the word "born" is accented: "All men are *born* with equality of opportunity." Then the implication might very well be that such equality need not continue to hold for men *after* they are born.

The fallacy of *special pleading* or *half-truth* may be considered a distinctive kind of illegitimate accent. For if one emphasizes only those circumstances favorable to his own case, and conveniently for-gets the unfavorable circumstances, he is wrongfully accenting or stressing only part of the truth. It must be admitted that special pleading is the stock in trade of the legal profession. One wonders indeed how an attorney, especially one who pleads his cases in court, could possibly build a successful practice without persistently and cleverly resorting to this fallacy. When an attorney becomes a jurist, however, it then becomes essential that he learn to detect and honestly evaluate special pleading on the part of lawyers be-tween whom he must adjudicate.

8.5 Amphiboly

Closely related to simple equivocation is the fallacy of amphiboly, or amphibology, as it used to be called. Equivocation, however, designates the ambiguity of a word or brief expression, while amphiboly refers to the ambiguity of a statement, and is due, not to multiple meanings of terms, but to the grammatical structure of a sentence.

If we are told that a certain number is equal to two times four plus three, the statement is amphibolous, since the answer might either be eleven or fourteen. Again, if we read on the society page that "After Mrs. Smythe boarded the Queen Mary, she thrust her huge nose toward the open sea and heaved mightily against the waves," we are confronted with two interpretations, one of which is more plausible, but the other perhaps more newsworthy.

Amphibolous statements have always proved exceedingly useful to persons who attempt to predict future events. For predictions can be worded in such a way that they cannot be falsified. Indeed, anyone wishing to gain a reputation as a seer, soothsayer, prophet, astrologist, palmist, Gypsy teacup reader, or something similar, could do no better than to become skillful at devising amphibolous predictions. There is little risk of error, for example, in telling a hopeful young girl that within six months she will meet a man, and he will have marriage on his mind. For surely she will meet *some* man in the specified time, and he will certainly be contemplating marriage, if not to her, then to someone else, either in prospect or retrospect. And if one wishes to establish himself as a prophet on a grander scale, he might try predicting that if Russia goes to war with the United States, a great nation will be defeated.

EXERCISES

Identify the fallacy of ambiguity most clearly committed in each of the following:

1. What is good for General Motors is good for the country.
2. Senator —— was much distressed by the reprimand given him by his colleagues. And since it is our duty to help those in distress, it is our duty to help Senator ——.

3. If all men were scholars, the human race would not survive. You, therefore, ought not to be a scholar.

4. The Germans are barbarians, for they killed thousands of Americans in the last war.

5. He was taken to the hospital and was badly hurt. It's not advisable therefore to be taken to a hospital.

6. The Irish are a pugnacious lot. Look at John L. Sullivan!

7. Our rights should be enforced by law, and since voting in this country is a right, it should be enforced by law.

8. My senator must have done a good job this year, for this last Congress was the finest in recent years.

9. Scripture tells us that "thou shalt not covet thy neighbor's wife." This means that we may only covet the wives of men who do not live in our neighborhood.

10. Meowing and purring contentedly, she picked the kitten up.

11. No individual can relieve his economic distress by increased expenditure, and therefore no nation can do so either.

12. Persons who are dependent upon others are unable to make their own way in life. Most wives, therefore, are in this category, since they are dependent upon their husbands.

13. All men must eventually die. Therefore, a time will come when the human race no longer exists.

14. Desegregation, since it will benefit the nation, is in the best interest of every American.

15. I have flipped a coin twenty times and got twenty heads. My next toss should be tails.

16. Dressed in white satin gown and demure veil, he led his bride happily back up the aisle. The church doors opened and they cheerfully clattered down the steps into a waiting car. He turned to plant a kiss with his heart beating on her lips.

9 FALLACIES OF PRESUMPTION

Certain fallacious arguments are characterized, not by the irrelevance of their conclusions or ambiguity of their language, but by the inclusion of an illegitimate assumption in their premises. These presumptive arguments are sometimes called *question-begging,* because by smuggling the conclusion into the wording of the premises, they beg or avoid the question at issue in the argument.

9.1 Complex Question

When a "yes" or "no" answer is demanded to a question containing two or more parts, each of which ought to be answered individually, it is said that the fallacy of complex question, or "many questions," has been committed. Facetious examples of this fallacy abound: "Have you left off beating your wife?" or "Is it true that you've stopped drinking so heavily?" or "Why is it that Americans are so crude?"

Each one of these questions is presumptive in the sense that it assumes an affirmative or negative answer to a question not directly asked. When one is questioned as to whether or not he has left off beating his wife, it is presumptively implied that an affirmative answer has been given to the previous question: "Have you *ever* beaten your wife?" Thus any answer to the complex question will be incriminating. A complete statement of the argument presupposed by this mischievous little question would run something like this:

> Either you are still beating your wife, or you have stopped beating her, or you have never beaten her. It is false that you have never beaten her (the illicit presumption), and therefore either you are still beating her or you have stopped beating her. Hence the question: Have you left off beating your wife?

Examples of complex question need not, of course, always be facetious. It is a favorite device of lawyers who wish to confuse a witness or defendant, or to incriminate them in the eyes of a jury. Legislative investigating committees, too, have been known to ask such questions as: "When did you give up your leadership of the Syndicate operating out of Baltimore?" or "Yes or no—Are you still a communist?"

9.2 Disguised Conclusion

A rather naive way of begging the questions is by the simple device of reaffirming a statement as the premise of an argument. The conclusion may be reworded when used as a premise, or it may merely be reasserted with more vigor. But in either case the question at issue has been begged, since any statement whatsoever can be "proved" by setting up a tautologous argument, in which the premise and conclusion are identical.

Usually this fallacy occurs when someone first makes an assertion, and then is called upon to give a reason for it. For example, it might be asserted that smoking is not good for a person. Then, when asked why this is the case, the reply might be: "Well, it simply isn't good for you," or "Because smoking is harmful to a person's health," or, more forcefully, "Every cigarette you smoke is a nail in your coffin." Each of these premises is a mere repetition of the statement to be proved, and therefore a commission of the disguised conclusion fallacy.

9.3 Question-Begging Definition

A more interesting fallacy, and one which is much harder to expose, is committed when a person defines his terms in such a way that his argument cannot possibly be disproved. This fallacy has plagued the entire history of science and philosophy, and even now periodically is found to be infesting the roots of some one of the special sciences or philosophic systems.

The simplest and most prevalent cases of question-begging definition occur when a generalization of some sort is criticized by pointing out an exception. For instance, the statement might be made that all Chinese are barbarians. Someone may then object to this generalization by pointing out that Confucius or Sun Yat-sen or Mr. Wong who runs the hand laundry around the corner are all Chinese, although they certainly cannot be called barbarians. Now if these exceptions are denied on the grounds that the men named are *not true Chinese,* the fallacy of question-begging definition has been committed. For the term "Chinese" has now been *defined* in such a way that no person, however Chinese he might seem, will be accepted as such unless he is a barbarian.

At the root of every question-begging definition is an illegitimate removal of the argument from the level of factual discourse to a purely linguistic plane. The person who commits this fallacy has redefined his terms in such a way that his contention cannot possibly be disproved. His argument, so to speak, is so conclusive that it is self-defeating. For no matter how cleverly language is used, it cannot directly change the facts to which it refers.

There are, without doubt, all sorts of warranted factual generalizations. The laws of physics are good illustrations. But even the laws of physics must be stated in such a way that a means of disconfirmation, a possible method of determining exceptions, can be *conceived.* If the generalizations or laws are actually sound, then no disconfirmation will in fact be forthcoming. But the possibility of finding an exception must still be present. And when such possibility is not present—when the means of disproving a contention cannot even be imagined—then that contention no longer refers to matters of fact, but is merely a linguistic exercise of some sort.

A more trivial example of a question-begging definition will perhaps serve to make this clear. Someone might contend that people living in Miami are blessed with beautiful Florida weather. Then, when it is remarked to this person that some days in Florida are rainy or cold or humid or rocked by a hurricane, he replies triumphantly: "Ah! but that is not what I mean by Florida weather!" And of course he has in this way irrefutably proved his case. But he is not talking about Florida weather.

Another illustration of this fallacy is the ever-popular argument of the cynic who maintains that all men act from selfish motives. It will not suffice to answer this thesis by pointing out that many parents, for example, seem almost completely unselfish in their devotion to their children; the cynic replies that a parent's affection for his children is evidence only of the personal pleasure he derives from being a parent. Nor will it be of any use to mention the behavior of a martyr who gladly sacrifices his very life for the sake of a friend or a principle. The cynic merely replies that a martyr is perhaps unconsciously willing to relinquish all the pleasures of an ordinary life in order that he may taste that one supremely pleasurable final moment during which all eyes are riveted upon him, and in which he realizes with exquisite satisfaction that he will forever be exalted by his posterity or God. At this point in the discussion, if not before, the non-cynic will have recognized that his adversary has redefined the notion of human motivation so as to exclude any possible disproof. All that remains is to walk away, or change the subject, or spend a possibly abortive half-hour in trying to explain the nature of question-begging definition.

In short, one should be immediately suspicious of any argument appearing so conclusive that all debate is stopped. It might be a good argument. But it might, on the other hand, be a redefinition of terms in such a way as to exclude any possible refutation. And in this case the argument has proved nothing about matters of fact except that its proponent is adept at the illicit use of language.

9.4 Circular Reasoning

Another very difficult fallacy to detect is that committed when an argument is presumptive in the sense of going around in a circle. This fallacy, sometimes called the "vicious circle argument" or by its Latin name, *petitio principii,* always involves at least two component arguments. The first argument need not itself be fallacious, although it usually has a premise the truth of which is doubtful. The fallacy of circular reasoning occurs when the truth of this doubtful premise is questioned, and an attempt is made to prove it, not by a new premise, but by the conclusion of the first argument.

Circular reasoning can be diagrammed in the following way:

$$P_1 = C_2$$
$$\downarrow \quad \uparrow$$
$$C_1 = P_2$$

Here P_1 stands for the doubtful premise of the first argument, C_1 for the conclusion of this argument, and the arrow for the relationship of "implies" or "yields up as a conclusion." The actual truth of P_1 is then called in question, so that it becomes C_2, the conclusion of a second argument. And the fallacy occurs when P_2, the premise used to prove C_2, is identical with, or perhaps a rewording of, C_1. For C_1 is the conclusion that was first at issue, and cannot logically be used to prove its own premise. To do so is to reason in a circle, thereby permitting one to prove any assertion whatever, since he argues from the premise to the conclusion, and then from the conclusion back to the premise.

Suppose it is asserted that the teachings of Mohammed are all true (C_1), because according to the Koran, Mohammed is the true prophet (P_1). Now suppose that the truth of this premise, that is, the authority of the Koran, is questioned. If the Koran is proved to be authoritative (C_2) by referring to Mohammed's claim that it was dictated to him by Allah (P_2), the fallacy of circular reasoning has been committed. For Mohammed's veracity was the issue at stake in the first place. And therefore, when the word of the Koran is used as evidence of Mohammed's truthfulness, Mohammed's word cannot be used as evidence of the Koran's truthfulness.

The logical circle involved in a circular argument may, as it is said, be narrow or wide. A narrow circle occurs when the component arguments are close together, permitting the circularity to be detected with comparative ease. But the most careful scrutiny will sometimes not reveal a wide circularity, because many chapters or volumes or lectures might be offered between the component arguments. Or numerous connecting arguments might form links in a chain of reasoning before the ends of the chain are closed in a circle. If, for example, it is argued in the first chapter of a long book that Francis Bacon could not have been the author of any plays attributed to Shakespeare, because Bacon had no particular dramatic talent, and if then it is argued in the final chapter of the same book that Bacon was not skilled in drama, because he never wrote any plays of note, the wide circularity of this argument might be exceedingly difficult to detect.

EXERCISES

A. Identify the fallacy of presumption most clearly committed in each of the following arguments:

1. Are these exercises the cause of your despondency?
2. Professor Jones is an expert in his field because he wrote the textbook used in his course. And that this textbook is authoritative is proved by Professor Jones's own testimony.
3. Keats' poetry is beautiful, because it is possessed of aesthetic quality.
4. A communist cannot possibly be a Christian. A communist who professes Christianity is either not a true communist or not a real Christian.
5. Why is it that women are more devoted to children than are men?
6. Scripture is true because it is the word of God, which in turn is attested to by Moses and other Biblical personages. That these are not capable of falsehood appears evident when we consider that their utterances are found in Scripture.
7. All politicians are dishonest. The expression "honest politician" is a contradiction in terms.
8. Polynesians are naturally prone to run away from danger, and therefore they are cowards.
9. An evil man cannot be happy. He might *seem* happy, but if you knew him better, you would see that he is necessarily miserable.
10. Haste makes waste, because hurried activity is careless activity.

11. Do you think that the people have been sufficiently informed of our tremendous military superiority over the Russians?

12. This man is insane and therefore is perfectly capable of committing the atrocity of which he is accused. There is no doubt that he is insane, for his behavior is that of a madman, and only a madman could be guilty of committing this atrocious crime.

B. A fallacy of definition, relevance, authority, ambiguity, or presumption has been committed in each of the following inferences or definitions. Identify the *specific* fallacy most clearly committed:

1. That astrology is a science should be obvious to anyone when he considers that kings, emperors, and rulers of all types have believed in astrology, and have guided the destiny of their nations by reference to the heavenly bodies.

2. The defendant is requested to answer with a simple, straightforward "yes" or "no"—Is he still in love with the murdered man's wife?

3. The movie star of whom you speak cannot be a great actress and should not be given the Academy Award, because she left her husband and, without bothering to get a divorce, lived with another man and had children by him.

4. A former all-American football player claims that this hair oil is the best. It must be good.

5. "Man" is a featherless biped.

6. "Man" is the animal who can send an artificial satellite aloft.

7. Viscaya is perhaps the most beautiful museum of art in the South, because no other Southern gallery possesses so many individually beautiful works of art, and in so beautiful a setting.

8. I don't believe in Santa Claus anymore, because nobody's ever been able to show that he exists.

9. A miracle cannot possibly occur, since a miracle is a temporary suspension of a law of nature, and if we were ever to discover such an occurrence, rather than calling it a miracle we would explain it by reference to a new law of nature. A miracle, therefore, is a contradiction in terms.

10. My reason for rejecting the evolutionary theory in biology is that the brilliant lawyer and statesman, William Jennings Bryan, was extremely critical of such theories.

11. No convincing reason for rejecting the evolutionary theory has ever been advanced. Hence we may rest assured that it is a sound theory.

12. The theories of racial purity defended by Ezra Pound are completely without merit, for their author has been confined to a mental institution.

13. If we can believe John Kaspar, however, Pound is not only sane, but is still possessed of a clear and powerful mind. And I do think we can rely on Kaspar's opinion, because Pound speaks very highly of him.

14. Each Latin American country is weak in a military sense. Very little military help, therefore, can be expected from that quarter in the event of war.

15. Every true criminal is mentally unbalanced. We can safely say of any man convicted of a crime, but who appears to act rationally, either that he has been wrongly convicted or that a psychiatric examination would reveal a streak of insanity.

16. "Criminal" is the word used for a person who has been, or who ought to be, convicted of a crime.

17. Call it what you will, but ever since I started to carry this silver dollar, my business has been growing by leaps and bounds.

18. Our local censorship board is composed of very prominent clergymen, politicians, and presidents of women's organizations, and hence its pronouncements upon good and bad art should carry a great deal of weight.

19. Indecent art, by definition, is bad art.

20. My client, your Honor, should not be sent to jail, since by your own admission, he is a good burglar. And I'm sure you won't send anyone who is good to jail.

21. The proposal that our contemporary theory of punishment should be based on the scriptural injunction: "An eye for an eye, and a tooth for a tooth," cannot be sound. For this injunc-

tion was given by an ancient tribe of semi-nomadic Middle Easterners.

22. If you wish to protect your American heritage, you will vote for Gary Mander, the people's choice for Governor.

23. Garbage collectors have a far more unpleasant job than do tool and die-makers, and therefore ought to earn at least as much money.

24. I cannot believe he is as depraved as you say. After all, he is a member of a very fine family.

25. Whenever we plan on going to the beach, it starts to rain. My lawn now needs watering, so I'm going to plan on leaving for the beach.

PART II

THE LOGIC OF PROPOSITIONS

10 VALID INFERENCES AND TRUE CONCLUSIONS

10.1 The Logical Form of an Inference

In the last part, we examined inferences in which the conclusion did not follow from the premises because the premises were irrelevant, ambiguous, or otherwise insufficient grounds for the conclusion. If we knew the meanings of the premises and conclusion, we could see how the premises contained information having little to do with the point to be established. But, sometimes, it was not quite clear what the premises meant and whether, therefore, they were grounds for the conclusion. At any rate, we had no rule to apply in determining whether a conclusion did or did not follow from the premises.

It is this rule which formal, deductive logic supplies. For formal logic abstracts meaning and significant content from the ambiguities of language, in order to show the *logical form or structure* or *pattern of relationships* of the inference. And that form shows whether or not the premises are so connected with the conclusion that it must follow from them. Many forms are shown either as primitive propositions or theorems in the Logic of Propositions. Their exposition and application to examples shall be our concern in this Part.

First, in order to illustrate what is meant by logical form, let us examine an inference which any driver of a car is always making:

> If the traffic light turns red, I should stop. And, since the light has turned red, I should stop.

Here, the first premise is what we shall call an implicative proposition. It is a statement of a simple traffic rule that must be known in order to secure a driver's license. It is so common that we often presuppose it. The second premise is a statement of a fact, which we shall take for granted. The inference states that, since the premises are true, the conclusion is also.

In order to find the structure of the inference, let us so far abstract from its meaning as to represent "the traffic light turns red" by R, and "I should stop" by S. We may then represent the inference, thus:

> If R is true, then S is true; and R is true. Hence S is true.

This is the logical form of the inference, a form showing the relationships of the propositions. This form establishes the conclusion to follow from the premises, as will be shown later.

Let us examine another common inference, this time from physics.

> If the electromagnetic laws governing the composition of matter hold, then a rod will contract along its line of motion. They are invariably assumed to hold; and hence a rod will contract along its line of motion.

Let us represent "the electromagnetic laws governing the composition of matter hold" by E, and "a rod will contract along its line of motion" by C. The logical form of the inference is:

> If E is true, C is true; and E is true. Hence C is true.

Finally, let us take a more complicated inference, one made by that hawk-nosed, hawk-eyed sleuth, Sherlock Holmes. In a mysterious murder, after Holmes has examined some footprints and other clues on the scene of the murder, he infers from them a complete description of the murderer, including the fact that "he was in the prime of life." His reasoning leading to the conclusion follows:

> "Well, if a man can stride four-and-a-half feet without the smallest effort, he can't be quite in the sere and yellow. That was the breadth of a puddle on the garden walk which he had evidently walked across. . . . There is no mystery about it"[1] [about the conclusion that the man was in the prime of life.]

---

[1] Conan-Doyle, Arthur, *Tales of Sherlock Holmes,* Grosset and Dunlap, New York, 1915, p. 34.

Now let us paraphrase the inference, keeping its meaning, in order to reveal its logical form. It becomes:

> If a man can stride four-and-a-half feet without effort, he is in the prime of life. A man strode four-and-a-half feet without effort. Hence, he is in the prime of life.

Let us symbolize "a man can stride four-and-a-half feet without effort" by S, and " he is in the prime of life" by P. The logical form of the inference is:

> If S is true, P is true; and S is true. Hence P is true.

The logical form of our three inferences all have something in common; they all reveal the same relationships between propositions, the same universal form. For if we let the more universal symbol, p, stand for the first proposition in all the inferences, and q for the second, the form common to all the inferences is:

> If p is true, then q is true; and p is true. Hence q is true.

Though the different inferences are about different things, about traffic lights and contracting rods and lengthy strides, they all exhibit the same pattern of relationships or general form. Many of our most common inferences, whether they deal with mathematical, scientific, or common-sense subject matters, have this basic logical form, connecting their premises with their conclusions.

10.2 Valid Inferences

This basic logical form, exhibited in our examples, is a *valid* form, as we will show in more detail later. Every inference with that form, no matter what its subject matter, is valid. A valid inference is one where, if the premises are true, the conclusion must be true also—it *cannot be false*. The premises are so related to the conclusion that their truth involves that of the conclusion, which may be said to follow from them.

In a valid inference, then, the conclusion is as true as the premises. If they are true, the conclusion is true also. Now in many inferences, as in the above examples, the premises may be granted to be true. Yet, in many inferences, the premises are either doubtful or false. However, these inferences may still be valid, exhibiting a valid form. *If* the premises were true, the conclusion would be true. That the premises are not, as a matter of fact, true, does not alter the valid logical form of the inference.

For example, consider the following inference:

> If John is courageous he will say what he thinks; and John is courageous. Hence, he will say what he thinks.

Let us symbolize "John is courageous" by *C*, and "he will say what he thinks" by *S*. The form of the inference is:

> If *C* is true *S* is true; and *C* is true. Hence *S* is true.

We see that this inference illustrates the same universal form that our other valid inferences did. It is therefore valid. *If* the premises are true, the conclusion will be true also. But, here, we could easily suppose that either or both of the premises are factually false, in situations say, where it is the better part of valor not to say what one thinks, or where John is timid. In either case, the *conclusion could be either true or false,* as can easily be seen. Neither its truth nor falsity follows from the false premises. Nevertheless, the inference is valid. *If* the premises were true, the conclusion would be true. For the factual falsity of the premises does not affect the valid logical form.

10.3 True Conclusions

Nevertheless, in the scientific and practical inferences we make, where we aim to arrive at true conclusions, we take care that our premises are factually true. When the driver of a car concludes that he ought to stop, he must carefully ascertain whether the light actually has turned red. When the scientist establishes a theory, he must be very sure about the grounds on which he bases it. When Sherlock Holmes reasons out the true characteristics of the murderer, he must carefully ascertain the evidence. In all our inferences, where we wish to establish a conclusion as factually true, we argue from premises which are factually true. For we assume the logical principle that only if the premises of an inference are true, must the conclusion be true also.

Yet, in order to establish the conclusion of an inference as true, it is not sufficient that the premises be true. As we saw, the inference must have a valid logical form, connecting its premises to its conclusion in such a way that if they are true the conclusion will be true. Thus, in each of our first three examples, the conclusion is established as true because it is linked to the premises by such a valid form. Unless we can discern the valid form of an inference, we cannot call it valid.

If an inference does not have a valid form, the conclusion does not follow from the premises, and so is not established as true. An invalid inference establishes nothing—and ostensibly concludes anything. Whether its premises are true or false, its conclusion can be either true or false. For there is no logical connection between the premises and conclusion.

Let us give an illustration of an inference which has an invalid form:

> If the traffic light turns red, then I should stop. And I should stop (as all the passersby are shouting at me!). Hence, the light has turned red.

The form of the inference, using the same symbols as before is:

> If R is true then S is true; and S is true. Hence R is true.

This form, as we shall later explain more in detail, is invalid. The conclusion does not follow from the premises. For, even if they are true, the conclusion could well be false. For instance, we know that the fact that we should stop may be indicated by nails projecting from a board in the road, rather than by a red traffic light. Thus, the premises do not establish the conclusion as true.

These results may be summarized graphically in a table. In any argument, the premises may be true or false, the reasoning valid or invalid, and the conclusion true or false. Eight different combinations are possible; as shown in the following table.

TABLE OF ARGUMENT-COMBINATIONS

Premises may be:	Reasoning may be:	Conclusion may be:
1. True	Valid	True
*2. True	Valid	False
3. True	Invalid	True
4. True	Invalid	False
5. False	Valid	True
6. False	Valid	False
7. False	Invalid	True
8. False	Invalid	False

Of these eight combinations, only Number 2 is an impossible kind of argument. A false conclusion cannot be drawn from true premises in a valid argument. In other words, when the premises of a valid argument are true the conclusion cannot be false, but must be true. If valid reasoning leads us to a false conclusion, at least one of our premises is false.

For, only if (a) the inference is valid, and (b) its premises are true, must its conclusion be true. Yet, as logicians, we cannot determine (b)—whether the premises are factually true or not. For the logician is not omniscient. He cannot say what is true in all fields of investigation. His problem is to determine (a)—whether the inference is valid. To do this, he must find the form or pattern of relationships between the propositions of an inference.

In the chapters which follow there will be many examples of inferences, taken from daily life as well as from the exact sciences. Fortunately, we will not have to determine whether or not the premises are factually true—an often doubtful point. But we will have to discern the logical form of the inferences. To do so will often require ingenuity and insight into the meaning of the inference, since the logical form may differ from the verbal form, which obscures it. In the earlier inferences, which will therefore seem stilted and unlike our idiom, the verbal form will reflect the logical form, so that the latter may be separated out and stated. But only if this form is found may we say that the conclusion follows necessarily from the premises and only then may we confidently say that, if the premises are true, the conclusion must be true.

EXERCISES

1. Carefully restate at least one of the examples of inferences. What are the premises? The conclusion?
2. Find, in your reading, an inference having the same logical form as the example.
3. What is the logical form of an inference?
4. Must the premises of a valid inference be factually true? The conclusion?
5. May the premises of a valid inference be false? If they are false, must the conclusion be true? *May* it be true? Explain.
6. Can you make up a valid inference whose premises are true and conclusion false?
7. Must the conclusion of an invalid inference be true? May it be true?
8. When is a conclusion established as true?

11 PROPOSITIONS: NEGATION AND CONJUNCTION

11.1 Symbolization of Propositions

Let us turn now to the justification of forms of valid inferences. These forms, we have seen, are valid for all inferences regardless of their subject matter. They are the pattern of relationships of the propositions composing an inference. For, in the Logic of Propositions, propositions are the units whose relationships constitute the form of the inference. Before we can consider inferences, then, we must consider the nature and precise statement of propositions.

A *proposition,* it was stated in Chapter 3, is the meaning of a sentence in its descriptive function. Yet even its meaning is disregarded in formal logic. It is expressed by a complete sentence, which asserts or proposes something for belief, *something which may be true or false.* No matter what it says, whether it is factually true, false, or doubtful, universal or particular, affirmative or negative, categorical or hypothetical, it is still a proposition if it is capable of being true or false. For a proposition, in formal logic, is only an entity capable of being true or false and of entering into relations with other propositions.

Examples of propositions are:

> Miami is south of New York.
> Miami is not south of New York
> All people make mistakes.
> If the temperature rises, the metal expands.

In order to treat propositions only as formal entities having certain relations to other propositions, logic designates propositions by symbols. Symbols enormously simplify, point out what is essential, and make procedure precise. The universal symbols for propositions, according to logical usage, are the middle letters of the alphabet, p, q, r. Any of these symbols may stand for *any* proposition, regardless of factual truth, provided that each stands for the same proposition throughout the argument. These symbols have been called *propositional variables.*

Recently it has become customary to symbolize specific inferences and specific propositions by using other symbols than the propositional variables. These symbols have been capital letters, usually the initial letter of definitive words in the propositions, as M may symbolize "Miami is south of New York" or G may symbolize "Any man has his good points." These symbols have been described as the *values* the propositional variables may take. Thus, any law stated universally in terms of propositional variables of course also will be true if stated in the more specific symbols. Here, we shall symbolize specific inferences with the more specific symbols.

11.2 Negation of Propositions

A basic logical relation is that of *negation*. If p stands for any proposition, then $\sim p$ symbolizes the negation or denial of p. The negative of a proposition says that what the proposition says is false. Accordingly, to express the negative of a proposition, we must deny its assertion or main verb, or prefix the proposition with "it is false that. . . ." But whether, as a matter of fact, p or $\sim p$ is true, is irrelevant to logic, which regards propositions as formal units which enter into relations with other propositions. Hence, regardless of whether p symbolizes a true, false, affirmative, or negative proposition, $\sim p$ symbolizes its denial, that what is said by p is false.

Thus, if M symbolizes the proposition:

Miami is south of New York.

then $\sim M$ symbolizes its negative or denial,

Miami is not south of New York,

or,

It is false (not true) that Miami is south of New York.

We could still use the same symbolism, even if M were false and $\sim M$ were true.

Though p may stand universally for *any* proposition, whether negatively or positively worded, we will find it convenient, in the classroom, to let a specific symbol such as M stand for a positively worded proposition, wherever possible. Then $\sim M$ will stand for a negatively worded proposition. We cannot always do this, since we cannot always say whether a proposition is positively or negatively worded, as:

He failed to answer.

In such cases, our assigning of symbols is arbitrary or is determined by the proposition which occurs first. But, whenever possible, for the sake of class uniformity, we shall keep to the convention of symbolizing a positive proposition by A or M, and its denial by $\sim A$ or $\sim M$.

11.3 Law of Double Negation

If $\sim M$ stands for:

> Miami is not south of New York

then $\sim \sim M$ stands for:

> It is not true that Miami is not south of New York

or, if we cancel out our two negative words;

> Miami is south of New York.

This proposition is the one we formerly symbolized as M. We may write:

$$M = \sim\sim M.$$

This law holds true for every proposition, and is stated:

$$p = \sim\sim p.$$

It is called the *law of double negation,* and is faithfully reflected in our idiom. We may always replace $\sim \sim p$ by p, or remember that the negation of $\sim p$ is p, just as the negation of p is $\sim p$.

11.4 Conjunction of Propositions

Propositions always occur in a context, having relations to other propositions. Many propositions are stated as *true at the same time.* When two (or more) propositions are both said to be true in a joint statement, they are related by *conjunction,* symbolized by a dot in the middle of the line. Thus:

$$p \cdot q$$

means that the two propositions, p and q, are true at the same time. For example, consider the sentence:

He is uneducated but he is very intelligent.

This sentence says that two propositions, "he is uneducated" and "he is intelligent" are both true. Symbolizing the first proposition by U and the second by I, their conjunction is symbolized:

$$U \cdot I.$$

We may use the words *and, but, while* to link propositions in conjunction. When the propositions are negative, we may use *neither . . . nor* as in:

She can neither swim nor dive,

which means:

She cannot swim and she cannot dive.

Symbolizing "she cannot swim" by $\sim S$ and "she cannot dive" by $\sim D$, their conjunction is:

$$\sim S \cdot \sim D.$$

Sometimes, when the entire sentence depends on a negative verb, *or* signifies conjunction, as in:

The man couldn't read or write,

which means:

The man couldn't read and he couldn't write.

Symbolizing "the man couldn't read" by $\sim R$ and "the man couldn't write" by $\sim W$, the conjunction is:

$$\sim R \cdot \sim W.$$

Already, in these simple examples which consider conjunction only, we see that the verbal or idiomatic order is not the logical order. We have to reword and fill out sentences to reveal the nature of the logical connections.

11.5 Commutative Law

When p and q are true at the same time, then q and p are true at the same time. The order of the propositions of a conjunction makes no difference to their truth. We may write this law:

$$p \cdot q = q \cdot p.$$

This is the *commutative law* for conjunction.

For example, the conjunctive proposition,

The metal glitters but is not gold,

can be symbolized, using M for "the metal glitters" and $\sim G$ for "it is not gold" as:

$$M \cdot \sim G.$$

Substituting M for p and $\sim G$ for q in the commutative law, we have:

$$M \cdot \sim G = \sim G \cdot M.$$

EXERCISES

A. Symbolize the following propositions, assigning specific symbols in capital letters to the component propositions.

> *For example:* "The strangers ate but did not drink."
> Let A stand for "the strangers ate."
> Let $\sim D$ stand for "they did not drink."
> $A \cdot \sim D.$

Do not neglect to write out the propositions symbolized. They will not always be obvious.

1. He was a profound thinker and a forceful writer.
2. He rose to speak and the applause was deafening.
3. A statesman must envisage ideals but not be an irresponsible dreamer.

4. She wanted to go dancing but he was tired and wanted to stay home.

5. The stranger was neither young nor old.

6. Men may come and men may go but I go on forever.

7. Mary talked but Jim didn't say a word.

8. He had neither the time nor the inclination to do that.

9. The detective could not accept either the theory that Ralph made the footprints or that someone happening to have the same kind of shoes made them.

10. Harry Truman is neither a communist nor a fascist.

11. The porcupine can curl up but can't swim.

12. The Holy Roman Empire was neither holy nor Roman nor an empire.

13. His eyes were closed and he took no notice.

14. Children must not play on or near the escalator.

15. You are old, Father William . . . and your hair has become very white and yet you incessantly stand on your head.

16. A lever is free to move around an axis and makes an angle with it.

17. You aren't allowed to laugh or talk at those meetings.

18. The gravitational attraction between two objects is directly proportional to the product of their masses and inversely proportional to the square of the distance between them.

19. Her eyes were open but she was not seeing.

20. I came; I saw; I conquered.

21. She is forbidden to dance or play cards.

22. The first guinea pig sickened and died while the second lived.

23. Neither my wife nor my secretary understands me.

24. Work should not be overwearisome or overanxious.

25. "Water, water everywhere,
    And all the boards did shrink;
Water, water, everywhere,
    Nor any drop to drink."

B. Do both sentences in these pairs have the same meaning? Symbolize them, showing why or why not.

1. He is a good man. It is false that he is a good man.
2. She is beautiful but dumb. She is dumb but beautiful.
3. Chicago is west of New York. It is false that Chicago is not west of New York.
4. She remembered her tickets, but forgot her directions. She forgot her directions, but remembered her tickets.
5. She stayed at home but did not work. She worked but did not stay at home.

12 IMPLICATION

12.1 Implication

Some disappointed students were discussing the football game, which had been lost. The argument seemed to hinge on whether the player, because of whose play the team had been penalized, had been "unnecessarily rough." On this point, some of the students disagreed with the officials. But, on one point, they all agreed. This was:

If a player is unnecessarily rough, his team is penalized.

What does this proposition mean? It says that *if* one proposition, "a player is unnecessarily rough," is true, *then* another proposition, "his team is penalized" is true. Provided that the first is true—or that the officials consider it to be true—the second must be true also. The truth of the first insures or involves the truth of the second.

When two propositions are so related that, if one is true, then the other is true also, they are said to be related by *implication*. Implication is a relation which connects many of our statements, both practical and scientific; and underlies all inference and reasoning. It enables us to pass from the truth of one proposition to that of another. When two propositions are joined into an implicative proposition, the first is said to *imply* the second, which *is implied by* the first. Symbolizing the first proposition by *p*, the second by *q*, and implication by the "horseshoe," ⊃ , we may symbolize the formal properties of the implicative proposition by:

$$p \supset q$$

p is the *antecedent* (or implicans), and *q* is the *consequent* (or implicate).

Generally, as in our example, we use the words *if . . . then* to show that one proposition implies another. However, we may omit the *then*. Or we may replace the *if* by *when* or *whenever,* as in:

When the sun shines through the rain there is a rainbow.

We may use *on the condition that,* as in:

On the condition that you get here early you will get a seat.

We may invert the verb and the subject of the conditional clause, as:

Should I see her, I'll tell her.

Very often, we may use *unless* for *if . . . not,* as in:

Unless you look carefully, you'll miss it,

which means:

If you do not look carefully, you'll miss it.

Verbal idiom often places the *if* clause after its consequent, as:

You'll miss it if you do not look carefully,

which has the same meaning as the previous example and the same logical structure. The clause following *if* or *unless* is always the logical antecedent, no matter where it may be placed in the sentence. We see again that the verbal order is not always the logical order, the order which we must always try to discern in our sentences.

In all of these examples, the antecedent is a condition of the truth of the consequent. It is called the *sufficient condition;* for it is enough that it be true for the consequent to be true also. On the other hand, the consequent is called the *necessary condition* of the antecedent, since it is necessary for it to be true for the antecedent to be true. In other words, in an implication, the consequent cannot be false if the antecedent is true.

We must not confuse sufficient and necessary conditions. A sufficient condition may not be a necessary one, as "he plays tennis" is a sufficient but not necessary condition of "he gets exercise." A necessary condition may not be sufficient, as "he studies" is a necessary but not sufficient condition of "he is a good student."

Let us illustrate these two conditions in an implication, or implicative proposition:

If a footprint is in the sand someone has been here.

Let us symbolize "a footprint is in the sand" by F, "someone has been here" by S, and the implicative proposition by

$$F \supset S.$$

Now, it is sufficient for F to be true for S to be true. The truth of the antecedent is all we need to affirm the truth of the consequent. Footprints left in the sand are enough to "implicate" a maker of the footprints.

Moreover, the consequent, S, is a necessary condition of F. It is essential that S be true and not false for F to be true. "Someone has been here" must be true if it is true that "footprints are in the sand." Unless someone had been there, there could be no footprints.

On the other hand, the antecedent, F, though a sufficient, is not a necessary condition of S. For "there are footprints in the sand" is not necessary to the truth of "someone has been here." For instance, someone might have been here and left no footprints remaining in the sand. We *cannot* say that our implication is equivalent to:

If someone has been here a footprint is in the sand.

In symbols:

$$F \supset S \neq S \supset F.$$

Neither can we say that our implication is equivalent to:

If there is not a footprint in the sand, no one has been here.

For, again, "a footprint is in the sand" is not a necessary condition of "someone has been here," so that it must be true (and not false) for the latter to be true. Even if there is no footprint, someone might have been here. In symbols:

$$F \supset S \neq {\sim}F \supset {\sim}S.$$

12.2 Counterimplication

A third possibility remains. Does our example mean:

If no one has been here a footprint is not in the sand?

We reflect that, in our original implication, "someone has been here," being the consequent or necessary condition of "a footprint is in the sand," must be true for the latter to be true. Unless "someone has been here" it is false that "a footprint is in the sand." And that is just what the above sentence says. Hence, it is equivalent to our original implication, and we may write:

$$F \supset S = {\sim}S \supset {\sim}F.$$

The latter implication is called the *counterimplication* of the former, since the antecedent and consequent are denied and interchanged.

Thus, we have illustrated the meaning of implication by examples of its application to our speech. The Logic of Propositions defines or establishes these results, generally and formally, as properties of implication. In general symbols, they are:

$$p \supset q \neq q \supset p.$$
$$p \supset q \neq {\sim}p \supset {\sim}q.$$
$$p \supset q = {\sim}q \supset {\sim}p.$$

Implication as thus symbolized is material implication as defined in Whitehead and Russell's *Principia Mathematica*. It may be abstractly defined, as in the truth-tables of Chapters 27 and 28, as that relation which is true when p and q are both true, or when p is false, but false when p is true and q false.

Here, however, $p \supset q$ has been defined as meaning "if p is true then q is true." As such, it is more than an abstract relation between "truth-values"; it is a relation holding between propositions in such a way that the truth of one is the sufficient condition of the other. It is a relation between a proposition and the consequences which flow from it, if it is true. And, even if we later show the antecedent to be factually false, we must see what it would imply if it were true.

Though $p \supset q$, considered formally, is an abstract relation, we will use it to symbolize the implications between propositions which underlie inferences. For the *formal laws of implication are necessary conditions for the truth of any implication holding between propositions*. Any implications must obey these formally stated laws of logic.

Many logicians have distinguished different kinds of implication, such as material, causal, mathematical, depending on the kinds of subject matter to which implication is applied. Here, no such distinctions will be made. For it is held that implication, applied to any subject matter, is the same logically defined relation, obeying the same logical laws. Whether it actually applies, whether it is exact or probable, and how probable, is a matter of factual truth but not of formal logic. Its meaning for logic remains: If p is true then q is true.

EXERCISES

A. Symbolize the following propositions as implications between propositions, using specific symbols:

Example: "On the condition that you don't tell, I'll tell you."
Let $\sim T$ stand for "you don't tell."
Let I stand for "I'll tell you."
$\sim T \supset I.$

1. If a pass is intercepted, the other team gets the ball.
2. If water is poured into strong sulphuric acid there is an explosion.

3. If he becomes angry at customers, he will lose his job.
4. If a figure is a square it is a rectangle.
5. If the child is hungry he'll eat his spinach.
6. The goblins will get you if you don't watch out.
7. If he does not honk his horn he is to blame for the accident.
8. Unless you're quiet you'll waken the baby.
9. A patient has fever if he has smallpox.
10. If the picture is not expensive it is not a genuine Rembrandt.
11. If a player has thirteen trumps, he makes a grand slam.
12. You'll miss the train unless you hurry.
13. Whenever it rains, my sidewalk is covered with water.
14. Should anyone squeal on him, he would be a hunted man.
15. Unless A always precedes B, A is not the cause of B.
16. If he likes music, he will be both quiet and attentive.
17. He never works unless he feels like it.
18. If a student graduates, he must have 120 credit hours.
19. If a girl is beautiful she attracts men.
20. If a player uses his hands for offense his team is penalized.
21. If the pressure on the gas increases, the gas contracts.
22. If a man lives he must eat.
23. If a painting is artistic, it must be unified.
24. Unless he has a *C* average he cannot play on the team.
25. If a body is immersed in water, it displaces water and loses weight.

B.

1. What is an implication? What is its antecedent? Its consequent?
2. What is the sufficient condition of an implication? The necessary condition?
3. What is the counterimplication?

13 INFERENCES BASED ON IMPLICATION

13.1 Inference and Implication

We come, now, to a study of inferences and of when they are valid or invalid. An inference is the drawing of a conclusion from premises, the transition from something which has been accepted as true to something new, whose truth the inference aims to establish. It is a mental leap from the premises to the conclusion. It is not merely a logical relation between them, but an assertion or judgment that such a relation holds. As such, it goes beyond formal logic.

Inferences may be valid or invalid. They may correctly claim that the premises are so related to the conclusion that it follows from them, in which case they are valid. On the other hand, they may be incorrect in their claim that the conclusion is so related to the premises that it may be inferred from them. The conclusion may have no relation or intrinsic connection with the premises; in which case, the inference which draws the connection is invalid.

It is this relation between premises and conclusion, justifying valid inference, which logic studies. What is it? When does it hold and when does it fail to hold? The relation which justifies inference is the relation of implication. For, as we saw in the last chapter, two propositions are connected by implication when, if the first is true, the second is true. If one proposition implies a second, we are justified in inferring the truth of the second from the truth of the first. If the premises imply the conclusion, then the conclusion may be validly inferred from the premises. But, if the premises do not imply the conclusion, the inference from the truth of the premises to that of the conclusion is invalid.

The problem of determining whether or not inferences are valid, then, reduces to the problem of what propositions, related in what ways, imply what other propositions. Logic has found that there are certain basic combinations of propositions in which some of the propositions always imply others. These implications between propositions are the forms of valid inference. We shall turn, now, to an investigation of them.

13.2 Inferences based on Implication

A pattern of propositions, in which some propositions imply another proposition, underlies many inferences. Its properties have been studied since the dawn of logic. It is a type of implication, where the first proposition is itself an implication between two propositions. The second proposition, which is true in conjunction with the first, affirms or denies one of the propositions of the implication. Together, these two propositions are claimed to imply the affirmation or denial of the other member of the implication. In this pattern, there are traditionally considered to be four possibilities, as follows:[1]

$$[(p \supset q) \cdot p] \supset q$$
$$[(p \supset q) \cdot q] \supset p$$
$$[(p \supset q) \cdot \sim p] \supset \sim q$$
$$[(p \supset q) \cdot \sim q] \supset \sim p$$

We will consider the two valid forms first; then the two invalid ones.

The first form, one of the most common forms of inference, is valid. It is generally assumed as a postulate of logic, the truth of which must be accepted if there is a logic of inference. It finds application in our mathematical, scientific, and practical inferences. It was illustrated in the first chapter of this Part. It has been known as a form of valid inference for centuries, and has acquired a Latin

---

[1] Parenthesis and brackets will be used here with their usual significance as marks of punctuation: parentheses enclose the smaller units within the larger units enclosed by brackets. Thus $[(p \supset q) \cdot p] \supset q$ means that the proposition $p \supset q$, in conjunction with p, together imply q.

name, *modus ponens,* (short for *modus ponendo ponens,* "the mode of affirming by affirming"). We will refer to it as *M.P.*

We may also illustrate this form by reference to our definition of implication in terms of conditions. The first proposition of the form says that on the condition that p is true then q is true. The second proposition says that p *is* true, and the condition is satisfied. Hence q is true; and we may validly infer its truth from the truth of the first two propositions.

The fourth form is also valid, as can be shown from the first. For, if we substitute for $p \supset q$ its counterimplication, $\sim q \supset \sim p$, we have the first form, where $\sim q$ and $\sim p$ occur instead of p and q. This form, then, is one of valid inference. It, also, has acquired a Latin name, *modus tollens,* (short for *modus tollendo tollens,* "the mode of denying by denying"). We shall refer to it as *M.T.*

The second form is invalid. For its premises do not imply its conclusion. As we have seen, $p \supset q$ does not mean $q \supset p$, as it would have to if the second premise, q, were a sufficient condition for affirming the truth of p. Formally, it cannot be justified as a true implication. Any inference with that form is invalid, committing the fallacy traditionally called *affirming the consequent.*

The third form is also invalid. For, as we have seen, $p \supset q$ does not mean $\sim p \supset \sim q$, as it would have to if the second premise, $\sim p$, were a sufficient condition for affirming the truth of $\sim q$. Formally, it cannot be justified. Any inference with that form is invalid, and commits the fallacy traditionally called *denying the antecedent.*

In summary, then, the first and fourth of the above forms are valid; and any inferences, no matter what their subject matter, having those forms, are valid. The second and third forms are invalid, and any inferences having those forms are invalid.

13.3 Valid Inferences

Let us consider the inference:

If the law that entropy always increases holds, then the universe can never evolve backward. But the law that entropy always increases has a supreme position among the laws of nature. Therefore, the universe can never reverse its order.

Here, an inference is made from two premises to the conclusion that "the universe can never evolve backward" (reverse its order). Is this conclusion implied by the premises?

Let us symbolize "the law that entropy always increases holds" by E, and "the universe can never evolve backward" by $\sim B$. The form of the inference is:

$$[(E \supset \sim B) \cdot E] \supset \sim B.$$

Let us substitute, as we always must, the more universal symbol, p, for the antecedent—here E— and q for the consequent—here $\sim B$. Our form then becomes:

$$[(p \supset q) \cdot p] \supset q$$

This is the first of our four forms, $M.P.$ Our inference is thus an instance of a valid form, and is valid.

Let us consider another inference:

> If the people could not be won over to support dictators, there would be no dictators. Since there are, people can be won over to their support.

Let us symbolize the antecedent of the implication, "the people could (can) not be won over to support dictators," by $\sim S$; and the consequent, "there would be no dictators" by $\sim D$. Our inference is:

$$[(\sim S \supset \sim D) \cdot D] \supset S.$$

Writing p for $\sim S$, q for $\sim D$ and $\sim q$ for D, we have the fourth form, $M.T.$, which is valid. Our inference, being an instance of a valid form, is therefore valid.

13.4 Invalid Inferences

Let us consider the example:

> The driver in the accident is blameless, since he sounded his horn. But, if he hadn't sounded his horn, he would be to blame.

Does the conclusion, "the driver in the accident is blameless," follow from the premises?

Let us symbolize the antecedent of the implication, "he did not sound his horn," by $\sim H$, and the consequent, "he would be (is) to blame," by B. The form of the inference is:

$$[(\sim H \supset B) \cdot H] \supset \sim B.$$

If we replace the specific symbols by the general, $\sim H$ by p, B by q, H by $\sim p$, and $\sim B$ by $\sim q$, we have the third of our forms, that of *denying the antecedent*. Our inference, being an instance of an invalid form is invalid.

Lastly, consider the inference:

> If he did not take precautions, he would catch the disease. Since he did catch the disease, we must infer that he failed to take precautions.

Does the conclusion, "he failed to take precautions," follow from the premises?

If we symbolize "he did not take precautions," by $\sim P$ and "he catches the disease" by D, the form is:

$$[(\sim P \supset D) \cdot D] \supset \sim P.$$

Substituting p for $\sim P$ and q for D, we have the second of our forms, which is invalid, *affirming the consequent*. Our inference is invalid.

There are other inferences of this general type which, though not having either of the invalid forms given, are yet invalid. The four forms listed for this type of inference do not really include all the possible combinations of premises and conclusion. They include only the two forms accepted, explainable, and illustrated as valid, and the two *most common* ways of deviating from these forms. There are other forms, other deviations, which are neither so natural nor so common.

For example, consider the following inference:

> Unless the witness was lying, the accident was not John's fault. But, since it is evident that the accident was not John's fault, the witness was lying.

Symbolizing "the witness was lying" by L, and "the accident was not John's fault" by $\sim F$, we have:

$$[(\sim L \supset \sim F) \cdot \sim F] \supset L.$$

Substituting p for $\sim L$ and q for $\sim F$, we have:

$$[(p \supset q) \cdot q] \supset \sim p.$$

This is not one of the four forms given; since in the form with these premises, which is invalid, the conclusion is p. But this form is certainly invalid. For, arguing from the meaning of $p \supset q$, these premises cannot imply $\sim p$, any more than they can imply p.

There are many ways in which inferences may be invalid, and only certain established ways in which they may be valid. What is important for understanding logic is to know the ways in which inferences may be valid. Unexplainable deviations from these valid forms must be called invalid. In general, we may say that, *if an inference of any type has a form which is not explainable as valid, it is to be treated as invalid.*

EXERCISES

The following inferences have been worded to reveal their logical form. In each inference, the student should first designate the conclusion, in order to find whether the conclusion claimed to follow really does follow from the premises. To find the conclusion is not always easy. In our speech, the emphasis of the voice may help differentiate the conclusion from the premises. In written language, the nature of the conjunction introducing the premises or conclusion may differentiate them. The word or phrase *thus, so, hence, therefore, consequently, we may infer that* . . . etc., introduces a conclusion. Sometimes the conclusion is introduced by no conjunction, and must be singled out by eliminating the premises. These are introduced by words such as *for the reason that* . . . , *for, since, because,* etc.

Then, as in the examples in this chapter, the component propositions should be symbolized by specific capital letters taken from important words in the propositions. Replacing the specific symbols of the implicative premise by p and q, and the other specific symbols by the corresponding general symbols, the student should recognize what general form the inference exemplifies. Accordingly, he can say whether the inference is valid.

> *Example:* "If Mr. Brown does not direct this play, it will not be a success. But Mr. Brown promised to direct it; so it will be a success."
> Concl.: It will be a success.
> Let $\sim B$ stand for "Mr. Brown does not direct the play."
> Let $\sim S$ stand for "it will not be a success."
> $[(\sim B \supset \sim S) \cdot B] \supset S$
> $p/\sim B, q/\sim S: [(p \supset q) \cdot \sim p] \supset \sim q$
> Invalid; denies antecedent.

1. If the lawyer can show a preponderance of the evidence, he will win this case. He does show such a preponderance and hence will win it.

2. If Ralph made the footprints, then he was wearing studded shoes. But Ralph was wearing boots at the time, and so did not make the footprints.

3. He can call, if their telephone gets installed today. And it did get installed. So he can call.

4. Unless there are staples in this gadget, it doesn't work. But I have checked it, and found that it had plenty of staples in it. So you will have no trouble with it.

5. The amoeba is a form of life. For if an amoeba eats, it is alive. And we see this amoeba eat when we look at it with a microscope.

6. This brain will not develop unless its body produces nerve cells. And, since it does not develop, it must be that its body does not produce nerve cells.*

---

* An asterisk after an exercise indicates that its partial solution occurs in "Solutions to Selected Exercises" at the end of the book.

7. If I apply the doctrine of *res ipsa loquitur,* I will prove that he has been negligent. I have applied the doctrine; and therefore I have shown that he is negligent.

8. Unless his check had come, he would not be taking the girl to the theatre. But, since I saw them there, I guess his check came.

9. If my interpretation of this statute is correct, the judge will sustain my demurrer. Unfortunately, my demurrer was overruled, and so I must admit that my interpretation of the statute was wrong.

10. Unless the defendant denies that he was the thief, the jury will think that he is guilty. But, since he has denied it several times, the jury will hold him not guilty.

11. If her husband deserts her, she can sue for divorce. But her husband has no intention of leaving her, and so she cannot sue.*

12. If he is a Protestant, he believes in the right of private judgment in religion. Since he believes in the right of private judgment in religion, he must be a Protestant.

13. If a conclusion is established as true, the inference must be valid. Since the inference is valid, the conclusion is established as true.

14. Unless you have opportunity, you have no initiative. But you do have opportunity, and so also initiative.

15. We'll win if there are women on the jury. But since there are no women on the jury, we'll lose.

16. These darker areas on Mars are not water surfaces; for, if they were, they would reflect the rays of the sun, and they do not.

17. If the moon were formed from a big bulge on the surface of the cooling earth, it should be made from the stone of the surface. Now the moon is formed from such stony materials. Therefore. . .?

18. If knowledge is about the changing qualities of the sensory world only, stable knowledge is impossible. But science shows that there is stable knowledge. Hence, knowledge is not only about the changing qualities of the sensory world.

19. Socrates reasoned that if justice is to do good to friends and evil to enemies, it is just to injure someone. But to injure is to destroy

and make worse, and can never be just. Hence, justice is not to do good to friends and evil to enemies.*

20. Hume argued that if our knowledge of causation came from reason, we could, by reason, know what would be the effect of a given cause, prior to any experience of it. But we cannot do this. Hence. . .?

14 IMPLICATION-IN-REVERSE

14.1 Only if

In many of our statements, the conditional clause is introduced by *only if* rather than *if*. These two words represent different relations, as may be seen by the following example:

Mr. Jones burst into his home one afternoon, breathlessly calling to his wife, "I want to catch the next train to New York. Only if you help me pack will I make it." Mrs. Jones promptly disconnected the iron, and got out her husband's valise. Yet, a half-hour later, when the Joneses dashed onto the station platform, the train was just disappearing in the distance.

Was Mr. Jones mistaken when he said:

"Only if you help me pack will I make the train"?

For his wife did help him pack, and he did not make the train. Yet he was not mistaken in his prediction, since he did not say, "If you help me pack I will make the train." If he had said this, events would have proved him wrong. Instead, he said something very different, something which was probably true. He said, in effect, that it was necessary that "you help me pack" in order to make the train. "You help me pack" is a necessary but not a sufficient condition of "I make the train." He meant:

If I make the train you (must) help me pack,

when he called out to his wife.

Only if you help me pack will I make the train.

Symbolizing the first proposition, introduced by *only if,* "you help me pack," by *H*, and the second proposition by *T*, the whole proposition is:

$$(T \supset H).$$

Whenever a proposition is introduced by *only if,* it is the necessary condition of the other proposition on which it depends. Hence it is the consequent of the other proposition, which implies it. It is related to the other proposition by implication-in-reverse.

Implication-in-reverse has not been given a separate name and symbol by logicians, since it is easily symbolized by a reversed implication. But it represents a different relation from implication, that of one proposition being a necessary condition of another, rather than its sufficient condition.

Even if the proposition introduced by *only if* comes after the other proposition, it is still its consequent. The above example could have been worded:

I will make the train only if you help me pack.

Only if still introduces the consequent in an expression of an implication-in-reverse.

14.2 Equivalence

Now two propositions may be related both by implication and by implication-in-reverse, as in the following example:

"If and only if a needle is magnetized will it be attracted to the North Pole."

Here, we have two assertions. The first is:

If a needle is magnetized it is attracted to the North Pole.

Symbolizing the first proposition by M and the second by N, we have:

$$(M \supset N).$$

The second assertion is:

Only if a needle is magnetized will it be attracted to the North Pole.

The two propositions are related by implication-in-reverse. Using the same symbols as before, we have:

$$(N \supset M).$$

The entire proposition may be symbolized:

$$(M \supset N) \cdot (N \supset M).$$

Here, M and N are both true or both false, as may be seen by their counterimplications. Such propositions are called *equivalent,* and are related by equivalence. The relation may be expressed by an equality sign with three bars. Using the universal symbols we have:

$$[(p \supset q) \cdot (q \supset p)] = (p \equiv q).$$

EXERCISES

Using specific symbols, symbolize the following propositions:
1. If he goes, he will enjoy himself.
2. Only if he is an expert mechanic can he find what's wrong with this car.
3. If and only if you have a ticket will you be admitted.
4. Only if he puts a lot into his work will he get a lot out of it.
5. If and only if a number is divisible by two is it even.
6. If and only if an action is done from obligation does it have moral worth.

7. Only if a language can reflect the basic logical distinctions is it developed.

8. If and only if the premises are true and the inference is valid will the conclusion necessarily be true.

9. If and only if you fulfill the conditions of the contract will the deal be closed.

10. Only if a person has fever does he have smallpox.

11. If he is sincere in what he says he will act on it.

12. If and only if you follow directions will you find the house.

13. He works only when he feels like it.

14. The violinist will play an encore if and only if the audience claps for a long time.

15. Only if you pass the physical can you enlist in the armed forces.

16. I will tell you if and only if you promise not to tell.

17. The picture will be accepted only if it fulfills certain requirements.

18. Only if you are lucky can you win the game.

19. If you know how you can do it.

20. Only if he knows the rules can he follow the game.

21. Unless he takes precautions he might catch the disease.

22. He is a communist only if he believes in economic determinism.

15 INFERENCES BASED ON IMPLICATION-IN-REVERSE

15.1 Valid Inferences

Many inferences of the same type as the last contain a premise introduced by *only if* instead of *if*. Though these are worded in terms of implication-in-reverse, they may easily be given the form of implicative inferences. They must have one of the four forms of implicative inferences, and so are tested in the same way.

For example, the student in the chemistry laboratory reasons:

> This solution can't contain copper; for, only if it turns blue when I add acid does it contain copper, and it is reddish-brown.

Was the student validly drawing the conclusion that "this solution can't contain copper"?

Let us symbolize this inference, with specific symbols. Thus, symbolizing the proposition following *only if,* "it (a solution) turns blue when I add acid" by B, and "it contains copper" by C, we have as the symbolization of the inference:

$$[(C \supset B) \cdot \sim B] \supset \sim C.$$

If we replace the specific symbols B and C, by p and q, we recognize that this form is an instance of the fourth form, *M.T.*, given for implicative inferences. It is therefore valid;

Again, let us examine the inference:

> Only if he is the murderer does he know who committed the murder; and, since he knows who committed the murder, he is the murderer.

Symbolizing "he is the murderer" by M, and "he knows who committed the murder" by K, we have:

$$[(K \supset M) \cdot K] \supset M.$$

Replacing K and M by p and q, we recognize that this is the first of the implicative forms, *M.P.* The inference is valid.

15.2 Invalid Inferences

On the other hand, we may meet an inference like this:

> Only if he drives a car can he get to the beach; and since he drives a car, he can get to the beach.

Does the conclusion, "he can get to the beach," follow validly from the premises?

Symbolizing "he drives a car" by C, and "he can get to the beach" by B, and remembering that *only if* introduces the consequent, we have as the form of the inference:

$$[(B \supset C) \cdot C] \supset B.$$

But, replacing the specific by the general variables, we get our second form for an invalid implicative inference. Should we make it, we would be guilty of the fallacy of *affirming the consequent*. The inference is invalid.

Again, take the inference:

> She could get in only if she remembered her purse. But she evidently couldn't get in, since she is sitting on the doorstep. Hence, she must have forgotten her purse.

Is the conclusion, "she must have forgotten her purse," validly drawn?

Symbolizing "she could get in" by I, "she remembered her purse" by P, the form of the inference is:

$$[(I \supset P) \cdot \sim I] \supset \sim P.$$

We recognize our other form for an invalid inference. Should we make it, we would be *denying the antecedent*.

In general, whenever an inference contains a premise with an implication-in-reverse, it may be symbolized as an implicative inference, and tested in the same way as other implicative inferences.

EXERCISES

In the following inferences, designate the conclusion by the method explained for the last implicative inferences. Then, using specific symbols, symbolize the inferences, saying whether the premises validly imply the conclusions.

1. If the dives the father of the child star forced her to make were dangerous to a child, the father was negligent. Now all diving experts agreed that the dives were dangerous to a child. Hence, the father was negligent.

2. Since, only if the smoker is a man who habitually smokes a pipe, does he cup his hand about his cigarette, and since the smoker cups his hand about his cigarette, the smoker must be a man who habitually smokes a pipe.

3. If he were alone, anticipating his murder, he would have left a written record of his suspicions. The fact that he left no such record shows that he didn't anticipate being murdered.

4. Only if he had a strong motive would he have committed the murder. Since he did not commit it, he had no motive.*

5. Unless the governor carries out the decision of the Court, he will be cited for contempt. But it is predicted that he will not be cited for contempt. Hence, he will carry out the decision of the Court.

6. Only if gambling is stopped will there be good government. Since gambling has been stopped, the government will be good.

7. If he didn't sell his investments, he'd be swamped by taxes. But he did sell his investments; and so he need not worry.

8. John can hear the speaker only if he sits in a front row; and, since he heard the speaker, he must have sat in a front row.

9. The hurricane will come here only if the barometer falls. The radio says that the barometer is slowly falling. Therefore, the hurricane will come here.

10. The defendant argued that, if the woman beside him were his wife, he would not have been driving with one arm around her. Witnesses testified that the woman was his wife. Hence, the judge acquitted him of one-arm driving.

11. Only if the politician acts on what he says is he sincere. Since he acts on what he says, he must be sincere.

12. Unless he acts at once, the entire enterprise will fail. And he is hurrying to remedy the situation immediately. Hence he will rescue his enterprise.

13. When the solute is an electrolyte, its molecules tend to split up into ions. Since this solute's molecules do not split up into ions, it is not an electrolyte.

14. The ship will come in safely, since the pilot knows the bay by

heart. And a ship can enter safely only if its pilot knows the bay.*

15. Juvenile delinquency will decrease only if the slums are cleared up. Since juvenile delinquency sharply decreased, the slums are cleared up.

16. The detective reasoned that, unless the boys knew the buildings well, they could not have perpetrated the robbery. Therefore, since the boys were strangers, they were not the robbers.

17. If the hypothesis does not explain the data, it should not be accepted. So he claims that, since the hypothesis explains the data, it should be accepted.

18. Only if the man wore studded shoes could he have made the footprints; and, since the man wore boots, he could not have made them.

19. The candidate will be elected only if he carries the large cities. Since he is sure to carry the large cities, he will be elected.

20. Kant reasoned that only if the man's honest act were done from principle did it have moral worth. But the man's honest act was done from policy. Therefore, it did not have moral worth.

16 DISJUNCTION

16.1 Weak Disjunction

Another relation between propositions links them in such a way that one or the other of them is true. Let us illustrate by a quotation from Mill's famous essay *On Liberty*. There he shows how the greatest threat to individual liberty lies in the "tyranny of the majority." He explains that:

> The tyranny of the majority is exercised either by laws *or* by public opinion.

Now this statement illustrates a new relation: two propositions, "the tyranny of the majority is exercised by laws" and "the tyranny of the majority is exercised by public opinion," connected by a relation signified by *either . . . or*. It means that *at least one* of the propositions is true, and is called *disjunction*. Symbolizing the first proposition by *L*, the second by *O*, and the relation of disjunction by **v**, we can symbolize the above statement:

$$L \lor O.$$

The English language does not have so many words for disjunction as for conjunction. Sometimes we use *either . . . or* as in the above, and as in:

> Either he wanted to go or he thought he ought to.

Sometimes we use *or* only, as in:

> This precipitate contains zinc *or* manganese hydroxides.

In all of these disjunctive statements, at least one of the propositions, no matter which, is true.

Moreover, in the three examples above, at least one alternative is true *and possibly both* are true. Tyranny may be exercised both by laws and by public opinion. A person might both want and think he ought to go. The precipitate might contain both zinc and manganese hydroxides. Both alternatives *might* be true, although both are not said to be true. All that is said is that at least one is true. These propositions are said to be in *weak* or inclusive disjunction. The logical relation of disjunction symbolized by **v** is weak disjunction.

Moreover, weak disjunction is the common meaning of *or* in our everyday speech. We say:

> I shall see Tom or Dick this afternoon,

meaning that we shall see one and possibly both. We say:

Either the manager or his assistant will be there,

meaning that at least one and possibly both will be there.

16.2 Strong Disjunction

On the other hand, we sometimes wish to say that one *but not both* of two alternatives is true, that one and only one is true. We may say:

Either he did it or he didn't.
A proposition is either true or false.
He is in California or Florida.
You must choose one or the other road.

Here, one but not both of the alternatives is true. "He" did not both do it and not do it. A proposition is not both true and false. "He" is not in both California and Florida at the same time. You can't travel on both roads. These examples are in *strong* or exclusive disjunction. All contradictory statements are in strong disjunction.

Strong disjunction, which is really a complex relation, combining the relation of disjunction with that of incompatibility, has often been symbolized by $\underline{\vee}$. In the third example above, we may symbolize "he is in California" by C and "he is in Florida" by F, and the whole proposition by:

$$C \underline{\vee} F.$$

The difference between a weak and strong disjunction is not one that is expressed merely by the English *or* or *either . . . or*. Latin distinguished between the meanings, using the enclitic, *-vel,* for weak, and *aut . . . aut* for strong disjunction. But in English, the meaning of the sentence and the compatibility or incompatibility of the propositions in disjunction determine whether the disjunction is weak or strong.

Strong disjunction must not be confused with weak disjunction. In order to make clear when *or* signifies a weak disjunction, legal language uses the notation of *and/or*. A lawyer says:

This contract may be voided by the party of the first part **and/or** the party of the second part.

He thus specifies that the contract may be voided by either or both of the parties. If he did not so specify, and wrote only *or* instead of *and/or,* another lawyer might take the sentence to mean that the contract might be voided by only one but not both of the parties.

An example of the consequence of confusing the two meanings of disjunction is shown in the following newspaper item:

> C—— must finish serving his 60-day sentence for assault and battery, Circuit Judge W—— ruled, in rejecting a plea for a writ of habeas corpus. . . .
>
> R—— (C——'s lawyer) had contended that the law provides for either a fine or a jail term for assault and battery, but not for both.
>
> The judge had fined C—— $250 and sentenced him to 60 days. C—— has served 17 days of the sentence, and R—— asked for his release, saying that since he had already paid the fine he couldn't be forced to stay in jail. The County Solicitor then read the 1927 statute which states that when a law provides for fine 'or' imprisonment it really means 'both' if the trial judge wants to give both a fine and a jail sentence.[1]

Here, the difference between the two disjunctions is the difference between being released from and staying in jail!

16.3 Commutative Law

When we state a disjunction such as:

> Either Mr. or Mrs. Smith will be home,

we could just as well have said:

> Either Mrs. or Mr. Smith will be home.

The order of the propositions in disjunction makes no difference. Symbolizing "Mr. Smith will be home" by S, and "Mrs. Smith will be home" by H, we have:

$$(S \lor H) \equiv (H \lor S).$$

In general symbols, we have:

---

[1] *The Miami Herald,* Wednesday, November 18, 1953.

$$(p \vee q) \equiv (q \vee p).$$

This is the commutative law for disjunction.

16.4 The Negative of a Disjunction

Suppose I said to you,

That man must be either hungry or tired,

and you wanted to contradict me. You would not say that either that man is not hungry or not tired, since this proposition could be true at the same time as mine. You would have to say:

That man is neither hungry nor tired.

For, in order to deny that at least one of the propositions is true, it is necessary to say that neither is true. Symbolizing the first proposition by H and the second by T, we have:

$$\sim(H \vee T) \equiv (\sim H \cdot \sim T).$$

In general symbols:

$$\sim(p \vee q) \equiv (\sim p \cdot \sim q).$$

The law may be stated thus: The negative of a disjunction is a conjunction, the propositions of which are the negatives of those of the disjunction. The law is part of what has been called *De Morgan's law*.

Since strong disjunction is a special case of disjunction, which combines incompatibility with it, its negation is a special case, which denies either the incompatibility or the disjunction, thus:

$$\sim(p \circledv q) \equiv [(\sim p \cdot \sim q) \vee (p \cdot q)].$$

For example, the denial of

Either he will get social security payments or a union pension.

is:

Either he will get neither social security payments nor a union pension, or he will get both.

EXERCISES

Symbolize the following propositions, using specific symbols, and showing whether the disjunction is weak or strong. Then symbolize the negatives of the weak disjunctions.

1. The train is going north or south.
2. He was driving very fast or very carelessly.
3. We need something to fertilize the soil or hold the moisture.
4. That man is either a Protestant preacher or a Rabbi.
5. I impugn either your intelligence or your honesty.
6. Sulphur dioxide results from the ignition of certain sulphides or sulphates.*
7. Either he had good luck or remarkable ability.
8. If the flame from a substance held in a Bunsen burner is blue-violet, it contains either potassium or indium.
9. One of us will gain from the transaction.
10. She either needs it or wants it.
11. Either he would offend his patron or endure the contempt of his fellows.
12. Either the fish has shining scales or it is not a pompano.
13. Either he likes her or she likes him.
14. If the wife were a better housekeeper or the husband were more patient, the marriage would have been a success.*
15. Mr. Smith and/or his wife may draw on their joint account.
16. He is either an army supply sergeant or a practical joker.
17. You must say yes or no.
18. If a man lets his wife drive in that city, either he wants a new car or a new wife.
19. This watch is either defective or improperly regulated.
20. The punishment will be $600 or 6 months in jail.
21. Either he is a person of inferior intelligence or his emotions interfere with his thinking.
22. Either the examination was very easy or the candidates were very good.
23. Either he is happy or he seems to be.
24. Either the position or the momentum of the particle will vary.

25. He stays home while his wife goes out or she stays home while he goes out.
26. He forgot to do it or he didn't want to.
27. Either you forgot to mail the letter or I didn't get it.
28. Either Ralph made the footprints intentionally or unintentionally.
29. False conclusions either do not follow validly from their premises or follow from false premises.
30. "Whether you look, or whether you listen,
You hear life murmur or see it glisten." *

17 INFERENCES BASED ON DISJUNCTION

17.1 The Disjunctive Forms

The relation of disjunction gives us a new form of inference, where the first premise is a disjunction of two propositions, the second premise affirms or denies one of the propositions, and the conclusion denies or affirms the other. Again, there are four possibilities:

$$[(p \vee q) \cdot \sim p] \supset q,$$
$$[(p \vee q) \cdot \sim q] \supset p,$$
$$[(p \vee q) \cdot p] \supset \sim q,$$
$$[(p \vee q) \cdot q] \supset \sim p.$$

The first of these four forms is valid. For the disjunctive premise says that at least one of two propositions is true. The other premise says that the first proposition is false. Hence, we may conclude, the other proposition is the only one left to be true. Formally, this form may be proved from *modus ponens,* when disjunction is defined in terms of implication.

The second form is valid for the same reason. For the order of the propositions of a disjunction makes no difference to their truth, by the commutative law. Whenever one of the alternatives of a disjunction is denied, the other may be validly inferred to be true. We could refer to either form as *Disj.* This form is reducible to *modus tollens.*

The third and fourth forms are both invalid. For $p \vee q$ means that at least one and possibly both p and q are true. That one is true does not enable us to infer that the other is false. Formally, when disjunction is defined in terms of implication, these forms are equivalent to *denying the antecedent* or *affirming the consequent.*

In summary, any inference which has either of the first two forms is valid, and any inference which has either of the last two forms is invalid.

17.2 Applications

Let us examine some disjunctive inferences in our reasoning, starting with one in the Platonic dialogues.

The famous method of Socrates was to lead the man he was questioning to discern for himself the relations his beliefs had to each other, so that he could draw for himself the "logical" conclusion, which was usually disturbing to some of those beliefs. In the *Gorgias,* Socrates is questioning a young man named Polus, who has been maintaining the popular belief that to do injustice may be advantageous to the doer, and so is "better" than to suffer it. Socrates, step by logical step, leads Polus to admit that the exact opposite of his belief follows from his other beliefs. The last steps of the argument follow:

Socrates. Then, if doing wrong is more disgraceful than suffering, the more disgraceful must exceed in pain or evil or both: does not that also follow?

Polus. Of course.

Socrates. First, then, let us consider whether the doing of injustice exceeds the suffering in consequent pain: Do the injurers suffer more than the injured?

Polus. No, Socrates, certainly not.

Socrates. Then they do not exceed in pain?

Polus. No.

Socrates. But if not in pain, then not in both?

Polus. Certainly not.

Socrates. Then they can only exceed in the other?

Polus. Yes.

Socrates. That is to say, in evil?

Polus. True.

Socrates. Then doing injustice will have an excess of evil, and will therefore be a greater evil than suffering injustice?

Polus. Clearly.[1]

Let us paraphrase Socrates' argument, so that the logical form is revealed:

> Doing injustice exceeds suffering injustice in pain or in evil. But doing injustice does not exceed in pain. Hence, it exceeds in evil.

The first premise of the argument is a weak disjunction. Symbolizing "doing injustice exceeds in pain" by P, and "it exceeds in evil" by E, we have as the logical form of the inference:

$$[(P \vee E) \cdot {\sim}P] \supset E.$$

Substituting p and q for P and E, we have the first of our valid forms. The conclusion follows from the premises.

Again, consider the inference:

> This black precipitate contains sulphides of mercury or lead. But tests indicate that lead is absent. Hence, mercury is present.

Symbolizing "this black precipitate contains the sulphide of mercury"

---

[1] Plato, *Gorgias*, Steph. pp. 474–75.

by M, and "it contains the sulphide of lead" by L, the form of the inference is:

$$[(M \vee L) \cdot \sim L] \supset M.$$

Substituting p and q for M and L, we have the second of our valid forms. The conclusion is validly drawn.

Consider the following example:

> Either the speaker is convinced of the truth of what he says or he loses direct contact with the audience. Since this speaker is thoroughly convinced of his ideas, his appeal is immediate.

Symbolizing "the speaker is convinced of the truth of what he says" by C, "he loses direct contact with the audience" by L, and "his appeal is immediate" by $\sim L$, we have as the form of the inference:

$$[(C \vee L) \cdot C] \supset \sim L.$$

Substituting p and q for C and L, we have the third form, an invalid one. The conclusion of this inference does not follow from its premises.

Lastly, consider the following:

> Either I can't go to the dance or my Dad gives me the money. And, since I can't go to the dance, my Dad did not give me the money.

Symbolizing "I can't go to the dance" by $\sim D$, and "my Dad gives me the money" by M, the form is:

$$[(\sim D \vee M) \cdot \sim D] \supset \sim M.$$

When we replace $\sim D$ by p and M by q, we have the same invalid form as above. The conclusion does not follow from the premises.

17.3 Inferences Based on Strong Disjunction

Traditionally, logic texts give consideration to inferences based on strong disjunction. However, since disjunctions are to be regarded as weak unless the disjuncts are known to be incompatible, such inferences occur infrequently. The four forms are:

$$[(p \otimes q) \cdot \sim p] \supset q,$$
$$[(p \otimes q) \cdot \sim q] \supset p,$$
$$[(p \otimes q) \cdot p] \supset \sim q,$$
$$[(p \otimes q) \cdot q] \supset \sim p.$$

All four of these forms are valid. For if we know that one and one only of the disjuncts is true, and if we can either affirm or deny one of them, then we can conclude the denial or affirmation of the other. For instance, consider the strong disjunction:

The violinist is playing either in London or New York tonight.

Symbolizing "the violinist is playing in London tonight" by L, and "the violinist is playing in New York tonight" by N, we have:

$$L \otimes N.$$

Now if we know that L is true, we conclude that N is false, and if we know that L is false we conclude that N is true. The same thing holds when N or its denial is a premise.

EXERCISES

In the following inferences, designate the conclusion. Then symbolize the component propositions, give the form of the inference, and show what general form it illustrates, according to the method followed for implicative inferences.

1. The director insists that either the star is in the show or the show will be a flop. Since she came back to the show, it will be a success.
2. Either John or his brother knows the secret. Since John doesn't know it, his brother must know it.

3. Either the acoustics where I was sitting were poor, or the pianist did not play well. But the critics raved over his playing. Hence the acoustics were poor.

4. One or the other of us is all mixed up, and I think I'm right. Therefore . . . ?*

5. Either the boss thought the candidate was not good enough, or he had reasons of his own for rejecting him. But the candidate could not have had better qualifications. Hence the boss must have had his own reasons for rejecting him.

6. If my mother dislikes my partner, I can't go to the dance. Since she likes him very much, I'm sure I can go.

7. He must pay a fine or serve a jail sentence. Since he has already paid his fine, he can't be forced to stay in jail.

8. You will not admit that you are guilty. For, if you admitted your guilt you would run the risk of losing your social prestige; and that's something one with your pride will never do.

9. Either he is a citizen or he can't vote. But, since he is a citizen, he can vote.

10. The witness was either angry or afraid; and, since she was obviously very angry, we may infer that she wasn't afraid.

11. This diamond is the real McCoy. For only if it cuts glass is it genuine, and it cuts glass.

12. That man is either a genius or decidedly eccentric. Since everyone regards him as eccentric, he is not a genius.

13. It is well known that either the ambassador will say the usual things or he will be recalled. And, according to the paper, he said the usual things. So he will not be recalled.

14. She said she would not worry if she did not hear from Jim. But she did hear from him, so her worries are over.

15. You cannot find what caused the event. For either you must repeat the conditions or you will not find the cause, and you cannot repeat the conditions.

16. Only if you listen to reason will you get to the bottom of the matter; and, since you won't listen to reason, you won't understand the affair.

17. Either you go to the dentist or you have a toothache; and, since

you go to the dentist regularly, you aren't troubled by toothaches.

18. The footprints were made by Ralph or by someone else wearing studded shoes. Since they were not made by Ralph, they were made by someone else wearing the same kind of shoes.

19. If expressions containing such words as "ought" assert nothing, but are emotional interjections, they cannot be argued about. But people do treat such expressions as controversial. Hence they are meaningful assertions.

20. Either his first or his second premise must be wrong. But his first premise cannot possibly be admitted, and hence his second premise is right.

18 INCOMPATIBILITY

18.1 Negation of a Conjunction

A good government, according to democratic tradition, has as its ideal that:

> The people have liberty and equality.

Here, two propositions are related by conjunction, since they are said to be true at the same time. Symbolizing "the people have liberty" by L and "the people have equality" by E the conjunction is symbolized:

$$L \cdot E.$$

Now, political thinkers have often pointed out that, unless liberty is defined as something with obligations and restraints, the above conjunction is false. If liberty is unrestrained individualism, then:

$$\sim(L \cdot E).$$

It is not true that the people have both liberty and equality.

In denying or negating the conjunction, what have we said? We have not said that the people do not have liberty. We have not said that they do not have equality. We have not said that they do not have either. We have said that they do not have both. We have said that both propositions are not true together. In other words, we have denied the relation of conjunction between them, not the propositions themselves.

When, as above, we say that two propositions are not both true, we mean that at least one and possibly both are false. One or the other is false. We mean, in this example:

Either the people do not have liberty or they do not have equality.

Using our same symbols, we have:

$$\sim L \mathbf{v} \sim E.$$

This exemplifies the law for the negation of a conjunction, which is, in general symbols:

$$\sim(p \cdot q) \equiv (\sim p \mathbf{v} \sim q).$$

The rule may be read: The negation of a conjunction is a disjunction, the propositions of which are the negatives of those of the conjunction. It is the other half of De Morgan's law, the first half of which gives the negative of a disjunction.

18.2 Incompatibility

The name for the relation between propositions which is the negative of a conjunction is *incompatibility*, since it relates propositions which cannot be true together and so are incompatible. We could read the above example:

That the people have liberty is incompatible with their having equality.

Incompatibility is so commonly used in our speech that its verbal expressions are various. Moreover, the verbal expression of incompatibility differs from its logical form, so that it is often hard to recognize. Sometimes *it is false that both . . . and* signifies incompatibility, as when the lawyer at a trial may point out:

> *It is false that both* the first witness *and* the second witness are telling the truth.

Often, merely *cannot . . . and* are used, as a politician may urge:

> My opponent *cannot* favor such a policy *and* be a good American.

Though the factual truth of this, and any other example, is not our concern, let us examine its form. First, let us restate it, so that the verbal form reveals the logical form:

> It cannot be true both that my opponent favors such a policy and that he is a good American.

The incompatible propositions are both dependent on *it cannot be true,* which logically and grammatically governs the whole sentence, and which negates the conjunction of the two propositions.

Since we know the general form of an incompatibility, let us symbolize it by the specific symbols. Letting F stand for "my opponent favors such a policy," and A stand for "he is a good American," the form of the incompatibility is:

$$\sim(F \cdot A).$$

It must be noted that in our rewording of the politician's original statement, as in most other statements of incompatibility, *cannot be* is only a statement of *is not,* which emphasizes the necessity of the denial of the conjunction. The politician is not saying that "my opponent *can* hold such a policy" is incompatible with "he *can* be a good American." For the politician is speaking not about possibilities but actualities; and is saying that "he holds such a policy" is incompatible with "he is a good American," whatever that may mean.

Other examples of incompatibility abound in all our literature. For instance, William James says, pointing out the incompatibilities of our tendencies:

> The millionaire's work would run counter to the saint's; the bon-vivant and the philanthropist would trip each other up; the philosopher and the lady-killer could not well keep house in the same tenement of clay. Such different characters may conceivably at the outset of life be alike possible to man. But to make any of them actual the rest should be suppressed.[1]

Let us symbolize just one of these incompatibilities:

> The philosopher and the lady-killer could not well keep house in the same tenement of clay.

Since James is not talking about possibilities but actualities, let us symbolize "the philosopher keeps house in this tenement of clay" by *P*, and "the lady-killer keeps house in this same tenement of clay" by *L*. The incompatibility is:

$$\sim(P \cdot L).$$

EXERCISES

Reword the following sentences so that their logical form is revealed. Symbolize them, using specific symbols. Then symbolize the incompatibilities as disjunctions.

1. You can't have your cake and eat it too.
2. A tree cannot be both deciduous and an evergreen.
3. You can't vote for both the Republican and Democratic candidates.
4. Neither one nor the other has slept a wink.
5. Ralph couldn't have worn boots and have made the footprints.
6. The precipitate could not be lead chloride and not dissolve.*

---

[1] *Principles of Psychology.* New York. Henry Holt, 1890, vol. i, pp. 309–310.

7. The products of the land are owing to nature or to man's labor.
8. He can't marry both Jean and Sally.
9. The territory couldn't belong to both England and France.
10. It is impossible to work hard and not have some results.
11. A proposition cannot be both true and false at the same time.
12. She cannot be a concert artist and lead a normal home life.
13. He must have either brawn or brains.
14. This precipitate could not be nickel sulphide and be light grey in color.
15. The car cannot run without gas.*
16. He couldn't be a man of action and not make up his mind.
17. It is impossible to see the beauty of the storm while you fear for your life.
18. He is well-meaning, but lacks insight into what might help.
19. He can't be boastful and retain the approbation of his fellows.
20. It is impossible for a man to be a communist and believe in private ownership of utilities.
21. The substance is not both an acid and a base.
22. Schopenhauer's theories are incompatible with Nietszche's.*
23. That stone could not have been unsupported and have stayed there that long.
24. It is impossible for nations to stay at peace and not give up some of their powers to an international organization.
25. It is impossible for this solution to be blue and not contain copper.
26. He can't stay in the sun all day and not get sunburned.
27. They cannot spend their vacation in the mountains and at the seashore at the same time.
28. The hypothesis could neither be verified nor rejected.
29. She could not be a great actress and not have insight into the emotions.
30. It is impossible, said Spinoza, to search for the highest good while following the usual objects of desire.

19 INFERENCES BASED ON INCOMPATIBILITY

19.1 The Four Forms

The relation of incompatibility gives us another type of inference, where the first premise is an incompatibility between two propositions, the second premise affirms or denies one of the incompatible propositions, and the conclusion denies or affirms the other. Again, tradition considers four possibilities:

$$[\sim(p \cdot q) \cdot p] \supset \sim q,$$
$$[\sim(p \cdot q) \cdot q] \supset \sim p,$$
$$[\sim(p \cdot q) \cdot \sim p] \supset q,$$
$$[\sim(p \cdot q) \cdot \sim q] \supset p.$$

The first form is valid: The first premise states that two propositions cannot both be true. The second premise says that one is true. Hence, it may be validly concluded that the other proposition is not true. Formally, when incompatibility is defined in terms of implication, this form reduces to *modus ponens*.

The second form is valid for the same reason. By the commutative law for conjunction, the order of the propositions of an incompatibility makes no difference. No matter which proposition is affirmed, the other one may be denied. Moreover, it reduces to *modus tollens*. We could refer to either form as *Incomp*.

The third and fourth forms are invalid. For an incompatibility says merely that two propositions cannot both be true, not that they cannot both be false, which they well might be. That one of the propositions of an incompatibility is false is no reason for concluding that the other is true. It, too, might be false. Formally, when incompatibility is defined in terms of implication, these forms reduce to the invalid forms of *denying the antecedent* and *affirming the consequent.*

In summary, any inference having one of the first two forms will be valid, and any inference having one of the last two forms will be invalid.

19.2 Applications

What student does not remember his puzzle at registration, his efforts to fit the desired courses, meeting at set times, into a schedule with no conflicts? Part of solving this puzzle is reasoning such as the following:

> I can't attend both German and Logic meeting at 9:30 every Monday, Wednesday, and Friday. But I must have German at that hour. Consequently, I can't take Logic at that hour.

This inference is one which you make so commonly that you do not consider its form. Let us state it, symbolizing "I attend German at 9:30 on Monday, Wednesday, and Friday" by G and "I attend Logic at that hour" by L. The form of the inference becomes:

$$[\sim(G \cdot L) \cdot G] \supset \sim L.$$

Substituting p and q for G and L, we see that the inference has a valid form. The student is right in his natural conclusion that "I can't take Logic at that hour."

Now, having drawn the conclusion that you cannot take Logic at 9:30, your problem is still unsolved. For you must somehow get in Logic. The only other section of Logic which is open is at 2:30 on those days. So you juggle your schedule around some more, and reason:

> I can't attend both History and Logic at 2:30 every Monday, Wednesday, and Friday. But, since I must take Logic at that time, I can't take History at that hour.

Again, you confidently assume that the inference is valid. And, again, your confidence is justified. For, symbolizing "I attend History at 2:30 on Monday, Wednesday, and Friday" by H, and I take Logic at that hour" by L, the form is:

$$[\sim(H \cdot L) \cdot L] \supset \sim H.$$

Substituting p and q for H and L, we see that the inference has a valid form. As in the first inference, the premises imply the conclusion.

Because so many inferences based on incompatibility are both natural and valid, we often make invalid inferences just as naturally. For example, a fatalist may argue:

> He can't be fated to go both by way of the Street and the Avenue; and he evidently wasn't fated to go by way of the Avenue; (since he didn't.) Hence, he must have been fated to go by way of the Street.

Symbolizing "he was fated to go by way of the Street" by S, and "he was fated to go by way of the Avenue" by A, the form of the inference is:

$$[\sim(S \cdot A) \cdot \sim A] \supset S.$$

Substituting p and q for S and A, we have the last of our invalid forms. The conclusion, "he must have been fated to go by way of the Street," does not follow from the premises but from the fatalist's unverifiable assumption that he was fated to do whatever he did.

Finally, let us consider another example:

> You can't both observe community speed laws and not be out of step with the rest of the traffic. But, since you are out of step with the rest of the traffic, you aren't observing community speed laws.

Does the conclusion, "you aren't observing community speed laws" follow from the premises?

Let us symbolize "you observe community speed laws" by O, and "you are not out of step with the rest of the traffic" by $\sim T$. The inference becomes:

$$[\sim(O \cdot \sim T) \cdot T] \supset \sim O.$$

Replacing O by p, $\sim T$ by q, T by $\sim q$, and $\sim O$ by $\sim p$, we have:

$$[\sim(p \cdot q) \cdot \sim q] \supset \sim p.$$

This is an invalid form. The conclusion does not follow from the premises.

EXERCISES

In each of the following exercises, what is the conclusion? Symbolize, using specific symbols, and show whether the conclusion follows validly from the premises.

1. This water cannot be both hot and cold in reality. Since it has a high temperature, it cannot be cold (though it feels cold).
2. It was written that a man cannot serve both God and Mammon. And we know that this man worships money. Hence, he cannot serve God.
3. It is impossible to be sincere and always agree with others. Since he is always agreeing with others, he cannot be sincere.
4. We cannot both have our religion and attack it. But since we don't attack it, we have it after all.
5. He can't get his work done, since he went on vacation. For he can't get his work done and go on vacation, too.
6. Unless he takes his final examination, he will not get credit for it after all. He took the final examination, so now he will get credit for the course.
7. This pork roast is lean, since it can't be both cheap and lean. And it is not cheap.
8. Jim can't be alert at his job and stay up all night. Since he sleeps eight hours a night, he is right on the ball.*
9. It is false that John could have had the jury against him and have won his case. But he did win; so at least the jury was not against him.
10. Only if he had a strong motive would he have committed the murder; and, since he did not commit it, he had no motive.
11. A man can't keep to his principles and please his constituency.

Since, to judge from the papers, he didn't please his constituency, we may infer that he kept to his principles.

12. Since Jim can't both keep his job and say what he thinks about the management; and, since he lost his job, he must have said what he thought about the management.

13. It is agreed that the defendant could not possibly have been doing his duty as a watchman and have been asleep. But all you have shown was that he was not doing his duty as a watchman; and this does not prove that he was asleep.

14. Smith is honest only if his dishonesty will be detected and punished. Now he knows that his dishonest weighing of merchandise will not be found out. Hence he will make dishonest weights.

15. It is an indefeasible law that he could not disregard all moral laws and lead any sort of a satisfying life. Since he leads a full and satisfying life, he must obey moral laws.

16. The same substance cannot be both an acid and a base; and, since this substance is not an acid, it is a base.

17. Since the temperature cannot be both forty and forty-five; and, since the forty-five degree reading is unreliable, the temperature must be forty.

18. Schopenhauer said that a man could not be happy and follow his desires. Since a man follows his desires, he is not happy.

19. Both the corpuscular theory and the wave theory of light cannot be true. But the corpuscular theory has been discarded. Hence the wave theory is true.

20. Aristotle argued: Either the position of the stars does not change noticeably when you travel, or the earth is spherical. But the position of the stars changes noticeably when you travel. So the earth is spherical in shape.

20 THE EQUIVALENTS OF IMPLICATION

20.1 Counterimplication equivalent

All through this inquiry into the ways of propositions, we have treated the relation of implication as basic. We have said that implication is that relation which links two propositions in such a way that if the first is true the second is true. We shall now see that an implication between two propositions may be equivalently stated by other relations between them.

In the implication,

If a bird is an ibis, it has a long neck,

let us symbolize "a bird is an ibis" by I and "it has a long neck" by N. The implication is:

$$I \supset N.$$

In Chapter 12, we saw that this was equivalent to its counterimplication:

$$\sim N \supset \sim I.$$

If a bird does not have a long neck, it is not an ibis.

20.2 The Disjunctive Equivalent

Now implication has equivalents in other relations. Though often, but not always, implication may seem most natural to our idiom, these other equivalents say and mean exactly the same thing.

Consider our implication:

If a bird is an ibis it has a long neck.

This means, in terms of disjunction:

Either a bird is not an ibis or it has a long neck.

(If this sentence does not seem to say the same thing as the first, try merely inverting its order to "either a bird has a long neck or it is not an ibis.") Using our same symbols, we may write the equivalence:

$$(I \supset N) \equiv (\sim I \lor N).$$

In words, an implication between two propositions is equivalent to the disjunction of the negation of the *antecedent* and the consequent.

20.3 The Incompatibility Equivalent

Let us consider our implication:

> If a bird is an ibis it has a long neck.

This means, also:

It is false that a bird is an ibis and does not have a long neck.

Using our same symbols, we may write:

$$(I \supset N) \equiv \sim(I \cdot \sim N).$$

For, to say "if I is true then N is true" is to say "if I is true, N cannot be false," or "it is false that I is true and N is false."

20.4 The Table of Equivalents

Now the logic of propositions states generally that what holds for these examples holds for *any* two propositions; and it justifies these equivalences in its system. Many of the equivalences we have met before, as in counterimplication and De Morgan's law. And we have throughout presupposed:

$$(p \supset q) \equiv \sim(p \cdot \sim q).$$

For we defined implication as relating p and q in such a way that, p being true, q cannot be false. On the basis of this definition, we have said that one proposition did not imply another when, though it was true, the other was false.

Using the general symbols, since these equivalences hold for any propositions, we may put all our equivalences into one formula, where each relation is equivalent to each of the others:

$$(p \supset q) \equiv (\sim q \supset \sim p) \equiv (\sim p \ \mathbf{v} \ q) \equiv \sim (p \cdot \sim q)$$

Now, in finding the equivalents for an expression, let us use the specific symbols. For example, let us find the equivalents of:

Either he is lucky or he will lose the game.

Symbolizing "he is lucky" by L, and "he will lose the game" by G, we have:

$$L \ \mathbf{v} \ G.$$

Now the disjunction in our formula is $\sim p \ \mathbf{v} \ q$. Accordingly, let us replace $\sim p$ by L and q by G in our general formula. It will read:

$$(\sim L \supset G) \equiv (\sim G \supset L) \equiv (L \ \mathbf{v} \ G) \equiv \sim (\sim L \cdot \sim G).$$

The three equivalents of our disjunction are:

$\sim L \supset G$; "If he is not lucky he will lose the game."

$\sim G \supset L$; "If he does not lose the game he is lucky."

$\sim (\sim L \cdot \sim G)$; "He can't both be unlucky and not lose the game."

These propositions all say the same thing as our first proposition.

Of course we may not need to find all three equivalents. We may want to find only one, say an implicative equivalent. In that case, we shall substitute specific symbols only in the first (or second) expression. Here, the implicative equivalent of $L \ \mathbf{v} \ G$ would be either $\sim L \supset G$, or $\sim G \supset L$, its counterimplication. We note that a disjunction is equivalent to an implication whose antecedent is the negation of one of the disjuncts.

Suppose we have an incompatibility for which we wish to find the equivalents. Consider the incompatibility:

He can't have his cake and eat it, too.

Symbolizing "he has his cake" by H, and "he eats it" by E, the expression is symbolized:

$$\sim(H \cdot E).$$

Now the incompatibility of our general formula is $\sim(p \cdot \sim q)$. Accordingly, we shall substitute H for p and E for $\sim q$ in our general formula. We then have:

$$(H \supset \sim E) \equiv (E \supset \sim H) \equiv (\sim H \vee \sim E) \equiv \sim(H \cdot E).$$

The three equivalents of our incompatibility are:

$H \supset \sim E$; "If he has his cake he can't eat it."

$E \supset \sim H$; "If he eats his cake he can't have it."

$\sim H \vee \sim E$; "Either he doesn't have his cake or he doesn't eat it."

Again, the implicative equivalents of $\sim(H \cdot E)$ are $H \supset \sim E$ or $E \supset \sim H$, its counterimplication. An incompatibility is equivalent to an implication whose consequent is the negation of one of the incompatible propositions.

20.5 Equivalences Between Forms of Valid Inference

An amazing result of the equivalences between the four relations is that all of the forms of valid inference which we have studied so far are equivalent. For, if we substitute, say, the equivalent implication for the disjunction or incompatibility in the forms containing them, we have one of the two valid implicative forms. And, if we substitute an implication for its counterimplication, the two implicative forms reduce to one, as we have already shown.

For example, consider the disjunctive inference:

> We know that this solution contains either manganese or zinc, and experiment shows that manganese is absent. Hence, zinc must be present.

Symbolizing "this solution contains manganese" by M, and this solution contains zinc" by Z, the form of the inference is:

$$[(M \vee Z) \cdot \sim M] \supset Z.$$

This, we remember, is a form for a valid disjunctive inference.

Now let us substitute for $(M \vee Z)$ its implicative equivalent, $(\sim M \supset Z)$. The form becomes:

$$[(\sim M \supset Z) \cdot \sim M] \supset Z.$$

This is *modus ponens,* the form for a valid implicative inference.

Similarly, we may always substitute the implicative equivalent for the incompatibility in a valid form based on it; and we always obtain a valid implicative inference. An analogous substitution in an invalid form will always result in another invalid form.

We come to the inescapable conclusion that all of the basic forms for valid inference which we have been discussing reduce to one form. Though which form we consider basic depends on the order of development of the logical system, we shall take the form we developed first, that of *modus ponens*. It seems simplest and closest to our idiom. It is this form, this relationship between propositions, which gives logical cogency to many of our inferences. It recurs through all of our inferences, which are thus seen to be variations on one underlying theme.

EXERCISES

Symbolize the following propositions with specific symbols, and symbolize their three equivalents. Then write out the equivalent propositions in words, as shown in the examples in this chapter.

1. He can't be in both California and Florida.
2. If you know her you'll like her.
3. Only if men have freedom of speech do they have liberty.
4. If the fish is a pompano, it has shining scales.
5. Either conditions are just right or he doesn't fly.*

6. Only if he knows French can he get a scholarship in France.
7. The figure cannot have the area of a square and also of a circle.
8. Either you ask or you won't find out.
9. A man can't do good work and not have enough to eat.
10. She either needs it or wants it.
11. Unless you hurry you will miss your train.
12. In business, you either compete or fail.

21 MORE INFERENCES BASED ON IMPLICATIONS

21.1 Valid Inferences

We have studied the most commonly occurring forms of inference based on the equivalent logical relations, and have found that all of these forms of inference are equivalent. They are the strong threads on which many of our inferences are strung. These are the basic forms usually studied in logic texts. Yet there are many other forms or logical laws which may be the basis of inferences, as may be seen by an examination of all the laws which may be deduced in a complete exposition of the Logic of Propositions. Many of these are of negligible practical exemplification; and many we take for granted, such as the law that any proposition implies itself.

We shall study a few more of these forms. The next chapter takes up the most important, that of the *implicative series*. In this chapter we shall study a form which is practically the same as the implicative form we have studied already. The form brings out the fact that a proposition which is true in conjunction with the premise remains true in conjunction with the conclusion. This form is of frequent exemplification, since inferences do not occur in isolation but in a context. Always other propositions are true in conjunction with the premises, propositions whose truth may be emphasized in conjunction with the conclusion.

Let us examine the following inference:

> If prices rise, the government will put ceilings on them; but prices are rising and goods are scarcer; and so the government will put ceilings on prices and goods are scarcer.

Symbolizing, "prices rise" by P, "the government will put ceilings on them" by C and "goods are scarcer" by G, we have as the form:

$$[(P \supset C) \cdot P \cdot G] \supset C \cdot G.$$

Substituting general for specific symbols, we have:

$$[(p \supset q) \cdot p \cdot r] \supset q \cdot r.$$

This can easily be shown, from our form for a valid implicative inference and other logical laws, to be a valid form.

Again, let us take the example:

> If the message had come, fighting would have been prevented. But fighting broke out and communications were cut. So the message did not come and communications were cut.

Does the conclusion follow validly from the premises?

Symbolizing "the message had come (or, came)" by M, "fighting was prevented" by F, and "communications were cut" by C, we have as the form of the inference:

$$[(M \supset F) \cdot \sim F \cdot C] \supset \sim M \cdot C.$$

This form is the same as the implicative form where the consequent is denied, with an added proposition in both the premise and conclusion. Of course, by the commutative law, the added proposition may be before or after the proposition to which it is joined by conjunction. This form, too, is a valid form; and any inference having this form will be valid.

21.2 Invalid Inferences

Previously, in this book, certain common invalid forms were given. For in each general type of inference, there were four possibilities, where the second premise either affirmed or denied one of the two propositions of the first premise. Two of the possibilities yielded valid conclusions; the other two were invalid. Yet inferences could have been invalid in other ways; the general type might not have been conformed to, or the second premise might have been irrelevant to the first or to the conclusion. No forms were given for these kinds of invalid inferences.

From now on, no specific forms will be given for invalid inferences, since we do not have such simple or such circumscribed types. There are countless ways in which inferences can be invalid. Our test for the invalidity of an inference will simply be that we can find no valid form for it. If a given inference does not have a form which we know to be valid, it is invalid so far as we know. Yet it will not be shown to be invalid by having a given invalid form.

Let us take an example of an invalid inference of this type:

> If everyone in the family has a car, there will be four cars parked in the two-car garage. There are four cars in the garage, and at least one car is usually blocked. So everyone in the family has a car, but at least one is usually blocked.

Let us use specific symbols, since we are not stating a general form. Symbolizing "everyone in the family has a car" by C and "there will be four cars in the garage" by F, and "at least one car is usually blocked" by B, we have:

$$[(C \supset F) \cdot F \cdot B] \supset C \cdot B.$$

The inference is invalid, since this form is neither of the valid forms we have above. In this case, it is a more complex version of the invalid form of *affirming the consequent.*

EXERCISES

Designate the conclusion of the following inferences, symbolize them with specific variables, and show whether the conclusion follows validly from the premises.

1. If John is drafted he will have to interrupt his work. He is drafted but is willing to go. So he interrupts his work, but is willing to go.
2. If Brown wrote the novel, he's a literary genius. But he not only wrote it but is the illustrator. Therefore he's a literary genius and also an illustrator.
3. If the enemy attacks us now, we will be unable to withstand the attack. And not only will the enemy attack us now but also he will attack our allies. So, not only will we be unable to withstand the attack, but our allies will be attacked.
4. Unless he has the car keys he cannot start the car. But he starts the car and heads for town. So he has the car keys and heads for town.
5. If a radio station serves the public, it will be a force for good. This radio station takes little advertising, makes no money, and serves the public. Hence it takes little advertising, makes no money, and is a force for good.*
6. If I had the tools, I could repair the sink. But, since I can neither repair it nor do I have the time for it anyway, I neither have the tools nor the time to repair it.
7. If he makes out a budget, he will know how much money he should spend on entertainment. He makes out a budget and he works on it all his spare time. So he knows how much money he should spend on entertainment, but he works on his budget all his spare time.
8. If I get a new phonograph, I will play records every evening. Since I play records every evening, and disturb my roommates, I have a new phonograph and disturb my roommates.
9. If the moon is seen as full, it is in opposition to the sun. The moon is full, and rises soon after sunset. Hence the moon is in opposition to the sun, and rises soon after sunset.
10. If he makes more money, he can afford to buy a sailboat. Now he is making a lot of money, and is too busy for boating. Hence

he can afford to buy a sailboat but he is too busy for boating.

11. If A is the cause of B, B never occurs without A. Yet not only does B often occur without A, but seldom occurs with A. Hence A is not the cause of B, which seldom occurs with it.

12. Unless he believes that everything makes for the best, he is not an optimist. Now he is not an optimist but a pessimist. Hence, he is a pessimist and does not believe that everything makes for the best.*

13. If time alone were the decisive factor, equivalent pleasant and unpleasant experiences which occurred equally long ago should be equally well remembered. But we tend to remember best our pleasant experiences, and even magnify them. So time alone is not the decisive factor in remembrance, and we tend to magnify our pleasant remembrances.

14. Only if she can swim may she go out in the canoe. She knows how to swim, but she can't paddle a canoe. So she may go out in the canoe, but she can't paddle it.

15. If the salesman dies, and his wife collects the insurance, she can pay for the house. The salesman dies and his wife collects his insurance, but there's nobody to live in the house. So his wife can pay for the house, but there's no one to live there.

22 THE IMPLICATIVE SERIES

22.1 Transitivity of Implication

The astronomer reasons:

> If the moon had an atmosphere, the light of a star coincident with it would be refracted, and if the light were refracted its deviation could be observed. Consequently, if the moon had an atmosphere, deviation of the light of a star could be observed.

This type of argument seems both familiar and cogent. We use it daily in our reasoning. Symbolizing "the moon has an atmosphere" by A, "the light of a star coincident with it is refracted" by L and "its deviation could be observed" by O, the form is:

$$[(A \supset L) \cdot (L \supset O)] \supset (A \supset O).$$

This illustrates the general form:

$$[(p \supset q) \cdot (q \supset r)] \supset (p \supset r).$$

Now this form, which we shall call that of the *implicative series,* is valid. This may be shown from the previous implicative form and other logical laws. However, it is often given as defining a basic property of implication called *transitivity*. A relation has transitivity or is transitive when, if it links one entity to a second and the second to a third, it will also link the first to the third, passing over the second. Other familiar transitive relations are *is less than, is greater than, is equal to,* and all relations of direction on a straight line, such as *is left of, is beneath, is north of*. Blood relationships are not transitive, nor are the logical relations of disjunction and incompatibility.

Let us mark certain regularities in the form of the implicative series. They are:

(1) The antecedent of the first premise is the antecedent of the conclusion.

(2) The consequent of the second premise is the consequent of the conclusion.

(3) The other proposition in the premises, which is the consequent of the first premise and the antecedent of the second, is the same in both premises. For otherwise we could not jump over it in order to link the first proposition to the last.

These three regularities are laws of the implicative series, and must be found in every valid argument having that form. And any argument obeying these three laws is valid.

22.2 Valid Inferences

Many an argument does not obviously have the characteristics of an implicative series. Often the order of the premises must be changed, or the counterimplication substituted for the implication, in order that the argument may manifest these characteristics. For example:

> If art copied nature exactly, it would be mechanical. But if art expresses the personal way the artist looks at nature it is not mechanical. Hence, if art expresses the personality of the artist, it does not copy nature exactly.

Letting C stand for "art copies nature exactly," M for "it is mechanical," and E for "art expresses the personality of the artist," the inference is symbolized:

$$[(C \supset M) \cdot (E \supset \sim M)] \supset (E \supset \sim C).$$

In order that the antecedent of the conclusion be the antecedent of the first premise, let us put the second premise first. Next, in order that we have a common proposition to go over, let us substitute its counterimplication for the other premise. We then have:

$$[(E \supset \sim M) \cdot (\sim M \supset \sim C)] \supset (E \supset \sim C).$$

Replacing the specific variables by p, q, r, we have the form of a valid implicative series obeying all three of the rules, and the inference is valid. For the premises imply the conclusion.

Sometimes an implicative series has more than two premises. But no matter how many implicative links in the implicative chain, if no links are missing, the chain is still sound. If a proposition—call it z— is implied by another, and that by another, and so forth up to the first antecedent, p, then z is always implied by p.

In our first example, we could have had another premise, thus:

> If there is life on the moon, there is (would be) an atmosphere; and if there is an atmosphere the light of a star would be refracted, in which case the deviation would be observed. Hence, if there is life on the moon the deviation of the light of a star would be observed.

Using the same symbols as in our first example, and adding M for "there is life on the moon," the form becomes:

$$[(M \supset A) \cdot (A \supset L) \cdot (L \supset O)] \supset (M \supset O).$$

By two successive applications of the implicative series, this may be shown to be valid.

Sometimes an implicative series is combined with our previous form for an implicative inference, thus:

> If any water existed on the moon, it would evaporate, forming a vapor which would make itself known to our scrutiny. But no vapor has been observed. Hence there is no water on the moon.

Symbolizing "water exists on the moon" by W, it would evaporate" by E, and "vapor has been observed" by O, we have:

$$[(W \supset E) \cdot (E \supset O) \cdot {\sim}O] \supset {\sim}W.$$

This is the form of a valid implicative inference, as may be easily shown.

22.3 Invalid Inferences

The implicative series is the only form of inference we can justify which, from two implications between three propositions, concludes to an implication between two of the propositions. And a valid implicative series obeys the three laws stated above. Hence, if an inference of this type disobeys even one of the three laws, it is invalid. There are so many ways to violate the three rules that we shall give no forms for invalid inferences of this type. We shall say only that an inference which violates even one of the three laws is invalid.

Let us take just one example:

> If the child is interested, he will pay good attention; and unless he pays good attention he will not learn. So if the child is interested he will learn.

Symbolizing "the child is interested" by I, "he will pay good attention" by A, and "he will learn" by L, we have:

$$[(I \supset A) \cdot (\sim A \supset \sim L)] \supset (I \supset L).$$

No matter how we rearrange our implications, we cannot find a common proposition to jump over, and at least our third rule is violated. Hence the inference is invalid.

EXERCISES

Symbolize the following inferences by specific symbols, showing whether they have the form of a valid implicative series.

1. I'm afraid that if Mrs. Jones is worse the doctor won't be at the reception. For, if Mrs. Jones grows worse the doctor can't leave the hospital, and if he can't leave the hospital he can't be at the reception.
2. Unless it rains the concert will be held on Monday night; and she'll be able to sing if it's held that night. So unless it rains on Monday night she'll be able to sing.
3. Only if Hal has no class before 10:30 can he get a ride to school. But if he takes German, he must take an 8:30 section. Hence, if he takes German, he can't get a ride to school.
4. If John takes the job, he will not have time to study. And if he gets a scholarship he must have time to study. Hence, if he gets a scholarship, he cannot take the job.
5. If the tariff is increased, imports will decrease; if imports are

decreased foreign countries will have less buying power. If foreign countries have less buying power our exports will decrease and so some of our factories will close down; and if some of our factories close down there will be unemployment. Hence, if the tariff is increased there will be unemployment.

6. Unless the minority is willing to accept the majority decision, there can be no democracy. But unless the majority respects the rights of the minority, the latter will be unwilling to accept the majority decision. Hence, unless the majority observes the rights of the minority, there can be no democracy.*

7. If you throw a stone directly upward, the effect of gravity is progressively to diminish its velocity; and if its velocity is diminished it will finally fall. Hence, if you throw a stone directly upward it will finally fall.

8. If a country is defeated in war, it loses what it is too weak to defend. And if it has lost what it is too weak to defend it will later try to win back what it has lost. But, if it does there will be a new war. Hence, if a country is defeated in war, there will later be a new war.

9. If I get a music scholarship, I must go to rehearsals. But if I take physics lab I cannot go to rehearsals. Hence, if I get a music scholarship I cannot take physics lab.

10. His campaign manager told him that a speech like that would ruin his chances of election; since a speech like that would offend many people and so lose their support, and if he lost their support he wouldn't have enough votes.

11. If he is interested in finding out who committed the robbery, he will ask about it; but, if he is guilty, he isn't interested in finding out who committed the robbery. Hence, if he is guilty, he will avoid asking about it.

12. If he had been there he would have known the answer, and if he knew the answer he would have passed. But he flunked; and so he could not have been there.

13. Unless the payments are promptly made, your mortgage is foreclosed. And if you have the money you can pay promptly. So if the mortgage is not foreclosed, you have the money.

14. Mill said: If an authority suppresses the expression of opinion, he denies it to be true, and so he assumes that he has knowledge of what is true, and is consequently infallible. Hence, if an authority suppresses an opinion, he assumes his own infallibility.

15. If the whole truth on any subject may emerge, all opinions on it must be allowed to collide and be discussed. But if an opinion is suppressed, not all opinions are discussed. Hence, if an opinion is suppressed, the whole truth cannot emerge.

16. Unless an opinion is vigorously contested, its meaning will be deprived of any vital effect on character, and hence it will not do any good. Hence, unless an opinion is vigorously contested, it will not do any good.

17. Mill reasoned further: Unless we know the grounds of an opinion, we do not understand it; and, unless we know why it is better than contrary opinions, we do not know its grounds. But if the contrary opinions are suppressed we do not know why our opinion is better than they are. Hence, if opinions contrary to ours are suppressed, we do not understand it.

18. John Dewey argues that if the end of an action is wisely chosen, the entire train of consequences of the action must be taken into consideration. But, if only pleasure is taken as the end, no such cool and farseeing judgment of consequences is possible. He concludes that, if pleasure only is taken as the end of conduct, the end cannot be wisely chosen.*

23 VARIATIONS OF THE IMPLICATIVE SERIES

23.1 Series Containing Disjunction

Many inferences do not look like implicative series, since they contain one or more disjunctions. However, they may easily be shown to be implicative series by substituting equivalent implications for the disjunctions. We must remember, from Chapter 20, that an implication is equivalent to a disjunction, one of whose disjuncts denies the antecedent. Conversely, a disjunction is equivalent to an implication whose *antecedent* denies one of the disjuncts, thus:

$$(p \vee q) \equiv (\sim p \supset q).$$

Let us consider the following example:

> Either the present sheriff does not remain in office or the law will not be enforced; and either the law is enforced or crime increases. Hence either the present sheriff does not remain in office or crime increases.

Does the conclusion, "either the present sheriff does not remain in office or crime increases," follow from its premises?

Let us symbolize "the present sheriff does not remain in office" by $\sim S$, "the law will be enforced" by L, and crime increases" by C. The inference becomes:

$$[(\sim S \vee \sim L) \cdot (L \vee C)] \supset (\sim S \vee C).$$

When we substitute the equivalent implications for the disjunctions, the form becomes:

$$[(S \supset \sim L) \cdot (\sim L \supset C)] \supset (S \supset C).$$

Substituting p for S, q for $\sim L$, and r for C, we have the form of a valid implicative series.

We may have one or more disjunctions in an implicative series, which we may always show to be valid or invalid by substituting equivalent implications, and testing for the implicative series.

23.2 Series Containing Incompatibility

Often, an incompatibility occurs as one link in a chain of implications. We must then substitute an equivalent implication for the incompatibility. We must remember, from the chapter on equivalents, that an implication is equivalent to an incompatibility one of whose terms is the denial of the consequent. Conversely, an incompatibility is equivalent to an implication whose *consequent* denies one of the incompatible propositions, thus:

$$\sim(p \cdot q) \equiv (p \supset \sim q).$$

Consider the following examples

We cannot be dead to pain and still have warning of physical injury. And either we have such warning or life would be short. Hence, if we were dead to pain, life would be short.

Is this a valid inference?

Symbolizing "we are dead to pain" by D, "we have warning of physical injury" by W, and "life is short" by L, we have:

$$[\sim(D \cdot W) \cdot (W \vee L)] \supset (D \supset L).$$

Here let us substitute the equivalent implication, $D \supset \sim W$, for the incompatibility, and $\sim W \supset L$ for the disjunction. The inference is:

$$[(D \supset \sim W) \cdot (\sim W \supset L)] \supset (D \supset L).$$

Replacing the specific variables by p, q, r, we see that this is an exemplification of a valid implicative series. The inference is valid.

23.3 Invalid Inferences

Here, again, no forms for invalid inferences will be given, since there are many ways in which an inference will fail to form a series obeying all three laws. If even one of the laws of a valid series is violated, the inference is invalid.

The implicative series is one of the most pervasive of forms; it runs through all our reasoning. To discern the fundamental theme of the implicative series in all its variations is to show that the inferences exemplifying it are valid.

EXERCISES

In the following inferences, designate the conclusion. Then symbolize them and reduce them to forms of the implicative series, thus showing whether they are examples of valid forms.

1. If Bob has Chem lab every afternoon, he cannot take oil painting. But either he takes Chem lab every afternoon or he can't complete his major. So, if he completes his major, he cannot take oil painting.
2. Either the game is in the afternoon or we don't play Florida. And if the game is in the afternoon, the players will be awfully hot. So either we don't play Florida or the players will be awfully hot.
3. Hobbes said that unless men have a strong government, they will have no security. Now men must have security, hence they must have a strong government.
4. The speaker claimed that poetry is either deceptive or is disguised history. For, if it is false, it is misleading; and, if it is true, it is history masquerading as art.*
5. Either a person enjoys his work or he doesn't do his best. But if he is the right person for the job, he must do his best. Hence, he can't be the right person for the job and not enjoy it.*
6. John reasoned that, if he went to school, he would have to pay for it, in which case he would have to get a full-time job. But, if he had a full-time job, he would not have time to study, and so his going to school would be useless. Hence, even if he went to school, it would be useless.

7. Mill argued that unless a belief is challenged by opposing beliefs it will be held as a formal pretension. And a belief cannot be a formal pretension and still have a vital effect on character. So, if a belief is vital it must be challenged.

8. If he knows what he's doing, he's dishonest; and, if he doesn't know what he's doing, he's ignorant. So he's either ignorant or dishonest.

9. If he has late examinations, he can't go home between semesters. But unless all his exams are crowded together, he will have a late examination. Hence, either he can't go home between semesters or all his exams are crowded together.

10. Unless Britain balances her budget, her security will be threatened. But if she has a defense with atomic weapons she cannot balance her budget. Hence, either she cannot have an atomic defense, or her security will be threatened.

11. If he plays in the band, his studies will be interrupted by band trips. But, unless he plays in the band, he will not have opportunity to play his trombone, and will be unhappy. So, unless his studies are interrupted, he will be unhappy.

12. Unless both husband and wife work, they cannot support their family. But if they both work their family will be neglected. So either their family is not supported or neglected.

13. John cannot be a good artist and not be precise about details. And either John is a good artist or he is wasting his time. So, if John is not careful about details, he is wasting his time.

14. Either we lose the game or we'll have a bonfire; and, if we have a bonfire, we'll need more wood. So either we lose the game or we'll need more wood.

15. If I go to the Conference, I will miss some classes. But, unless I go to the Conference, I will miss some good talks. So, I will miss either some classes or some good talks.

16. Either the fire was caused intentionally or our insurance is good. But if our insurance is good, we can rebuild our plant. So it is not true that the fire was not caused intentionally and that we cannot rebuild the plant.

17. If the danger of destruction increases, the system of balance of

power will be abandoned. But unless there is a system of international cooperation, the system of balance of power will remain. Hence, if the danger of destruction increases, there must be a system of international cooperation.

18. Unless a hypnotist has knowledge and experience, he will neglect something in removing the hypnosis. And either he neglects nothing or the hypnotised subject may become mentally ill later. Hence, if a hypnotist is an amateur, the hypnotised subject may become mentally ill later.

24 CONTRADICTORIES, CONTRARIES, AND SUBCONTRARIES

24.1 Contradictories

Contradiction meets us on all sides. Everyone has opinions; and others contradict those opinions. Someone claims, "When the Republicans are in there will be good government;" and someone else hotly denies or contradicts the claim. Someone claims, "Government ownership is desirable in certain enterprises;" and others emphatically contradict the claim. Yet, though people may feel very sure about what may be contradicted, they are not always so sure about what contradiction involves.

Whenever we have symbolized a proposition as $\sim p$, we have symbolized it as the contradictory of p, as saying that what p says is false. And we have actually been presupposing two laws about contradictories.

The first law, the famous law of contradiction, is that contradictories *cannot both be true at the same time*. In other words, contradictories are incompatible. If we symbolize any proposition by p and its contradictory by $\sim p$, we may write:

$$\sim(p \cdot \sim p).$$

The second law, called, since Aristotle, the law of excluded middle, says that either a proposition or its contradictory must be true. There is no third alternative; at least one of the two must be true. We may symbolize the law:

$$p \vee \sim p.$$

Putting the two laws together, we may say that, if two propositions, p and $\sim p$, are contradictories, then:

$$\sim(p \cdot \sim p) \cdot (p \vee \sim p).$$

In short, they are in strong disjunction. One and only one of the two contradictories is true. They cannot both be true; and at least one is true, so that they cannot both be false.

Other examples of contradictories are:

> Napoleon was a great man.
> It is false that Napoleon was a great man.

and again:

> The number is even.
> The number is not divisible by two.

For the propositions can be neither true nor false together.

24.2 Contraries

Another kind of proposition, though we sometimes call them contradictories, are logically *contraries*. A politician might claim:

> The sales tax should be increased,

as against his opponent's claim that

> The sales tax should be decreased.

These claims may seem to be contradictory. But are they?

An examination of those claims show that they cannot both be true. The sales tax cannot be both increased and decreased. But the claims might both be false; for perhaps the sales tax should be neither increased or decreased, but abolished or kept the same. The propositions, then, are *not* contradictories. They are *contraries*.

Contraries are propositions which cannot be both true but which can be both false. Nothing is said about their falsity. In other words, they are incompatible but are not in disjunction. If p stands for any proposition and q for its contrary (of which there may be more than one) we may write *only:*

$$\sim(p\cdot q).$$

Other examples of contraries are:

He votes for the Republican candidate;
He votes for the Democratic candidate;

and again:

He is enthusiastically in favor of the theory,
He is strongly opposed to the theory.

For the propositions cannot be both true, though they could be both false.

24.3 Subcontraries

Still other propositions, though compatible, cannot both be false, and so are in disjunction. They are called *subcontraries*. Let us take as examples:

The sales tax should not be increased.
The sales tax should not be decreased.

These propositions could both be true, if the sales tax should remain as it is. However, they cannot both be false. For if they were, the sales tax should be both increased and decreased, which is impossible. At least one of our propositions, then, must hold, and possibly both.

They are in weak disjunction. In general, if p represents any proposition and q its subcontrary, we may write *only:*

$$p \vee q.$$

Other examples of subcontraries are:

> He does not vote for the Republican candidate;
> He does not vote for the Democratic candidate;

and again:

> He is not in China;
> He is in Asia.

For at least one of these propositions must be true, though possibly both.

It may easily be shown that the negatives of contraries are always subcontraries; since, by de Morgan's law,

$$\sim(p \cdot q) \equiv (\sim p \vee \sim q).$$

The relation of subcontrariety is expressed by *only one* of the conditions characterizing contradiction, that of *disjunction*. The relation of contrariety is expressed by the other condition *only,* that of *incompatibility*. Contradiction, which is expressed by *both* conditions, is the strongest relation of opposition between propositions. It is what is meant by negation.

EXERCISES

A. Symbolize the following pairs of propositions by specific symbols, and show how they are related as contradictories, contraries, or subcontraries.

1. He spoke English fluently; he spoke English poorly.
2. He never loses his temper; he always loses his temper.
3. He spoke English fluently; he did not speak English fluently.
4. The speech was in French; the speech was in German.
5. This substance is an acid; this substance is a salt.

6. Podunk Center is east of Metropolis; Podunk Center is west of Metropolis.*

7. Podunk Center is east of Metropolis; Podunk Center is not east of Metropolis.*

8. Podunk Center is not east of Metropolis; Podunk Center is not west of Metropolis.*

9. A conclusion may be validly inferred from a premise; it is not implied by the premise.

10. She adores playing tennis; she hates playing tennis.

11. Ralph wore boots; Ralph wore studded shoes.

12. The workers had many hardships; the workers had no hardships.

13. He is not at the theatre; he is not at the church.

14. He doesn't marry Sally; he doesn't marry Jean.

15. He is president of the CIO; he is president of the NAM.*

16. The room was crowded; the room was empty.

17. Some people like tea; some do not.

18. He drinks alcoholic beverages; he drinks nonalcoholic beverages.*

19. He is away from home; he is absent from school.

20. The figure is a closed curve with equal radii; the figure is not a circle.

21. He believes that God exists; he does not believe that God exists.*

22. He believes that God exists; he believes that God does not exist.*

23. No one loves an outlaw; everyone loves an outlaw.

24. He studies exactly six hours a day; he studies only two hours.

25. It is colored; it is not red.*

26. He votes for Jones; he votes against him.

B. Two pairs of the following propositions are related by contradiction, one pair by contrariety, and one pair by subcontrariety. Symbolize them, showing their relations.*

1. He plays golf every Saturday.
2. He never plays golf.
3. He does not play golf every Saturday.
4. He sometimes plays golf.

25 THE DILEMMA

25.1 The Four Forms

The dilemma is a form of argument which is famous—or infamous—from its use in public speaking and debate. It has often been used as a tool of sophistry, since its valid form creates the illusion that the conclusion must be true, although drawn from false premises and so possibly false. Yet, when its premises are true, the dilemma is a forceful way of presenting an inescapable conclusion. This conclusion has usually been an unwelcome one—but its character, welcome or unwelcome, is part of meaning and therefore not a concern of formal logic.

Logically, the dilemma is not so important as its historical notoriety would suggest. For any example of an argument which may take the form of a dilemma is also a form of the implicative series.

The dilemma is so called because one of its three premises consists of two propositions in disjunction, each of which is the antecedent of an implication in one of the other premises. The conclusion is also a disjunction of two propositions, except in simple dilemmas. The dilemma may take one of four forms:

$[(p \supset q) \cdot (r \supset s) \cdot (p \vee r)] \supset (q \vee s)$: *Complex Constructive Dilemma.*

$[(p \supset q) \cdot (r \supset q) \cdot (p \vee r)] \supset q$: *Simple Constructive Dilemma.*

$[(p \supset q) \cdot (r \supset s) \cdot (\sim q \vee \sim s)] \supset (\sim p \vee \sim r)$: *Complex Destructive Dilemma.*

$[(p \supset q) \cdot (p \supset r) \cdot (\sim q \vee \sim r)] \supset \sim p$: *Simple Destructive Dilemma.*

All four of these forms may be shown by logical laws to be forms of the implicative series and so valid. Any inferences shown to have any one of these forms is valid.

25.2 Constructive Dilemmas

In that famous series of debates between Abraham Lincoln and Stephen Douglas, Lincoln crystallized the issues in this way:

> If the Territories have the right to hold slaves, that right should be upheld by favorable legislation. If they do not have that right, the Dred Scott decision should be reversed. But they either do or do not have that right. Hence, either there should be favorable legislation supporting that right or the Dred Scott decision should be reversed.[1]

Both alternatives of this conclusion were unwelcome to Douglas.

Symbolizing "the Territories have the right to hold slaves" by R, "that right should be upheld by favorable legislation" by L, and "the Dred Scott decision should be reversed" by D, we have as the form of the argument:

$$[(R \supset L) \cdot (\sim R \supset D) \cdot (R \vee \sim R)] \supset (L \vee D).$$

Substituting p for R, q for L, r for $\sim R$, and s for D, we have the form of the *Complex Constructive Dilemma*. The inference is valid.

Again, consider the following dilemma, which often confronts us:

> If freedom of speech is allowed in wartime our democratic government will be undermined. If it is not allowed, our democratic government will be impaired. But either freedom of speech is allowed or not. Therefore, our democratic government will be impaired in wartime.

Since the conclusion, "our democratic government will be impaired in wartime" is a simple proposition, the inference must be a Simple Dilemma. Symbolizing "freedom of speech is allowed in wartime" by F, "it is not allowed" by $\sim F$, and "our democratic government is undermined (impaired) in wartime," by D, we have:

$$[(F \supset D) \cdot (\sim F \supset D) \cdot (F \vee \sim F)] \supset D.$$

---

[1] A free rendering of the argument at the end of Lincoln's reply to Douglas in the Alton, Illinois, debate, October, 1858.

Substituting p for F, q for D, and r for $\sim F$, we have the form of the *Simple Constructive Dilemma*. The inference is valid. If the premises are true, we are justified in drawing this disquieting conclusion about the effects of war on free speech.

In the last two examples, as in the majority of dilemmas, the two antecedents of the implications are contradictories. Logically, they could just as well be any two propositions in disjunction. If they are contradictories, their disjunction is often not stated but presupposed, since contradictories are always in disjunction. In case their disjunction is omitted, the student must supply it, to complete the form of the dilemma.

25.3 Destructive Dilemmas

Sometimes the dilemma denies rather than affirms a proposition (or propositions) of the premises. Then we have what have been treated traditionally as *Destructive Dilemmas*. For example, it might be argued:

> If he is a Marxist, he believes that class conflict alone causes social progress, and, if he is a democrat, he believes that agreement by the people causes social progress. Since either he does not believe that class conflict alone causes social progress or he does not believe that agreement by the people causes social progress, we may conclude that either he is not a Marxist or not a democrat.

Does the conclusion, "either he is not a Marxist or not a democrat," follow from the premises?

Symbolizing "he is a Marxist" by M, "he believes that class conflict alone causes social progress" by C, "he is a democrat" by D, and "he believes that agreement by the people causes social progress" by A, we have:

$$[(M \supset C) \cdot (D \supset A) \cdot (\sim C \vee \sim A)] \supset (\sim M \vee \sim D).$$

Substituting p, q, r, s for the four symbols, we have the form of the *Complex Destructive Dilemma*. The inference is valid.

The destructive dilemma is particularly useful in showing that propositions are incompatible, since $\sim p \vee \sim q$ is always equivalent to the incompatibility, $\sim (p \cdot q)$. In the above example, we may substitute $\sim (C \cdot A)$ and $\sim (M \cdot D)$ for the disjunctions. Sometimes, a destructive dilemma will be worded to contain an incompatibility, in which case a disjunction should be substituted for it.

Lastly, we may argue:

> If we were to believe the witnesses, this man was in China at the time; and, if we were to believe the witnesses, this man was in England at the time. But, since this man was not both in China and England at the time, we cannot believe the witnesses.

May we validly conclude that "we cannot believe the witnesses"?

Symbolizing, "we believe the witnesses" by B, "this man was in China at the time" by C, "this man was in England at the time" by E, we have:

$$[(B \supset C) \cdot (B \supset E) \cdot \sim (C \cdot E)] \supset \sim B.$$

Substituting p, q, r for B, C, E, and substituting its equivalent disjunction for the incompatibility, we have the form for the *Simple Destructive Dilemma*. The inference is valid.

The law sometimes called the *reductio ad absurdum* is a special form of the simple destructive dilemma, where $(\sim q \vee q)$ is assumed.

$$[(p \supset q) \cdot (p \supset \sim q)] \supset \sim p.$$

25.4 Dilemmas with False Conclusions

There are no invalid dilemmas, since any one of the four forms of the dilemma is valid; and an inference which does not have one of the forms is simply not a dilemma.

Yet, though the conclusion of a dilemma follows validly from the premises, it may be false. As has been said, the conclusion of a dilemma, though false, and following from false premises, may be palmed off as true. Hence, various ways have been developed for showing the premises of a dilemma to be false. One way, traditionally called "taking the dilemma by the horns," shows that either or both of the implications in the premises are false. Another way, called "escaping between the horns," shows that the disjunction is false, allowing for a third alternative. The way called "rebuttal" of a dilemma shows that there are other consequents of the implications which are contraries to those stated. But all of these ways show that the premises of a dilemma are false or misleading, not that the form is invalid. And it is only with the form of a dilemma that we are here concerned.

25.5 The Dilemma as a Form of the Implicative Series

In many inferences of this type, which may be solved as dilemmas, the student may find it simpler to find the validity by symbolizing them as implicative series. Symbolizing complex dilemmas is relatively simple. But, when the conclusion is a simple proposition, as in simple dilemmas, the proposition must be converted into an implication. This is done by means of two logical laws, (which are equivalent).

$$p \equiv (\sim p \supset p).$$

$$\sim p \equiv (p \supset \sim p).$$

Thus p (or $\sim p$) may always be replaced by an implication.

EXERCISES

In each of the following dilemmas, what is the conclusion? Symbolize the component propositions and then the form of the dilemma, showing whether it is an example of a valid form.

1. A chess player reasons: If I move my knight, my bishop will be captured, and if I don't move my knight, it will itself be captured. Hence, I lose either my bishop or my knight.*
2. "Well, I'll eat it," said Alice, "and if it makes me grow larger,

I can reach the key and get into the garden; and, if it makes me grow smaller, I can creep under the door and get into the garden. Either way, I'll get into the garden."*

3. If Tom doesn't do well at this difficult job he will be fired; and, if he becomes run-down, he will be fired. But either Tom doesn't do well or he becomes run-down. Hence, it is a foregone conclusion that he will be fired.

4. If a person is boastful, he talks about himself, and, if he is timid, he does not talk about himself. Since, either he talks about himself or not, either he is not boastful or not timid.*

5. If he comes out for his convictions, he will lose the votes which keep him in office, and so he can't work for them. But, if he doesn't come out for them, he can't work for them anyway. So he is driven to the conclusion that he can't work for them.

6. If he does what he ought, he will stay with his sick mother; and, if he does what he ought, he will travel for his business. But he cannot do both. Hence, he cannot do what he ought.

7. If I maintain my fees, I shall lose my clients; and, if I cut my fees, I shall lose my standing. Hence I must choose between losing my clients and losing my standing.

8. If the plaintiff's counsel is right, then the demurrer should be overruled; if the defendant's counsel is right, the demurrer should be sustained. But the demurrer cannot be both overruled and sustained. Hence, either the plaintiff's or defendant's counsel is wrong.

9. If the police obey the law, they will put an end to gambling; and, if they keep their jobs, they will allow it. But, since they cannot both end it and allow it, they either disobey the law or lose their jobs.

10. If Smith is president of the CIO he believes that the rights of labor unions should be increased; but if he is president of the NAM, he believes that the rights of labor unions should be decreased. Now, since he cannot believe that the rights of labor unions should be both increased and decreased, he is not both president of the CIO and NAM.

11. Depressions come no matter what is done. For, if people proceed

as if a depression were going to occur, they upset the economy and produce a depression; and if they proceed as if a depression were not going to occur, expanding production is bound to produce one.*

12. If he tells the truth, he betrays his friends and therefore his conscience; if he doesn't tell the truth he betrays his conscience. Hence, whatever he does, he betrays his conscience.

13. If he finishes balancing the accounts, he must hurry; but, if he succeeds in balancing them, he cannot hurry. Hence, he cannot finish balancing the accounts.

14. How can he vote to change the constitution? If he is a citizen he has sworn to uphold it and therefore can't try to change it; and, if he is not a citizen, he can't vote.*

15. If I go to school I must get a full-time job to pay for it. But if I go to school I must have time to study and can't get a full-time job. Hence, I can't go to school.

16. The attorney said: If the court rules that membership in the Communist party is a crime, I will indict these men, and they will be jailed. If the court rules that membership is not a crime, they will be jailed for contempt (for invoking the Fifth Amendment). In either case, they will be jailed.

17. A businessman reasons: If I'm away from home, I'll miss an important call; but, if I'm not in my office, I won't get my letters out. Since either I'm away from home or not in my office, I must conclude that either I'll miss an important call or not get my letters out.

18. The directors of the store reason: If we furnish a good puppet show as a shopping attraction, the people will watch it instead of doing their shopping. If we don't furnish one, people will do their shopping elsewhere. So we're bound to lose out.

19. If the commission fails to question Smith, the investigation will be a whitewash. If it does question Smith, the facts disclosed will destroy the party. So either the investigation will be a whitewash or the party will be destroyed.

20. "And what a life should I lead, at my age, wandering from city to city and always being driven out! For I am quite sure that

wherever I go, there, as here, the young men will flock to me; and, if I drive them away, their elders will drive me out at their request; and, if I let them come, their fathers and friends will drive me out for their sakes."—Socrates; *Apology.*

21. If she understood what she read, she was old enough to criticise it, and so her opinions could not be harmed; if she didn't understand it, no harm could be done. So, what harm could reading do her?

22. If we go on a trip, we must buy a new car. But, if we go on a trip, we cannot afford a new car; so I guess we can't go on a trip.

26 TELESCOPED INFERENCES

26.1 The Missing Premise

The great majority of the inferences we meet and use do not come to us with their premises and conclusions fully stated, ready to be symbolized. They may lack a premise or merely suggest a conclusion. The missing premise may be silently presupposed as a proposition which is obvious or indubitable or even one whose truth cannot bear examination. It becomes an important logical enterprise to find the missing premise which will result in a valid inference, and bring it out into the open, so that its truth may be examined.

The logical problem here differs from the problem which, up till now, we have been trying to solve. Formerly, we were given all the premises and conclusion of an inference in order to find out whether it was valid. Now we will be given only some of the propositions of an inference, and the fact that *it is valid,* in order to find out the missing proposition(s). For the inference must be assumed to be valid if the missing premise which alone will result in its validity may be found. Almost any proposition would result in an invalid inference.

Of course, if the conclusion is incompatible with the given premise, it can never be drawn validly from the premise. We shall consider here only those inferences which may be validly completed.

First, let us consider the following inference of a slandered politician:

My opponent cannot prove his charge, since it is not true.

Is this an inference; and, if so, does the conclusion follow from its premise?

Assuredly this is an inference, with the conclusion, "my opponent cannot prove his charge," asserted on the grounds of, for the reason that, or *since* "the charge is not true." Let us symbolize this premise by $\sim T$, and the conclusion by $\sim P$, using specific symbols since we are not dealing with a general form. The inference is symbolized:

$$\sim T \supset \sim P.$$

But does $\sim T$ imply $\sim P$ so that the inference is valid? There is no formal relationship between the propositions that would make an inference from one to the other justified. If the inference is valid, there must be a formal link between $\sim T$ and $\sim P$. If, as the politician presumably meant, the conclusion is validly drawn, that formal link must be presupposed.

The only way to complete the above inference so that it is a valid implicative inference is to write:

$$[(\sim T \supset \sim P) \cdot \sim T] \supset \sim P.$$

The "missing link," then, which connects $\sim T$ and $\sim P$ is $\sim T \supset \sim P$. It is the premise which is presupposed, and whose addition results in a valid inference. In words, it is:

If the charge is not true my opponent cannot prove it.

Our inference as first stated is not a valid one; for the conclusion is not implied by the premise. Only if the inference is completed by adding the suppressed premise, is the conclusion implied by the premises and the inference valid. Our inference, then, in presupposing what it does not state, is elliptical or *telescoped*.

Again, consider the telescoped inference:

> The solution must contain copper, for it turns greenish-blue when acid is added.

If this inference is valid, what is the presupposed premise?

Symbolizing the conclusion, "the solution contains copper" by C, and the premise, "it turns greenish-blue when acid is added" by B, we have:

$$B \supset C.$$

Now C could be implied and so validly inferred only if $B \supset C$ were true. For a valid form would be:

$$[(B \supset C) \cdot B] \supset C.$$

The missing premise, which we must supply if the inference is valid, is $B \supset C$, and reads:

> If the solution turns greenish-blue when acid is added, it contains copper.

26.2 Other Telescoped Inferences

Not all inferences are of this type. More rarely, an inference, instead of presupposing its implicative premise, presupposes its other premise. Consider this inference:

> If John doesn't have any money, he can't keep his car in repair. So he doesn't keep his car in repair.

Symbolizing "John doesn't have any money" by $\sim M$, and "he can't keep his car in repair" by $\sim R$, we have:

$$[(\sim M \supset \sim R)] \supset \sim R.$$

The missing premise here, which alone would result in a valid inference, is $\sim M$, or "John has no money."

All forms of inferences, including the implicative series and the dilemma, may be elliptical. In fact, we have dealt with elliptical inferences of both types, with a series where one of the propositions in the chain had to be repeated, and with a dilemma which presupposed an unstated disjunction. These missing propositions had to be stated if the inferences were valid.

A telescoped inference of an interesting and common type contains a disjunction. The following example is from *Alice in Wonderland,* that children's classic written by a logician. The Cheshire Cat says to Alice:

"You must be mad or you wouldn't be here."

Let us assume that the conclusion "you are (must be) mad," is validly drawn, and let us symbolize it by *M*. But what is the premise? It is not "you wouldn't be here," for that proposition is stated as an alternative to the conclusion. But, since the proposition "you wouldn't be here," is contrary to fact, it presupposes "you are here," which is the premise, and which we shall symbolize by *H*. The inference becomes:

$$H \supset M.$$

We can now proceed, as with our other telescoped inferences, to supply the other premise, $H \supset M$, which is presupposed by the Cat.

Infinite varieties of telescoped inferences meet us in all our speech and reading. In all of them, if they are assumed to be valid, a tacitly assumed premise enables us to validly link the premises to the conclusion. And in all of them, this premise must be supplied.

EXERCISES

In the following telescoped inferences, symbolize the premise and conclusion with specific symbols, and supply the other premise which will result in a valid inference.

1. Since the metal is expanding, its temperature must be rising.
2. Since the light turned red, I should stop.

3. This hut will soon fall, since it has weak supports.

4. You couldn't have walked faster than he does, or you would have been here first.

5. This liquid must be an acid, for it reddens litmus paper.

6. Since writing is an art, there will always be something inexplicable about it.

7. That bird must be an Indian cuckoo, or it would not have that call.

8. The witness can't be telling the truth, or her statement would not contradict her previous one.

9. Since Congress did not approve the League of Nations, it was prevented from becoming a reality.

10. Since Mr. Jones has not been in office so long as Mr. Smith, he can't know as much.

11. He must be wrong, or someone would agree with him.

12. He says what he thinks; so he must be courageous.

13. The American public is given to illusions, since it smiles so much.

14. He had occasional bursts of prosperity, or he could not have redeemed the watch.

15. His face is darkly tanned; so he must have been living in the tropics.

16. He must be very intelligent; for he answered all of these questions.

17. Since this planet deviates from its orbit, it must be attracted by an outside force.

18. He must have an iron constitution, or he could not stand the climate that long.

19. He must have an exceptional memory, or he would not have remembered the man for so many years.

20. Mill said that there should be freedom of speech; for such freedom leads to man's happiness.

21. Alice said that if they had lived on treacle, they'd have been ill. Hence they couldn't have lived on treacle.

22. The Dormouse replied that they were very ill. Hence they lived on treacle.

27 TRUTH-TABLE DEFINITIONS

If one were to ask for the exact *meaning* of the symbolic operations or relations in the logic of propositions—negation, conjunction, disjunction, and so on—the answers would have to be expressed in terms of the truth-values (truth or falsity) of component propositions. For example, we must define "conjunction" as that relation between propositions in which a conjunctive proposition is true if and only if each of its component propositions (conjuncts) is true. And disjunction, in its weak form, is false if and only if each of its disjuncts is false.

It follows then, since the meaning of symbols used in the logic of propositions is a function of truth-values, that a precise definition of each symbol will involve a statement of its truth-value under all possible circumstances, that is, for each possible truth-value combination of its component propositions. Definitions that are based in this way on an exhaustive list of truth-value combinations are called *truth-table definitions*.

An examination of truth-table definitions of symbols in the logic of propositions is useful for at least three distinct purposes. First, it introduces the exact meaning of the notions defined. Second, it lays the foundation for a mechanical method of deciding validity or consistency of all expressions or arguments in the logic of propositions. And third, the study of truth-table definitions is peculiarly adapted to showing the basis or nature of formal logic in general.

27.1 Negation

Since negation is not a relation between propositions, but an operation upon a single proposition or relation, an exhaustive list of truth-value possibilities for negation will contain only two values: the truth or falsity of any proposition p. A truth-table definition of negation, therefore, will look like this:

p	$\sim p$
T	F
F	T

Here, the T and F in the column headed p represent the truth or falsity of any given proposition p—that is, an enumeration of possible truth-values of a single proposition. The column headed $\sim p$ is a *definition* of negation: it shows that a negated proposition always has a truth-value opposite that of the proposition affirmed. Negation *means*, then, the denial—the assertion of the opposite truth-value— of any proposition, whether true or false. The negation of a true proposition is false, and the negation of a false proposition is true.

27.2 Conjunction

It was said that conjunction is true if and only if all component propositions are true. Conjunction is a relation between propositions, and its truth-table definition, therefore, must take into account at least two propositions: p and q:

p	q	$\sim p$	$\sim q$	$p \cdot q$
T	T	F	F	T
T	F	F	T	F
F	T	T	F	F
F	F	T	T	F

The first two columns, headed p and q, represent the possible truth-value combinations of two different propositions. These two columns are separated by a double line from the remainder of the table to indicate that they are the truth-value possibilities on which the definitions are based. The third and fourth columns, headed $\sim p$ and $\sim q$, are inserted simply to show how negation may be defined in a truth-table composed, not only of one, but of two propositions. And the final column is a definition of conjunction, showing clearly that a conjunction of two propositions is false unless both component propositions are true.

27.3 Disjunction

A disjunction of two propositions may be either strong or weak, and the exact difference between these two types of disjunction will be reflected in their truth-table definitions:

p	q	$p \vee q$	$p \;ⓥ\; q$
T	T	T	F
T	F	T	T
F	T	T	T
F	F	F	F

Weak or inclusive disjunction, in other words, is always true unless both (or all) disjuncts are false. Strong or exclusive disjunction is identical with weak disjunction, except for the first truth-value combination, in which both propositions are true. This combination is excluded by strong disjunction. Truth-table definitions of weak and strong disjunction, therefore, give a clear statement of the difference between "p or q or both" and "p or q, but not both."

27.4 Implication

The relation of implication is more difficult to define by means of a truth-table. We found conjunction and disjunction easy to define, because these logical connectives are used in ordinary language as truth-functions, that is, as compound propositions whose truth-values depend upon the truth-values of component propositions. But that implication is truth-functional in the same sense is not nearly so apparent. As commonly used, the "If p, then q" type of proposition seems to connote a more intimate relationship between antecedent and consequent than can be determined merely by reference to component truth-values.

Nevertheless, the meaning of implication must at least in part be truth-functional. For we would demand, even in common discourse, that an implication containing a true antecedent be considered *false* unless the consequent is also true. This gives us the partial definition:

p	q	$p \supset q$
T	T	T
T	F	F
F	T	
F	F	

But how shall we define implication when the antecedent is false? A reference to ordinary discourse seems now to be of little help. Consider, for example, the proposition: "If you cram all night, you'll pass the exam." This implication, we should say, is true if an all-night cramming actually does permit you to pass the examination, and false if such is not the result. That is what we have entered so far on our truth-table. But what if it is *false* that you cram all night? Is the *implication,* in that case, true or false?

It is tempting, at first thought, simply to leave the two spaces blank on our truth-table. But that this solution is unsatisfactory becomes apparent when we consider that any proposition, after all, is true or false by definition, and hence the antecedent of an implication might not only be true, but also false. Furthermore, as we shall see, it would be impossible to define "equivalence" as *mutual* implication if the definition of implication is not somehow completed.

Nor may we fill in the blanks with question marks or some other symbol denoting our inability to decide the implication's truth or falsity. For this, in effect, would give us a third truth-value— a useful device for a more complicated, multi-valued logic, but incompatible with a basic, two-valued logic such as the one we are now discussing.

Suppose we experiment with T's and F's in the blank spaces. We might, for example, say that a false antecedent implies neither a true nor a false consequent. But this will not do, because implication will then have exactly the same truth-value definition as *conjunction.* And if anything at all is clear, it is that implication does not mean the same as a joint assertion of propositions. Nor will it do to say that a false antecedent might imply a false consequent, but not a true consequent. For then implication will have the same meaning as that we soon must ascribe to equivalence. And of the two remaining alternatives, one possibility—that a false antecedent implies a true, but not a false, consequent—is unacceptable, not only because of its inherent implausibility, but also because this definition would make implication equivalent to its own consequent.

Only one possibility remains: that a false antecedent imply *any* proposition, true or false. A truth-table definition of implication in the basic logic of propositions, therefore, must be constructed in this way:

p	q	$p \supset q$
T	T	T
T	F	F
F	T	T
F	F	T

It must frankly be admitted that this definition of implication is paradoxical, in that it permits any proposition whatever to be implied by a false proposition. However this peculiarity is more than counterbalanced by various advantages obtained by such a definition. We have seen, for one, that the definition finally decided upon was the result of an elimination of other, even less acceptable possibilities. And there are many other systemic reasons—reasons originating in the construction of a system—for accepting the definition in question. Not the least of these reasons consists in the freedom we gain in transforming symbolic expressions from implicative into conjunctive or disjunctive forms, and back again.

Furthermore, there even seems to be a sense in which a false proposition *does* imply any proposition. A *true* proposition, we have seen, does not imply any consequent, true or false. Therefore to say that a *false* proposition *does* imply either a true or false consequent is perhaps simply to comment on the nature of falsity in general: that a false proposition is empty or is not binding upon us insofar as its implications are concerned.

One more reason must be added—probably the most important reason—for accepting the foregoing definition. This stems from the fact that there is a multiplicity of ways in which we use the expression: "If . . . , then. . . ." We might mean a causal connection, as when we say that "If a student crams all night, he'll be tired the next day." Or we might mean an inference, for example: "If no men are angels, then no angels are men." Or again we might mean to explicate the connotation of a term, as in the implication: "If this is red, then it is a color."

We may now ask: What is the common or broadest possible meaning of all these different usages of implicative propositions? And the answer would seem to be that each usage requires only that the case involving a true antecedent and a false consequent be rejected as a false implication. The broadest meaning, then, of implication—the meaning which comprehends all the more specific usages of this logical connective—is that which denies that a true proposition can imply a false proposition. And this is precisely the definition we have settled upon. A more sensitive logic of propositions, of course, would take into account some of the narrower meanings of implication. But such a logic is beyond the scope of an introductory text.

27.5 Equivalence

The notion of equivalence must now be defined. This will be simple, because equivalence has been interpreted earlier as mutual implication. An equivalence of two propositions, then, is a case of each proposition implying the other. This means that equivalence can symbolically be expressed as a conjunction of two implications: $(p \supset q) \cdot (q \supset p)$. We may therefore build up a definition of equivalence in the following manner:

		(1)	(2)	(3)	(4)
p	q	$p \supset q$	$q \supset p$	$(p \supset q) \cdot (q \supset p)$	$p \equiv q$
T	T	T	T	T	T
T	F	F	T	F	F
F	T	T	F	F	F
F	F	T	T	T	T

Columns (1) and (2) are definitions of implication in both directions, from p to q and from q to p. Column (3) defines the conjunction of columns (1) and (2), and hence is a definition of mutual implication. Column (4), defining equivalence, is identical with column (3), since we have taken equivalence as meaning mutual implication. It will be noted that column (4) gives exactly what one would expect in the way of a definition of equivalence. For what is intended by this notion is an equivalence of *truth-values*. And turning back to the original set of possible truth-value combinations, we see that only those combinations in which p and q have the same truth-values, that is, in which they are both true or both false, are considered true equivalences.

We may now summarize this chapter by gathering all the notions we have defined into one truth-table:

p	q	$\sim p$	$p \cdot q$	$p \vee q$	$p \varovee q$	$p \supset q$	$p \equiv q$
T	T	F	T	T	F	T	T
T	F	F	F	T	T	F	F
F	T	T	F	T	T	T	F
F	F	T	F	F	F	T	T

EXERCISES

A. Construct truth-table definitions of each of the following symbolic expressions: (Asterisks indicate that solutions appear in Appendix B)

1. $\sim(p \cdot q)$

2. $\sim(p \vee q)$*

3. $\sim(p \varovee q)$

4. $p \cdot (p \vee q)$

5. $p \vee (p \cdot q)$

6. $p \supset (p \cdot q)$

7. $q \supset (p \cdot q)$

8. $(p \cdot q) \equiv (q \cdot p)$

9. $(p \vee q) \equiv (q \vee p)$

10. $(p \supset q) \equiv (q \supset p)$*

B. Assuming *only* that the proposition: "The signal is green" is *true,* use your knowledge of truth-table definitions to determine whether each of the following propositions is *true, false,* or *doubtful.* (Your knowledge of any causal relationship holding between green lights and moving traffic must be disregarded.)

1. The signal is not green.
2. Either the signal is green or traffic is not moving (or both).
3. The signal is green and traffic is moving.*
4. Traffic is moving.
5. Traffic is not moving and the signal is not green.
6. It is false both that traffic is moving and that the signal is green.
7. Either traffic is moving or the signal is green (or both).
8. It is not true that either traffic is moving and/or the signal is not green.
9. If the signal is green, then traffic is moving.*
10. To say that the signal is green is equivalent to saying that traffic is moving.
11. If traffic is moving, then the signal is green.*
12. That the signal is not green and traffic is moving is false.
13. If the signal is not green, then traffic is moving.
14. It is not the case that if the signal is green, traffic is moving.
15. To maintain that if traffic is moving, then the signal is green, is not true.
16. Either the signal is green or traffic is not moving (but not both).
17. It can be denied that if the signal is not green, traffic is not moving.
18. The signal is green and traffic is not moving.
19. Traffic either is, or is not, moving.
20. It is false that the signal is either green or traffic is moving (but not both).

C. Assuming only that the proposition: "The signal is green" is *false,* state whether each of the propositions listed above is *true, false,* or *doubtful.*

28 TRUTH-TABLE METHOD

We are now able to use our knowledge of truth-table definitions to formulate a mechanical decision procedure for the logic of propositions, that is, a systematic means of testing the validity of all inferences and expressions in which propositions are taken as units. Since a valid inference is one which is perfectly conclusive because of the *meanings* of key terms involved, we might expect that the *definition* of an inference would give a clue to its validity. More specifically, the distinctive property of a valid argument is the fact that it is necessarily true under all possible conditions. And since a truth-table lists all possible conditions, that is, all possible truth-value combinations, we should expect that a truth-table column for a valid argument would contain only *T*'s.

28.1 Testing for Validity

Let us construct a truth-table for *modus ponens,* which we know to be a valid argument, and see whether or not our reasoning in this matter is correct:

(1)	(2)	(3)	(4)	(5)
p	q	$p \supset q$	$(p \supset q) \cdot p$	$[(p \supset q) \cdot p] \supset q$
T	T	T	T	T
T	F	F	F	T
F	T	T	F	T
F	F	T	F	T

Here, just as we had suspected, the truth-table definition of a valid inference reveals that it is true no matter what the truth-values of its component propositions. And in general we can take for granted that any valid argument, when tested by the truth-table method, as it is called, will yield a final column of *T*'s.

The manner in which the validity of *modus ponens,* in this example, has been tested, must be carefully analyzed by anyone wishing to become proficient in the use of truth-tables. Columns (1) and (2), of course, are the possible truth-value combinations of the two propositions found in *modus ponens.* Column (3) is simply a definition of implication, while Column (4) is a listing of the truth-values resulting from a conjunction of $p \supset q$ and p, that is, of Columns (3) and (1). Column (5) is once more a test for implication, this time with Column (4) as the antecedent and Column (2) as the consequent.

It is exceedingly important to ask, before filling in the truth-values of any column, what exactly is the relation or operation being defined. If it is conjunction, as in Column (4), then we look for at least one F in the appropriate line and columns; if we find it, the conjunction is false, and if we do not find it, the conjunction is true. But if we are testing *implication,* as in Columns (3) or (5), the procedure is different. We now have to pay attention to the direction of the relation, since we are testing to see if the antecedent implies the consequent, and *not* if the consequent implies the antecedent. For example, in entering the truth-values in Column (5), we must ask whether the truth-values in Column (4) imply those in Column (2), and not vice versa.

The following set of rules, extracted from the table of definitions in the preceding chapter, will be of help in testing arguments quickly and accurately by means of truth-tables:

(1) A *negation* always has the opposite truth-value.
(2) A *conjunction* is false if and only if one or more of its conjuncts is false.
(3) A *weak disjunction* is true if and only if one or more of its disjuncts is true.
(4) A *strong disjunction* is true if and only if its disjuncts have different truth-values.
(5) An *implication* is false if and only if its antecedent is true and its consequent false. (A different rule to the same effect: A false proposition implies any proposition, true or false, and

a true proposition is implied by any proposition, true or false.)

(6) An *equivalence* is true if and only if its equivalents have the same truth-value.

One more caution needs to be observed in the construction of truth-tables. It will be noted in the foregoing truth-table for *modus ponens* that the implication $p \supset q$ was defined *before* the conjunction $(p \supset q) \cdot p$ could be defined. If the parentheses had been disregarded and the conjunction $q \cdot p$ defined first, followed by a definition of the implication between p and $q \cdot p$, the truth-table would have been constructed wrongly. Unless the table is built up step by step, proceeding from the elements inside parentheses to those outside, the results cannot be guaranteed. The premises of *modus ponens* consist of a conjunction of an implicative with a single or elementary proposition. Thus the implicative proposition must be defined first, before the conjunction. And since the argument as a whole consists of an implication between a conjunction of premises and the conclusion, the conjunction of premises must be defined before this final implication. In fact, the final column in a truth-table for any ordinary inference will always be a definition of the implication between premises and conclusion.

The following truth-table furnishes a demonstration of the validity of a disjunctive inference. Note especially the order in which the columns are set down:

p	q	$p \vee q$	$\sim p$	$(p \vee q) \cdot \sim p$	$[(p \vee q) \cdot \sim p] \supset q$
T	T	T	F	F	T
T	F	T	F	F	T
F	T	T	T	T	T
F	F	F	T	F	T

28.2 Testing for Invalidity

The invalidity of an argument is demonstrated by the presence of *at least one F* in the final column of a truth-table. Consider, for example, an implicative argument in which the antecedent is denied:

p	q	$p \supset q$	$\sim p$	$(p \supset q) \cdot \sim p$	$\sim q$	$[(p \supset q) \cdot \sim p] \supset \sim q$
T	T	T	F	F	F	T
T	F	F	F	F	T	T
F	T	T	T	T	F	F
F	F	T	T	T	T	

We need proceed no further than the third truth-value in the final column, because this shows that there is one truth-value possibility (namely, when p is false and q is true) of the inference being falsified. Such an inference is not necessarily true, and hence is invalid.

28.3 Testing for Equivalence

It must be noted that the truth-table method need not be restricted in application to arguments involving implications between premises and conclusion. Suppose, for instance, we wanted to determine whether the relation of implication was really equivalent (as remarked in the preceding chapter) to a denial that the antecedent is true and the consequent false. The equivalence to be tested may be written: $(p \supset q) \equiv \sim (p \cdot \sim q)$, and its validity demonstrated in the following manner:

p	q	$p \supset q$	$\sim q$	$p \cdot \sim q$	$\sim (p \cdot \sim q)$	$(p \supset q) \equiv \sim (p \cdot \sim q)$
T	T	T	F	F	T	T
T	F	F	T	T	F	T
F	T	T	F	F	T	T
F	F	T	T	F	T	T

28.4 Testing Inferences Containing n Propositions

When the inference to be tested is composed of more than two propositions, the truth-table is constructed exactly the same way, except that an appropriate number of truth-value combinations must be added. The formula used to determine the proper number of truth-value combinations is: $C = 2^n$, where C is the number of combinations, 2 stands for the number of truth-values (truth and falsity), and n is the number of propositions in the argument being tested. Thus an inference containing three propositions will yield eight truth-value combinations ($C = 2^3$), an inference composed of four propositions will yield sixteen combinations, and so on.

As an illustration of this extension of the truth-table method, let us test the validity of the argument: $[(p \supset q) \cdot p \cdot r] \supset (q \cdot r)$:

p	q	r	$p \supset q$	$(p \supset q) \cdot p \cdot r$	$q \cdot r$	$[(p \supset q) \cdot p \cdot r] \supset (q \cdot r)$
T	T	T	T	T	T	T
T	F	T	F	F	F	T
F	T	T	T	F	T	T
F	F	T	T	F	F	T
T	T	F	T	F	F	T
T	F	F	F	F	F	T
F	T	F	T	F	F	T
F	F	F	T	F	F	T

A listing of the eight truth-value combinations in the above example, although it may look complicated, is really very simple. For it consists merely of a listing of the four combinations under p and q, each of which may be combined with the *truth* of r, and a second listing of the same four values under p and q, each of which may be combined with the *falsity* of r. The student who wants to become adept at using truth-tables should learn some such systematic method of listing truth-value combinations of complex inferences, and should always check to see if the correct number of combinations has been listed.

28.5 Testing for Consistency

Oftentimes it proves desirable to test, not for validity, but for consistency. By the term "consistency" in logic is meant "self-consistency" or "noncontradictoriness." A set of propositions is consistent, in other words, when it is *possibly true,* and inconsistent when it is *necessarily false.*

That the truth-table method may be used for determining consistency is at once apparent. The consistency or possible truth of an expression is demonstrated by the occurrence of at least one T in the final column of its truth-table, and its inconsistency is demonstrated by a final column made up entirely of F's. Consider the following table:

p	$\sim p$	$p \vee \sim p$	$\sim(p \vee \sim p)$	$p \cdot \sim p$
T	F	T	F	F
F	T	T	F	F

We may interpret this table as indicating that the proposition p itself, or its denial $\sim p$, is invalid but consistent, since it may either be true or false. However, the statement that a proposition is either true or false, $(p \vee \sim p)$, is valid, while the denial of such a statement, $\sim(p \vee \sim p)$, is inconsistent. And finally, the conjunction of an assertion and denial of the same proposition, $p \cdot \sim p$, is inconsistent.

A test for consistency is not so important in examining an inference as it is in examining premises and conclusion separately. If a set of premises leads by valid reasoning to an inconsistent, that is, a necessarily false conclusion, we may rest assured that at least one of our premises is false. For, as we saw in Chapter X, a valid inference containing true premises will necessarily yield a true conclusion. This may be expressed and tested symbolically:

p	q	$\sim q$	$q \cdot \sim q$	$p \supset (q \cdot \sim q)$	$\sim p$	$[p \supset (q \cdot \sim q)] \supset \sim p$
T	T	F	F	F	F	T
T	F	T	F	F	F	T
F	T	F	F	T	T	T
F	F	T	F	T	T	T

In other words, any given premise p, if it implies the inconsistent conclusion $q \cdot \sim q$, will always imply that p, the premise, is false.

With respect to inconsistent *premises,* we know that the conclusion of a valid inference need not be true if the premises are not true. Therefore an argument can at once be rejected as unsound if its premises are shown to be inconsistent. The following truth-table demonstrates that a pair of contradictory propositions in any set of premises will render that entire set inconsistent:

p	q	$\sim p$	$p \cdot q \cdot \sim p$
T	T	F	F
T	F	F	F
F	T	T	F
F	F	T	F

It is interesting to observe that an argument with inconsistent premises is always valid, since a false conjunction of propositions implies any conclusion, true or false. But even though valid, such an inference is always unsound. For validity, as mentioned before, is not enough to ensure the soundness of an argument. True premises are also required if the conclusion is to be ascertained as true.

EXERCISES

A. By means of the truth-table method, test each of the following inferences and equivalences for *validity*:

1. $p \equiv p$

2. $p \equiv q$

3. $(p \cdot q) \supset p$

4. $p \supset (p \lor q)$

5. $\sim(p \cdot q) \equiv (\sim p \cdot \sim q)$

6. $\sim(p \cdot q) \equiv (\sim p \lor \sim q)$

7. $[(p \lor q) \cdot p] \supset \sim q$

8. $[(p \veebar q) \cdot p] \supset \sim q$

9. $(p \supset q) \equiv (\sim q \supset \sim p)$

10. $(p \supset q) \equiv (\sim p \supset \sim q)$

11. $[(p \supset q) \cdot (q \supset r)] \equiv (p \supset r)$

12. $[(p \supset q) \cdot (r \supset q) \cdot (p \vee r)] \supset q$

13. $[(p \supset q) \cdot (r \supset s) \cdot (q \vee s)] \supset (p \vee r)$

14. $[p \cdot (q \vee r)] \equiv [(p \cdot q) \vee (p \cdot r)]$

15. $[p \vee (q \cdot r)] \equiv [(p \vee q) \cdot (p \vee r)]$

B. Test the following symbolic expressions for *consistency*:

1. $p \supset q$

2. $p \supset \sim p$

3. $p \vee p$

4. $p \otimes p$

5. $p \cdot q \cdot r \cdot \sim p$

6. $(p \vee q) \cdot \sim (p \vee q)$

7. $(p \vee q) \cdot \sim p \cdot \sim q$

8. $(p \otimes q) \cdot p \cdot q$

9. $(p \supset q) \cdot p \cdot \sim q$

10. $(p \equiv q) \cdot p \cdot \sim q$

C. Symbolize the first five arguments in Chapter 30, and test them for validity by means of the truth-table method.

D. Given the proposition: "Either it's love or it's insanity (or both)," each of the propositions listed below falls into one and only one of the following five categories:

(a) equivalent to the given proposition.

(b) implies the given proposition, but is not equivalent.

(c) is implied by the given proposition, but is not equivalent.

(d) inconsistent with the given proposition (*i.e.*, a contradictory of the given proposition).

(e) consistent with the given proposition, but not related by implication.

Now, by means of truth-tables, determine which of these categories may correctly be applied to each of the following propositions (—unless otherwise specified, all disjunctions should be considered weak):

1. It's love and it's also insanity.*
2. It is false that it's either love or insanity.
3. If it's not love, then it's insanity.
4. Either it's not love or it's not insanity.*
5. It's love.*
6. To say it's love is equivalent to saying that it's insanity.
7. If it's not insanity, then it's love.
8. Either it is or it is not love.
9. It's not love and it's not insanity.
10. It is not true that if it's love then it's not insanity.
11. It's insanity but of a harmless type.
12. It is false both that it's love and that it's not insanity.
13. If it's both love and insanity, then we know it's insanity.
14. Either it's love or insanity, but not both.
15. If it's love, then it's insanity.
16. It is not the case both that it's not love and not insanity.
17. If it's not insanity, then it's not love.
18. It is false that it's both insanity and not insanity.
19. To maintain either that it's not love or that it's not insanity is not true.
20. It is denied that if it's not love, it's insanity.

29 SHORTER TRUTH-TABLE METHOD

The truth-table method, as we have seen, is a perfectly mechanical and reliable procedure for determining the validity or consistency of any expression in the logic of propositions. Its application, however, requires a good deal of time, paper, and patience. A truth-table often seems cumbersome and time-consuming when it is used for testing the validity of ordinary inferences. The purpose of this chapter, therefore, is to formulate a method of testing validity which, although not so general in application as the truth-table method, will enable us to save considerable time in determining the validity of most arguments. We may call this new technique the *shorter* truth-table method, since it involves a more concise application of truth-table definitions and, in effect, requires us to select the most pertinent information contained in a truth-table.

29.1 Invalid Inferences

Let us examine carefully the full truth-table for an invalid argument, say, the invalid inference based on incompatibility:

p	q	$p \cdot q$	$\sim(p \cdot q)$	$\sim p$	$\sim(p \cdot q) \cdot \sim p$	$[\sim(p \cdot q) \cdot \sim p] \supset q$
T	T	T	F	F	F	T
T	F	F	T	F	F	T
F	T	F	T	T	T	T
F	F	F	T	T	T	F

An inspection of this table reveals that the argument is invalid because one possible truth-value combination, when p and q are both false, leads to a false implication between premises and conclusion. In other words, when false propositions are substituted for the variables p and q, we are forced to call the conjunction of premises, $\sim(p \cdot q) \cdot \sim p$, *true,* while the conclusion q is *false.* And since a true proposition does *not* imply a false proposition, the premises, in this one case, do not yield up the conclusion. The inference is possibly false and hence is invalid.

Note, however, that if our purpose was only to discover the invalidity, the possible falsity, of the inference in question, most of our work in constructing a truth-table was superfluous. It was not necessary to know that the premises do actually imply the conclusion in three out of four possible cases. Only the fourth truth-value combination was pertinent to our inspection for validity, since no matter what the other combinations lead to, if we can find one possibility of falsifying the inference—one F in the final column—the inference can at once be proclaimed invalid.

Is there any way, then, of directly turning up a truth-value combination which falsifies an invalid argument without having to explore all possible combinations? It would appear significant that the *only* possibility of getting an F in the final column of a truth-table elaboration of an invalid argument occurs when the premises column contains a T and the conclusion column an F. Thus, for the purpose merely of testing an argument, we can *assume the conclusion to be false,* and then if we can in any way *make the premises true,* we will have demonstrated that the argument is *invalid.* For this would be the only case—true premises and false conclusion—in which the inference could be falsified.

Let us see whether this can be done with the example of an invalid inference we have been using. The inference may be expressed symbolically and an F written under the conclusion to show that we are assuming it to be false:

$$[\sim(p\cdot q)\cdot\sim p]\supset \underset{F}{q}.$$

Now if q is false in the conclusion, it must also be false in the premises. We may therefore carry the F over to the premises and, to help us in determining whether the premises can be made true, the symbols and punctuation of the inference are brought down:

$$[\sim(p\cdot F)\cdot\sim p]\supset F.$$

Our proposed test consists in falsifying the conclusion and then attempting to make the premises true. Hence, as our next step, we can assume the second premise, $\sim p$, to be *true,* since premises are always conjoined, and a conjunction is true if and only if every conjunct is true:

$$[\sim(p\cdot F)\cdot T]\supset F.$$

Now if $\sim p$ is true, then p is false:

$$[\sim(F\cdot F)\cdot T]\supset F.$$

And a conjunction of false propositions is itself false:

$$[\sim(F)\cdot T] \supset F.$$

And the negation of a false proposition is true:

$$[T\cdot T] \supset F.$$

But a conjunction of two true propositions is true:

$$T \supset F.$$

Thus we have succeeded in making the premises true while the conclusion is assumed to be false. And since a true proposition does not imply a false proposition, we are left simply with:

$$F.$$

This is precisely the F that had turned up on our complete truth-table as a consequence of the truth-value possibility of both propositions being false. However we have arrived at this possible falsification directly, by means of the principle that only an invalid argument can contain true premises and a false conclusion. And while it took a little time to explain this test, in actual practice the time required to determine the invalidity of most arguments is only a fraction of that used in constructing a full truth-table.

Ordinarily the work involved in applying the shorter truth-table method can be somewhat more condensed than in the foregoing example. A test of an implicative argument in which the antecedent is denied would look like this:

$$[(p \supset q)\cdot \sim p] \supset \sim q$$
$$[(F \supset T)\cdot \ T] \supset F$$
$$[T \quad \cdot \ T] \supset F$$
$$T \qquad \supset F$$
$$F$$

In this example the proposition $\sim q$ is the conclusion that must be assumed false, and in order for this to be the case, q itself must be considered true. Similarly, if the second premise, $\sim p$, is assumed to be true, then p is false. Rather than carrying down an expression in which variables and truth-values are combined, time is saved by substituting at once the appropriate truth-values for both variables.

29.2 Valid Inferences

The shorter truth-table method seems well adapted to the task of demonstrating the invalidity of an inference. But will it show that an inference is *valid*? Let us see what happens when we apply the method to *modus ponens*:

$$[(p \supset q) \cdot p] \supset q$$
$$[(T \supset F) \cdot T] \supset F$$

Thus far we have assumed the conclusion to be false, have carried over this assumption to the occurrence of q in the premises, and, since we are trying to make the premises true, have substituted a T for the second premise and therefore a T also for the antecedent of the implicative premise. We call one premise true, but are forced to consider the other premise false, since a true antecedent does not imply a false consequent:

$$(F \cdot T) \supset F$$

One false conjunct renders a conjunction false, and so:

$$F \supset F$$

But a false proposition implies any consequent, true or false, and hence we are left with a final T, which may be interpreted as representing the final column of T's in the full truth-table elaboration of a valid inference. In other words, after falsifying the conclusion, we were unable to make the premises true, showing that the inference is valid. For, by the principle that true premises cannot lead to a false conclusion by valid reasoning, when only false premises can consistently be found for a false conclusion, the reasoning involved must be valid.

However, the objection might be raised in connection with the foregoing example that, if we had called p false, then the implicative premise could have been made true. But, as we see in the following slightly different test, when we make the implicative premise true, we are forced to consider the other premise false:

$$[(p \supset q) \cdot p] \supset q$$
$$[(F \supset F) \cdot F] \supset F$$
$$[T \quad \cdot F] \supset F$$
$$F \quad \supset F$$
$$T$$

And we thus are led to the same result as before.

29.3 Inferences Containing Compound Conclusions

The inferences we have so far tested by the shorter truth-table method have contained only single propositions as conclusions. But the method may still be profitably applied to inferences containing conclusions of more than one proposition, as long as there is only one truth-value combination which will falsify the conclusion. The implicative series or any of its variations, for example, can be tested in the following manner:

$$[(p \supset q) \cdot (q \supset r)] \supset (p \supset r)$$
$$[(T \supset T) \cdot (T \supset F)] \supset (T \supset F)$$
$$(T \quad \cdot \quad F) \quad \supset \quad F$$
$$F \quad \supset \quad F$$
$$T$$

We see there is only one set of truth-values that will falsify the conclusion $p \supset r$, namely that in which the antecedent p is true while the consequent r is false. Carrying these truth-values over to the premises, we find that in order to make the first premise true, the consequent q must be true, which makes the second premise false. (We could, of course, have made the second premise true by calling q false, but this would have forced us to call the first premise false.) Thus because we were unable to make the premises true, the inference is valid.

Similar considerations hold when the conclusion is disjunctive, as in a complex dilemma:

$$[(p \supset q) \cdot (r \supset s) \cdot (p \vee r)] \supset (q \vee s)$$
$$[(F \supset F) \cdot (F \supset F) \cdot (F \vee F)] \supset (F \vee F)$$
$$(T \quad \cdot \quad T \quad \cdot \quad F) \quad \supset \quad F$$
$$F \qquad\qquad \supset \quad F$$
$$T$$

Since there is only one way of falsifying the disjunctive conclusion $q \vee s$, that is, when q and s both are false, we are permitted to carry over these truth-values to the premises. Then, in assuming the two implicative premises to be true, we are obliged to consider the disjunctive premise false, showing the conjunction of premises to be false, and the inference valid—thus accomplishing very quickly a task that would otherwise have required a truth-table with sixteen different truth-value combinations.

29.4 Limitations of the Shorter Method

When the conclusion of an inference is conjunctive or strongly disjunctive, however, there is more than one possibility of falsifying such conclusion, and the shorter method is usually not so economical as we might desire. A conjunction of two propositions, for example, can be false in three ways: when one or the other or both of the conjuncts are false. Thus three separate applications of the shorter method would be required in order to test the validity of an inference. If such an inference contained three or four different propositions, calling for a truth-table of eight or sixteen combinations, then a saving in time might still be effected by using the shorter method. But if the argument contained only two propositions, a full truth-table might well be preferable to the shortened version.

An *equivalence* between propositions is a mutual implication—a reciprocal inference, so to speak—and hence will usually require two applications of the shorter method. Suppose, for example, we wished to know if one of DeMorgan's Laws could be extended to include a third variable:

$$\sim(p \cdot q \cdot r) \supset (\sim p \vee \sim q \vee \sim r) \qquad (\sim p \vee \sim q \vee \sim r) \supset \sim(p \cdot q \cdot r)$$

$$\sim(T \cdot T \cdot T) \supset (F \quad \vee \quad F \vee \quad F) \qquad (F \vee F \vee \quad F) \supset \sim(T \cdot T \cdot T)$$

$$\sim T \qquad \supset \qquad F \qquad\qquad F \qquad \supset \qquad \sim T$$

$$F \qquad \supset \qquad F \qquad\qquad F \qquad \supset \qquad F$$

$$T \qquad\qquad\qquad\qquad\qquad T$$

In this way, we would have determined, in perhaps half the time required for constructing a truth-table, that $\sim(p \cdot q \cdot r) \equiv (\sim p \vee \sim q \vee \sim r)$ is valid. And still more time would have been saved, of course, if the equivalence had been *invalid,* and if the first test for implication had revealed this invalidity by reducing to an *F*.

EXERCISES

Symbolize each of the following inferences and test for validity by means of the shorter truth-table method. When in doubt as to the accuracy of your evaluation, check your work by constructing a full truth-table:

1. The philosopher Nietzsche was either a genius or else a madman. And since he died insane, he was not a genius.*
2. Astrology is not a mere superstitution, because it has a scientific aspect; and astrology, like any field of learning, must either be scientific or superstitious, but not both.*
3. If smoking is the cause of lung cancer, then heavy smoking will shorten a man's life by about ten years. This is not true however, and consequently smoking is not the cause of lung cancer.
4. Only if a significant correlation is discovered to hold between cigarette smoking and lung cancer may we say that the one is the cause of the other. Since this correlation has actually been found, we may be sure that cigarette smoking causes lung cancer.

5. Smoking is not the cause of lung cancer, because other causal conditions have been discovered, and lung cancer cannot be caused both by smoking and by other causal agents.

6. If you are unhappy, you have too many responsibilities. But if you are poor, you do not have too many responsibilities. Hence, if you are poor, you are happy.

7. Pity the poor student! He must either be a grind or a spendthrift. For either he studies hard, or else he neglects his studies. In the former case, he's a grind; in the latter case, he's wasted his tuition money.

8. Pity also the poor male! If he gets married, he's henpecked, and if he stays single, he's lonesome. So no matter what he does, he leads a miserable life.

9. The politician's dilemma is this: If he lies, he ruins his own character, and if he tells the truth, he's voted out of office. But the only other alternative is that he doesn't talk at all, in which case he's certainly not a politician.

10. Either the butler or the nephew killed the old man. But if the old man didn't leave a will, he didn't have any money, and either the butler found the will, or the old man didn't leave one. Therefore, since it's not true both that the old man was broke and that he was still killed by his nephew, if the butler didn't find a will, he, the butler, must be guilty of the murder.

30 REVIEW

At this point, after searching for and finding the logical form of many inferences, we know better what is meant by logical form. We can recognize the forms that so connect the premises to the conclusion of a valid inference that, if the premises are true, the conclusion must be true. And we know that, if an inference does not have one of these forms, it is invalid—no matter how persuasive or emotionally attractive its conclusion.

Yet there are many forms other than those we have studied which validly link the premises to the conclusion. Many more of them have been developed in the systematic deduction of logical laws from a few basic postulates in Symbolic Logic. But we have applied to the varied inferences of discourse the most commonly used laws governing the combination of propositions into inferences.

In this investigation, our units have been propositions, regarded formally and as unanalysed wholes, irrespective of content or internal structure. They could be connected by the fundamental logical relationships of *negation, conjunction, disjunction, implication, implication-in-reverse, incompatibility*. When propositions were related in certain ways they were also related by implication to one or more other propositions. The implied propositions could then be validly inferred from those which implied them. The logical forms of these implications were the forms of valid inferences.

These logical forms, where the premises imply the conclusion, are forms of deductive reasoning. As we saw in the Introductory Chapter, deductive reasoning is distinguished from so-called inductive reasoning, studied in scientific methodology. Yet, even inductive reasoning contains much deduction. Moreover, as our examples have shown, deductive reasoning permeates our inferences, not only in mathematics and the mathematical sciences, but also in all of our natural and social sciences, and even our practical affairs. All of these inferences, to be valid, must illustrate one of the basic logical forms. The laws of logic apply to all of our reasoning.

The student has been developing an ability to recognize and state these laws as they are applied to our discourse. In the following exercises, in all of which are exemplified laws he has studied, he can further develop his ability to discern the forms of inferences pertaining to the varied fields of science and of life.

EXERCISES

In the following exercises, designate the conclusion. Then show whether it follows from its premises, by symbolizing the component propositions and stating the logical form.

1. The accused is not guilty; for, if he were guilty, he would not have stayed on the scene of the crime, which he did.
2. In the near future, either the U.S.S.R. or the U.S.A. will have developed long-range rocket-type guided missiles. Since the U.S.A. will surely develop them, the U.S.S.R. will not.
3. Only if they are brought to the UN, can the comprehensive problems of international economics be discussed broadly. Since they are not brought to the UN, they cannot be discussed broadly.
4. John can't own a large house and pay his taxes every year. But he has no record of tax delinquency; so he doesn't own a large house.
5. If my mother dislikes my partner, I can't go to the dance. Since I can go, she must like my partner.
6. It would be impossible for John to be sincere and not hurt someone's feelings. But John isn't sincere; so he never hurts the feelings of others.
7. If destruction is available to any nation, universal disarmament will be necessary for survival. In the future, destruction will become available to everyone. Hence, disarmament will become a necessity.
8. Only if the acting is good, will the play be a success. Since it has played to capacity audiences for months, the acting must be good.
9. I know that if Mr. Smith knew that the speed limit is thirty-five miles an hour, he would not have been driving at sixty. Since the policeman says he was driving at sixty, he must have been ignorant of the law.
10. The attorney has grounds for preferring his own case only if he can refute his adversary's case; but, since he does not even

know his adversary's case, he hasn't sufficient grounds for his own case.

11. If a sensitized film is large-grained, all the detail of the moving object photographed will be blurred; and, if it is fine-grained, the speed of the film is slower than that of the moving object, and its photograph will be blurred. Consequently, a photograph of a fast-moving object will be blurred.

12. If the aim of the artist were to exactly imitate external objects, he would have to be a duplicating machine with no individuality. But the artist must see things in his individual way. Hence his aim cannot be the imitation of external things.

13. You know that it is impossible to laugh at a thing and admire it at the same time. Since you see how hard he is laughing at it, you may infer that he doesn't admire it.

14. Because of the nail the shoe was lost; because of the shoe the horse was lost; because of the horse the rider was lost; because of the rider the battle was lost. Therefore, because of the nail the battle was lost.

15. He couldn't have been wearing gloves and have left finger-prints. Since he left fingerprints, he was not wearing gloves.

16. Either you are not a good citizen or you did not fail to vote yesterday. But you did vote yesterday. So you are a good citizen.

17. You cannot use our product and not be satisfied with it. Since you don't like it, you haven't used it.

18. If the danger of destruction increases, the system of balance of power will be abandoned. But unless there is a system of international cooperation, the system of balance of power will have to remain. Hence, if the danger of destruction increases, there must be a system of international cooperation.

19. The city can't afford both to pave the streets when necessary, and build the schools that are needed. But it never can afford to pave the streets. Hence it certainly can't build the needed schools.

20. It is not true that the species of animals are fixed and that new ones are formed. But we know that they are not fixed. So there must be new ones.

21. Either you don't get a 3-percent tax reduction or you pay taxes

before the end of the month. But it is the following month, and you didn't pay your taxes. So it is obvious that you can't get the reduction.

22. Extremely high tides could have risen on the earth, if the period of the sun's tidal forces ever coincided with the free oscillation of the liquid earth. Since the free oscillation of the liquid earth coincided with the sun's tides at that time, extremely high tides could have risen on it.

23. Unless a doctor has experience in the tropics, he will not diagnose the disease. And either he diagnoses it or the patient will become very ill. Hence, either the doctor is experienced in tropical diseases, or the patient will become dangerously ill.

24. The existentialist, Kierkegaard, maintained that it was impossible for a belief to be genuine and not to be absurd. Now this belief is absurd, and hence must be accepted as genuine.

25. A microscope is either in focus or it gives an obscure view of the slide. And this microscope is in focus. Hence it gives a clear view of the slide.

26. Unless he knows what's good for others, he can't do good to them. But since he's always doing good to others, he must know what's good for them.

27. The rest of this gaseous material must have been somehow removed, either by falling into the sun or by being dispersed into surrounding interstellar space. Since the first possibility would result in much too rapid axial rotation of the sun, we have to accept the alternative that the gaseous excess material was dispersed into space.

28. If forms of life containing alchohol instead of water were possible, they would be found in our polar region. But no such alcoholic animals or plants have been found; so we surmise that they are impossible.

29. If planets support life, they must have oxygen or carbon dioxide or moisture in their atmospheres. Since these planets have atmospheres containing neither oxygen nor carbon dioxide nor moisture, there is hardly a chance for life on them.

30. If a man is a good artist or poet, he must have many emotional

experiences. But if a man is a financier, he does not have time for many emotional experiences. Hence, if a man is an artist or poet, he cannot be a financier.

31. If six small pearl buttons and two larger ones are found in the ashes of cloth, a man's shirt has been burned. And if a shirt has been burned, its owner wanted to conceal it, in which case it has tell-tale blood stains on it, and must have been the murderer's shirt. So if shirt buttons are found in the ashes, they must be from the murderer's shirt.

32. Sartre says: Both of us cannot be at the same time objects for each other. For when he sees me as an object, and I am sucked into his world, then I experience him as subject.

33. He continues: If the other is an object for me, he is contemplated and placed within my world. But if the other is a subject to me, I am his object and part of his world. Consequently, when the other is a subject to me, the other as an object is shattered.

34. He also says: We can take a consistent attitude toward another only if we were revealed at the same time as subject and object, which is in principle impossible. Hence we cannot take a consistent attitude toward another.

35. If the isolationists fight the middle-of-the-road policies of their own leadership, it would be better for them to establish their own party. But if they wish to win votes, it would not be better for them to establish their own party. Hence, if the isolationists want more votes, they will not fight the middle-of-the-road policies.

36. A seventeenth-century test for witches was as follows: the suspected witch was thrown into the water. If she sank, she was innocent. If she floated, she was a witch and so was burned at the stake. In either case, the unfortunate suspect perished.

37. Either this is an exceptionally good class or the test was too easy. Since the class did exceptionally well, the test must have been too easy.

38. The woodjoints could not have been made by a carpenter and be badly fitted. Since they were well-fitted, they were made by a carpenter.

39. Schopenhauer argued; If a man has desires, he is frustrated and so he suffers. If a man does not have desires, he is bored and so he suffers. In either case, man suffers.

40. If the X party nominates Y, it will lose the labor vote, in which case it will lose in the industrial areas. If it loses in these areas, it will not be able to make up in those areas by polling more votes in other areas, and in that case it will lose the election. So, if the X party nominates Y, it will lose the election.

41. If one has early classes one has to get up early. Either one has early classes or afternoon classes. Therefore, if one doesn't have afternoon classes, one has to get up early.

42. A pacifist argues: If I go to war when I'm called I violate my principles. If I don't report for induction, I'll be imprisoned, my family will be unprovided for, and so I'll violate my principles. In either case, I violate my principles.

43. The Greek philosopher, Zeno, argued: If a body moves, it moves in the place where it is or the place where it is not. But it can neither move in the place that it is nor in the place that it is not. Hence, a body cannot move, and motion is impossible.

44. One can't examine his own life and think he's always right at the same time. But unless one examines his own life he doesn't think. Hence, if he thinks, he doesn't think he's always right.

45. Albert Schweitzer argues: Only if we have reasoned ethical ideals may we have a true civilization. But since we have no reasoned ethical ideals, we have no true civilization.

46. Certain optical or electrical consequences of the earth's motion would have been observed unless a contraction of just the right amount to compensate them occurred. These electrical consequences were not observed. Hence the compensating attraction had occurred.

47. If he is a Socialist, he believes in public ownership of utilities. If he is a Republican he believes in private ownership of utilities. But he can't believe in both public and private ownership of utilities. Hence he is either not a Socialist or not a Republican.

48. Whenever the earth comes between the sun and the moon, a shadow is cast on the moon; whenever a shadow is cast on the

moon there is an eclipse. Hence, whenever the earth comes between the sun and the moon there is an eclipse.

49. He figures that if he studies hard he won't have to work outside of school. For either he will write a good examination or he doesn't study hard; and if he writes a good examination he will get the scholarship, and then he won't have to work outside of school.

50. If nations settle their differences by war, they will be driven to self-destruction; and, if they settle their differences peaceably, they must give up some of their powers to an international order. So either nations give up some of their powers to an international order, or they will be driven to self-destruction.

51. If there is no freedom of choice, a person is not free to choose the better end; and, if a person is not free to choose the better end, knowledge of the end is useless. Hence, if there is no freedom, ethical knowledge of ends is useless.

52. If the Chinese do not release American prisoners, the UN surely will not admit the Chinese. And if they do release American prisoners, the Chinese will offend Russia. So they will either not be admitted to the UN or they will offend Russia.

53. Either John does not get his degree early or he can go to graduate school before entering the Army. But he has flunked so many courses that it is impossible for him to get his degree early. He will therefore have to serve in the Army before entering graduate school.

54. If the ambassador believed his own statements he would welcome an impartial UN investigation. Since he opposes UN observers, he cannot be sincere.

55. If we rent the ballroom, we must charge $25 a plate. But, if we charge $25 a plate, not enough people will come and we can't rent the ballroom. Hence, we can't rent the ballroom.

56. Socrates said to the rhapsode, Ion, that, if he had knowledge of Homer's poetry which he recited, he was not acting honestly in not explaining it. But, if he did not have knowledge of it, he was divinely inspired. Hence, he was either dishonest or inspired.

57. The conclusion of Michelson's experiment is that either the earth is always stationary in the ether or that there is something wrong with the fundamental principles on which the interpretation of the experiment relies. But the motion of the earth is well-established. Hence, there is something wrong about the fundamental principles of science.

58. Newton reasoned that the motions of the satellites of Jupiter could not be so regular if the circumsolar force were not equally exerted upon Jupiter and all its satellites in proportion to their weights. Hence, since the motion of the satellites is regular, the circumsolar force must attract them in proportion to their weights.

59. Mill says that, in suppressing the expression of opinion, mankind loses a benefit. For, if the opinion is right, they are deprived of the opportunity of exchanging error for truth; if it is wrong they lose the benefit of the clearer perception of truth produced by its collision with error.

60. Socrates showed Cephalus that if justice were to speak the truth and pay one's debts, then one ought to tell the truth and return arms to a madman. But Cephalus did not think that we ought to do this. Hence he could not maintain that justice was to speak the truth and pay one's debts.

61. Lucretius, following Epicurus, argued thus: Space is boundless, and after our manner of speaking is infinite. For, if a man stood on the outermost boundary of space and hurled a javelin outward, it would either fly from his hand or something beyond it would stop it. If it flew from his hand, he would, contrary to his supposition, not be at the boundary of space: and, if it were prevented from flying from his hand, there would have to be some barrier beyond. In either case there would always be space beyond. So space has no outer boundary and is infinite.

62. When radioactive elements in rocks decay they pass through a number of intermediate stages and end up as common lead, whose accumulated amount can be measured. If the lead produced by the radioactive decay can be measured, the time it took to form the decay can be calculated. Hence, when radioactive

elements decay, the time they took to decay can be measured.

63. If the force of gravity decreases with the distance, the part of the earth nearest the moon will be attracted more strongly than the center of the earth, which, in turn, is attracted more strongly than the farther side. If the different parts are attracted differently, the earth and its waters will be elongated in the direction of the moon, and tidal waves on opposite sides will be produced. Hence, because of the force of gravity, there are tidal waves.

64. If the attraction of the moon for all parts of the earth and ocean were equal at all times, there would be no tides. Since there are tides, the attraction must vary.

65. If he is a gentleman I do not send him a bill, and either he pays his account or he is not a gentleman. So either he pays his account or I send him a bill.

66. The Principle of Indeterminacy states that it is impossible to determine with precision both the position and the momentum of a particle. The more accurately we determine the position, the less accurately we determine the momentum.

67. Leibniz wrote: If space were absolute there would happen something for which it is impossible that there would be a sufficient reason. But everything must have a sufficient reason for happening. Hence space is not absolute.

68. If the earth's axis of rotation is inclined to the plane of its orbit, then for six months the northern hemisphere (and for another six months the southern) is turned to the sun, a fact which results in one hemisphere receiving more heat than the other. Now either all surfaces of the earth receive a similar amount of heat at all times, or there are seasonal changes. So it is a consequence of the earth's inclined axis that there are seasonal changes on the earth's surface.

69. In a familiar brain-teaser, a king painted a red spot on the forehead of each of three aspirants for the post of prime minister, telling each only that his spot was either blue or red. Then he brought the three together and asked anyone who saw two blue spots to laugh, and anyone who reasoned out the color of his

own spot to raise his hand. No one laughed. Then one of the three raised his hand. He reasoned, "If the spot on my forehead were blue, either of the others, seeing it, could reason that his own spot was not blue, and would raise his hand. But, since neither of the others does this, the spot on my forehead is not blue but red." Is this reasoning valid? To go beyond formal logic, are its premises and hence its conclusion true?

THE LOGIC OF PROPOSITIONAL FUNCTIONS

PART III

THE LOGIC OF
PROPOSITIONAL
FUNCTIONS

31 QUANTIFIED PROPOSITIONS

31.1 The Generality of Propositions

We have begun to analyze the inferences we hear, read, and use in our sciences, literature, and discussions. We have learned that a deductive inference, to be valid, must have a logical form in which the premises imply the conclusion; and that, if an inference does not have that form, its conclusion does not follow logically from the premises. For instance, the enthusiastic voice over the radio may urge us to vote for Jones, who is so interested in the welfare of the people of the state. That he is truly interested in the welfare of the people—the voice warmly continues—is to be concluded from the fact that, if he is interested in their welfare, he wants better highways, and he has always devoted himself to the cause of better highways. But, despite the contagious zeal of the voice, we, as logicians, are not convinced of the conclusion, that "he is interested in the welfare of the people." We see that "he is for better highways" is only a consequent of "he is interested in the people's welfare;" and, therefore, that affirming its truth does not imply the truth of the conclusion. We realize that the validity of an argument does not depend on its eloquence, emotional force, congeniality, or insistence; but only on the logical connection between the premises and the conclusion. And this logical connection is missing from the politician's argument.

In an inference such as the above, later premises and conclusion contain propositions which merely affirm or deny propositions exactly as they occur in the earlier ones. Only such forms may be analyzed according to the logic of propositions, which we examined in the last Part. There, we studied propositions as unanalyzed wholes, symbolizing them by the propositional variables, p, q, r . . . , or by their more specific symbols, regardless of their generality. When a proposition, p, occurred, it had to recur in exactly the same statement or in its negation. This fact limited the kind of inferences which could be so analyzed.

In this Part, we shall extend our analysis of propositions to show their generality, or range, of reference or application. For propositions say things, not only about one specified individual, but more extensively about one or more or all individuals meeting certain conditions. For instance, consider the following statements:

> All men make mistakes.
> Some men make mistakes.
> This man makes mistakes.

The propositions make the same assertion about all, some, and one man or men; and so differ in generality.

This difference of the range of reference is part of the internal structure of propositions. When we can symbolize it, we can relate propositions in new ways. We will then have a much more flexible type of inference, and one more commonly found in the inferences we meet.

31.2 The Term Variable

A symbolism which shows the different generality of propositions has been developed by modern symbolic logic. It is developed as the "theory of Propositional Functions," and is one of the greatest achievements of logic since Aristotle. Though we cannot go into its complete theory here, we shall use some of its symbols, especially those of the *term variable*.

The term variable, usually designated by x, y, or z, symbolizes an individual about which the proposition says something. When only one term variable is used, as here, x is the common symbol. It symbolizes an individual thing, entity, or member of the universe of discourse. It is an abstraction, and free of any characteristics, which it receives only in the proposition containing it. In itself, the individual is unknown; it is any individual thing, entity, or member of the universe of discourse.[1] It may be progressively characterized

---

[1] The "universe of discourse" is the totality of entities being discussed.

by the propositions throughout the argument; and it must keep its identity, as characterized by the propositions about it.

Such an abstraction is not essentially different from the arithmetical abstraction symbolized by 0 (zero); and who knows what kind of thing 0 symbolizes? Yet 0 is a very convenient notation, which the student could not get along without. Similarly, the student will find the term variable a very convenient notation in analyzing the difference in the range of individuals to which a proposition refers.

31.3 Propositional Functions

A proposition must say something about one or more of these individual variables. To do this, the proposition must be symbolized by quantifiers of the variable, and by *propositional functions*. The latter are expressions—abstract and incomplete in themselves—which say something about x. They may be illustrated by:

> x plays football.
> x makes a touchdown.
> x is a hero.

Each function says something about an unknown individual x. Since the functions each say something different about x, they may be symbolized, respectively:

$$fx,\ gx,\ hx,$$

where x stands for the term variable and the letter preceding it stands for what is said about it. It is customary to start lettering a function with its initial letter, f, though many logicians have used the corresponding Greek letter.

However, when we symbolize functions in the exercises, we will not use these general symbols, fx, gx, hx. For, as with propositions, we will find it more convenient to use a capitalized initial letter of an important word in the proposition to symbolize the function. For instance, the above three propositional functions could be symbolized:

$$Fx,\ Tx,\ Hx.$$

A propositional function, such as "x plays football," is not a proposition, since, as long as x is unknown, it cannot be shown to be true or false. Yet it may become a proposition when x takes a value which will make the expression true or false. Hence, *all the laws which hold for propositions also hold for propositional functions.* In this Part, then, all the laws which were shown in the last Part to hold for propositions will be assumed to hold.

As there was for propositions, for each propositional function, fx, there will be a negative, $\sim fx$, which denies what fx says. We also will follow a convention similar to that for propositions in symbolizing a negatively worded function by a negative symbol. For instance, we can symbolize:

$$x \text{ does not play football}$$

by $\sim Fx$.

31.4 Universal Propositions

When propositional functions are combined with *quantifiers,* they may symbolize propositions. Let us consider how they may symbolize the following propositions:

(1) If a person is happy, he has wide interests.
(2) Some people are happy and have wide interests.
(3) This person is happy and has wide interests.

These three propositions say the same thing about different ranges of individuals; hence, they must be symbolized differently.

The first proposition says something about any person, about each and every individual we may mention. It says that *if* any individual is a happy person, then he has wide interests. If a happy person is found, he will be one who has wide interests. Now a happy person, like the traditional honest man of Diogenes, may not be found. Though we hope that there are happy people, whether or not there are any does not affect the truth (or the falsity) of the proposition. For the proposition says only that *if* there is a happy person, then he will have wide interests. And the truth of this assertion does not depend on the existence of any members of the universe who meet the qualification of being happy persons.

All universal propositions, of which this example is one, are hypothetical. A universal proposition may be defined as one which asserts of *every member of the universe that if it meets one qualification then it will meet another.* Moreover, it says something about every member of the universe. This universal reference is symbolized in the theory of propositional functions by:

$$(x)$$

which is read "for every *x*," and is called the *universal quantifier.* It always precedes the symbolization of a universal proposition.

Let us now symbolize our universal proposition. We shall let *Hx* stand for the function, "*x* is a happy person," and *Wx* for "*x* has wide interests." We then have:

$$(x) \ (Hx \supset Wx).$$

All universal propositions may be symbolized in a similar way. In general, then, we may write:

$$(x) \ (fx \supset gx).$$

31.5 Particular Propositions

Let us examine the second proposition:

Some people are happy and have wide interests.

This proposition differs from the first in two ways. First, it does not say something about *any* members of the universe, but about some particular members, though the members are not identified. In logic, *some* is taken to mean *at least one,* so that the proposition makes an assertion about at least one member of the universe. It asserts about at least one member that he is a happy person *and also* that he has wide interests.

Second, this proposition asserts that this member *exists.* If there were no members of the universe who had the qualification of being happy people, the proposition would not hold. It makes an assertion about some existent happy people. It is, accordingly, *existential*. It is not hypothetical, as is the universal proposition.

To show that the particular proposition says something about at least one existent member of the universe, the *particular quantifier* has been used, and symbolized by:

$$(Ex).$$

It is read "there exists at least one x such that . . . ," and is prefixed to every particular proposition.

Let us now symbolize our particular proposition. Using the same symbols as before, we have:

$$(Ex)\ (Hx \cdot Wx),$$

which is read:

> There exists at least one x such that x is a happy person and has wide interests.

All particular propositions are symbolized in a similar way.

31.6 Singular Propositions

Let us analyze the third proposition:

> This person is happy and has wide interests.

We see that this proposition is similar to the particular one. Certainly, it asserts the existence of a member of the universe with the stated specifications. However, instead of saying that at least one unidentified x with the given qualifications exists, it says that a definite, unique, identifiable individual with the qualifications exists. The proposition is what has traditionally been called a *singular proposition*.

A singular proposition, then, is a specific type of particular proposition. But it does not, as the latter does, say something about at least one unidentified though existent member of the universe. It says something about a unique, identified, demonstrable individual. To show this, a *singular quantifier* must be used. It may be symbolized:

$$(Ei)$$

where i is an abbreviation for x_i, *an individual value of x*. It is read, "there exists an individual x such that . . ." and is prefixed to singular propositions.

Let us symbolize our singular proposition. Using the same symbols as before, we have:

$$(Ei) \ (Hx \cdot Wx).$$

All singular propositions may be symbolized in this way.

Using such a symbolization for the universal, particular, and singular propositions, we can symbolize the generality and internal structure of a wide variety of propositions. We can build inferences on other relationships than those we have used before, including the relation of a universal proposition to a particular or individual instance of it. But, first, we shall explore these different formulations of propositions.

EXERCISES

1. What is meant by a term variable? By a propositional function?
2. What is meant by a universal proposition? A particular proposition? A singular proposition?
3. Explain the differences between these three types of propositions.
4. Symbolize the following propositions, explaining their meaning:
   (a) If a student has an average of 100 percent, he will be excused from the final examination.
   (b) Some students have an average of 100 percent and are excused from the final examination.
   (c) This student has an average of 100 percent and is excused from the final examination.
5. Make up examples of the different kinds of propositions.

32 OTHER WORDINGS OF QUANTIFIED PROPOSITIONS

32.1 Universal Propositions

The proposition used to illustrate universal propositions in the preceding chapter was:

If a person is happy, he has wide interests.

This proposition may be reworded in many ways. It obviously means:

A happy person has wide interests,

which is symbolized in the same way. If we use the same symbols, we have:

$$(x) (Hx \supset Wx).$$

In our flexible English idiom we find other wordings of the same proposition, as follows:

Any (every) happy person has wide interests.
Happy people have wide interests.
All happy people have wide interests.

Other universal propositions may be negatively stated. Consider the proposition:

A happy person is not preoccupied with himself.

This means:

If a person is happy he is not preoccupied with himself.

Let us symbolize "x is a happy person" by Hx, and "x is not preoccupied with himself" by $\sim Px$. We then have:

$$(x) (Hx \supset \sim Px).$$

The same proposition may be worded:

> No happy person is preoccupied with himself.
> No happy people are preoccupied with themselves.
> Happy people are not preoccupied with themselves.

Again, we must note that the existence of happy people is not asserted by this proposition, which is hypothetical. Its truth is not affected by the existence or nonexistence of happy people. It says only that *if* there is a happy person, he will not be preoccupied with himself.

Many universal propositions state specifications which, obviously, no existent x may satisfy or which it is possible that no existent x does satisfy, as:

> All trespassers will be prosecuted.
> Any resemblance to actual characters is strictly coincidental.
> Anything which moves this lever will be caught in the trap.
> Anyone who could answer these questions is omniscient.
> A perfectly just man will be happy.
> A squared circle is a circle with the area of a square.

However, many universal propositions have an implicit reference to particular members, and so make a double assertion, as:

> All the people in this room are Republicans.

Since existent people are referred to in this proposition, it may be broken down into the two propositions:

> (x), if x is a person in this room, x is a Republican.
> (Ex), x is a person in this room and a Republican.

But, since only the hypothetical interpretation is common to all universals, it will be used here.

32.2 Particular Propositions

The particular proposition used as an example was:

> Some people are happy and have wide interests.

We symbolize this, using the same symbols as before:

$$(Ex)\ (Hx \cdot Wx).$$

Now this proposition means:

> Some happy people have wide interests.
> A few (many) happy people have wide interests.
> At least one happy person has wide interests.
> There are happy people with wide interests.
> There is at least one individual who is a happy person and who has wide interests.

Particular propositions, too, may be negative. We may say:

> At least one person is happy and is not preoccupied with himself.

Using the same symbols, we have:

$$(Ex)\ (Hx \cdot \sim Px).$$

We may also say:

> Some happy people are not preoccupied with themselves.
> A few happy people are not preoccupied with themselves.
> Not all happy people are preoccupied with themselves.

The rather ambiguous statement:

> All happy people are not preoccupied with themselves.

is usually taken to have the same meaning as the preceding sentences, and is symbolized in the same way.

32.3 Singular Propositions

As an example of a singular proposition, we had:

> This person is happy and has wide interests.

The proposition may be symbolized:

$$(Ei)\ (Hx \cdot Wx).$$

A singular proposition, too, can be negative, as:

> This happy person is not preoccupied with himself.

Using the same symbols as before, we have:

$$(Ei)\ (Hx \cdot {\sim} Px).$$

A singular proposition is often about an individual designated by a proper noun, as:

> John has wide interests.

We may symbolize "x is John" by Jx, and "x has wide interests" by Wx. Our proposition becomes:

$$(Ei)\ (Jx \cdot Wx).$$

Or, alternatively, we could let Jx stand for what the two functions in conjunction stood for, "x is John, and has wide interests." The proposition, then, would be symbolized:

$$(Ei)Jx.$$

Whether we symbolize a conjunctive proposition by one or by two or more functions in conjunction will be determined by our convenience in symbolizing the inference in which it occurs.

EXERCISES

Symbolize the following propositions, using capital letters from some word in the proposition to symbolize the propositional functions.

1. All rational people need to use symbols.
2. Any advantages are concealed by the disadvantages.
3. No work of art should be confused.
4. Any person passing by may see it.
5. No one who makes the most of himself spends his time in personal contention.
6. John is intelligent and asks many questions.

7. No idealist could be happy with the results.
8. A freely falling body has uniform acceleration.
9. All bodies fall toward the earth.
10. Some people like cold weather; others do not.
11. People in glass houses shouldn't throw stones.
12. Shots were heard.
13. Copenhagen is the capital of Denmark.
14. At least one member of the jury thought him innocent.
15. Some people are afraid of open places; others are not.
16. Not all people need eight hours of sleep.
17. People who are perfect themselves may criticize others.
18. The unexamined life is not worth living.
19. Someone made footprints leading to the window.
20. Nobody knows the troubles I've seen.
21. Fools rush in where angels fear to tread.
22. There were those who dissented.
23. A man of understanding holdeth his peace.
24. People who talk about their exploits are not usually those who do the most.
25. A man was seen looking at the wreck.

33 OTHER RELATIONS WITHIN QUANTIFIED PROPOSITIONS

33.1 "Only" Propositions

Now that we can symbolize the different kinds of propositions, recognizing them in their idiomatic variations, we are ready to relate them in inferences. But, first, let us show how propositions containing relations other than implication and conjunction may be symbolized in terms of them.

Here, as throughout, we may assume that all the laws established to hold between propositions, in the previous Part, also hold between propositional functions. For, since the latter are only abstract propositions which say something about an abstract x, they must obey the same laws as propositions. Thus we see that the laws which we found to govern unquantified propositions also govern relations in and between quantified propositions.

Let us consider the proposition:

Only if a man reasons precisely is he a good scientist.

This is a universal proposition about any x, whose components are related by implication-in-reverse. Symbolizing "x is a man who reasons precisely" by Rx and "x is a man who is a good scientist" by Sx, we have:

$$(x) \ (Sx \supset Rx).$$

This sentence may also be worded:

Only one who reasons precisely is a good scientist.

33.2 Disjunctive and Incompatible Propositions

A proposition such as:

Either a man works or he doesn't eat,

is a universal proposition containing a disjunction. Symbolizing "x is a man who works" by Wx and "x is a man who doesn't eat" by Ex, we have:

$$(x) \ (Wx \ \lor \sim Ex).$$

We may replace this expression by either of its implicative equivalents:

$$(x) \ (\sim Wx \supset \sim Ex), \text{ or, } (x) \ (Ex \supset Wx).$$

Again, consider a sentence such as:

One can't have one's cake and eat it too.

Let us symbolize "x has his cake" by Hx, and "x eats his cake" by Ex, and the entire incompatibility by:

$$(x) \sim(Hx \cdot Ex).$$

This may be replaced by its implicative equivalents:

$$(x)\ (Hx \supset \sim Ex),\ \text{or},\ (x)\ (Ex \supset \sim Hx).$$

33.3 Particular Propositions

A particular proposition, too, may contain any of the relations between propositions, in addition to conjunction. Let us illustrate by the following:

If some people look down from high places they become dizzy.

This is a particular proposition, about at least one existing person. Let us use three functions to symbolize it: Px for "x is a person," Lx for "x looks down from high places," and Dx for "x gets dizzy." The proposition becomes:

$$(Ex)\ [Px \cdot (Lx \supset Dx)].$$

However, in inferences, we may often let Lx stand for the conjunctive proposition, "x is a person who looks down from high places," so that the proposition reads simply:

$$(Ex)\ (Lx \supset Dx).$$

Similarly, a particular proposition may contain any of the other relations. Let us consider the proposition:

Some people can't talk and drive at the same time.

If we symbolize "x is a person" by Px, "x talks" by Tx, and "x drives" by Dx, we have:

$$(Ex)\ [Px \cdot \sim(Tx \cdot Dx)].$$

More simply, we may let Tx stand for "x is a person who talks," and

Dx for "*x* is a person who drives." The proposition is:

$$(Ex) \sim(Tx \cdot Dx), \text{ or, } (Ex) \ (Tx \supset \sim Dx).$$

EXERCISES

Symbolize the following sentences:

1. If a man is a human, he is neither a God nor a beast.
2. A figure is not a circle if it is a square.
3. A person who denies it flies against common sense.
4. Only if a player obeys the rules, may he play the game.
5. If a man hurries too much, he makes a mistake.
6. If some people eat mangoes, they get mango-poisoning.
7. A person can't be fair and always act from selfish motives.
8. Only an expert would know that.
9. If some people are always happy, they become unsympathetic.
10. Only if a person follows directions, will he find it.
11. Unless a person follows directions, he won't find it.
12. Only sulphur dioxide has that odor.
13. If anyone receives a Russian stamp, he should lay it aside.
14. Unless a person knows the language he will learn little.
15. If anyone answers to the description, he should be detained.
16. In order to learn, one must desire to learn.
17. Either the passers-by see the sign or they don't look.
18. Except a man be born again, he cannot enter the kingdom of heaven.
19. A person can make himself useful only if he is able.
20. People are either too shy or too ignorant to object.
21. Except for having one fault, he was a fine man.
22. No one could refuse an offer like that.
23. There is a man who is one hundred and fifty years old.
24. Anyone who knows the good will do it.
25. A people cannot be impoverished and retain its culture.

34 CONTRADICTORIES OF QUANTIFIED PROPOSITIONS

34.1 Contradictories of Universal Propositions

The history of science is scattered with discarded theories and hypotheses. These theories and hypotheses may have served their purpose in paving the way to more adequate hypotheses; but facts have disproved them. For a scientific hypothesis is universal, and says about every member of the universe that if it meets certain conditions or specifications, it will also meet others. This hypothesis is contradicted or shown incorrect if even one well-authenticated instance which meets the first conditions does not meet the others. Just one instance in which a supposedly universal law does not hold is enough to show that it does not hold for all instances; if it fails to be true for even one instance, it fails to be true for all.

Take, for example, a discarded scientific hypothesis, a universal theory which was generally accepted until the late sixteenth century:

All heavy bodies fall with velocities proportional to their weights.

This was a theory believed to hold universally for all members of the universe which were heavy bodies. Reputedly, Galileo made experiments in which he dropped different weights from the Leaning Tower of Pisa. He showed that:

Some heavy bodies do not fall with velocities proportional to their weights.

His experimental result *contradicted* the former theory. He showed that in some instances the theory did not hold. Hence, the theory was false, and it was rejected.

The universal theory and its denial in particular instances are contradictories. For, as the logic of propositions has shown, contradictories are propositions of which one must be true, but cannot be true together. Certainly the universal theory and Galileo's experimental result cannot be true together; a theory cannot hold in all cases and fail to hold in one. Moreover, one of the two must be true; either a theory holds for all instances or it does not.

Galileo's experimental result, then, is the contradictory of the previously accepted universal theory. Let us symbolize the theory, using Hx for "x is a heavy body," and Px for "x falls with a velocity proportional to its weight," in this way:

$$(x) \ (Hx \supset Px).$$

Galileo's experimental result may be symbolized:

$$(Ex) \ (Hx \cdot \sim Px).$$

These two propositions are contradictories.

As a general rule, we may say that:

$$\sim(x) \ (fx \supset gx) = (Ex) \ (fx \cdot \sim gx).$$

From the logic of propositions we remember that $p \supset q$ is the contradictory of $p \cdot \sim q$. Hence, we may say that a universal proposition, holding for every x, is contradicted by a particular proposition, saying that at least one x exists for which the universal proposition is false.

Let us take a simpler example. Let us contradict our familiar, universal proposition:

All happy people have wide interests.

which we symbolized:

$$(x) \ (Hx \supset Wx).$$

It is not contradicted by:

No happy people have wide interests.

For these propositions, though they cannot both be true if there are happy people, might both be false. They would both be false if some happy people did and some did not have wide interests. They would be, then, contraries. They are not, however, contradictories. Rather, the original proposition is contradicted by:

Some happy people do not have wide interests.

for these propositions can be neither true nor false together. At least one proposition must be true, since either all happy people have wide interests or some do not. The propositions are contradictories, and we may write:

$$\sim(x)\ (Hx \supset Wx) = (Ex)\ (Hx \cdot \sim Wx).$$

34.2 The Contradictories of Particular Propositions

Conversely, the particular proposition is contradicted by the universal proposition. If we invert the order and substitute Wx for $\sim Wx$ in the above statement of contradictories, it is equal to:

$$\sim(Ex)\ (Hx \cdot Wx) = (x)\ (Hx \supset \sim Wx).$$

In words, the pair of contradictories would be:

Some happy people have wide interests.
No happy people have wide interests.

The contradictories of all particular propositions are similarly symbolized.

34.3 Contradictories of Singular Propositions

The contradictories of singular propositions pose a problem in which the difficulties with singular propositions are apparent. Let us examine a singular proposition:

This solution contains copper.

Symbolizing "x is a solution" by Sx and "x contains copper" by Cx, it is:

$$(Ei)\ (Sx \cdot Cx).$$

What is its contradictory?

Now, if the proposition were particular, its contradictory would be:

$$(x) \ (Sx \supset \sim Cx)$$

or, "No solutions contain copper."

Yet this last proposition is not the contradictory of the first, although it could not be true at the same time and is incompatible with the first. The propositions might both be false, since some solutions might contain copper, even though "this" one did not.

Nevertheless, it will often be convenient to treat the singular proposition as if it formed its contradictory in the same way as the particular, for the singular proposition:

$$(Ei) \ (Sx \cdot Cx),$$

implies the particular,

$$(Ex) \ (Sx \cdot Cx),$$

which is the contradictory of the universal proposition,

$$(x) \ (Sx \supset \sim Cx).$$

In practice, often a singular proposition is said to contradict the universal proposition which really contradicts its corresponding particular. Thus, Galileo's result, given at the beginning of this chapter, may be phrased as the singular proposition:

> These heavy bodies do not fall with velocities proportional to their weights.

It is said to be contradictory to the universal proposition:

> All heavy bodies fall with velocities proportional to their weights.

Though these propositions are not contradictory, but only incompatible, scientists seek merely an observation incompatible with a general law, so that if the observation is true the law is false.

Nevertheless, the true contradictory of

> This solution contains copper

would seem to be:

> This solution does not contain copper.

These propositions must be interpreted:

> This is a solution which contains copper.
> This (same individual) is not a solution which contains copper.

Only as thus interpreted can they be neither true nor false together.

Letting Cx stand for "x is a solution which contains copper," the contradictories are:

$$(Ei) \ Cx.$$

$$(Ei) \sim Cx.$$

We must remember that the x in the singular quantifier exists and keeps its identity in both expressions.

Let us state the laws for contradictories, using general symbols:

$$\sim(x) \ (fx \supset gx) = (Ex) \ (fx \cdot \sim gx),$$
$$\sim(Ex) \ (fx \cdot gx) = (x) \ (fx \supset \sim gx),$$
$$\sim(Ei) \ fx = (Ei) \sim fx.$$

EXERCISES

Symbolize the contradictories of the sentences in the exercises of Chapter 32, and write them out.

35 INFERENCES CONTAINING EXISTENTIAL PROPOSITIONS

35.1 An Application of a Universal Proposition to a Special Instance

At the beginning of the last Part, we examined an inference of the perspicacious detective Sherlock Holmes. The inference was:

> "Well, if a man can stride four-and-a-half feet without the smallest effort, he can't be quite in the sere and yellow. That was the breadth of a puddle on the garden walk which he had evidently walked across. . . . There is no mystery about it."— [That he was in the prime of life.]

Paraphrased to reveal its logical form, it read:

> If a man can stride four-and-a-half feet without effort, he is in the prime of life; a man can stride four-and-a-half feet without effort; hence he is in the prime of life.

Symbolizing "a man can stride four-and-a-half feet without effort" by S, and "he is in the prime of life" by P, we symbolized the inference:

$$[(S \supset P) \cdot S] \supset P.$$

This was an example of the valid form, *modus ponens*.

Yet, strictly, we had no right to let S stand for "a (any) man can stride four-and-a-half feet without effort" and also "a (some) man can stride four-and-a-half feet without effort." For, as we now recognize, the former is a universal, the latter a particular proposition; and they make statements about a differently quantified x. If Sx symbolizes "x is a man who can stride four-and-a-half feet without effort," the former would be symbolized as $(x) Sx$, and the latter by $(Ex) Sx$. And if Px symbolizes "x is a man in the prime of life," the inference is symbolized:

$$[(x) (Sx \supset Px) \cdot (Ex)Sx] \supset (Ex)Px.$$

We have no form to show that this inference is valid, though we suspect that it is.

Now Sherlock Holmes was assuming that his generalization about men who strode so far held for the individual man whose footprints showed him to be so far-striding. In fact, his inferences were due to quick application of the generalizations with which his mind was stocked to the pertinent individuals.

In our reasoning, both in everyday affairs and in theory, we are always applying general principles to individuals. If we know that all men must die, we readily assume that this, existing man must die sometime. If all dogs have four legs, this dog, too, must have four legs. If a happy man has wide interests and there exists a happy man, he will have wide interests. And if a man who can stride four-and-a-half feet is in the prime of life and there exists a man who can stride that far, he is in the prime of life.

Thus, we are assuming that a general law holding for any individuals having certain qualifications will also hold for an existing individual with those qualifications. In other words, what holds universally of every x conforming to certain conditions will also hold of an individual x conforming to those conditions. We may symbolize this law:

$$[(x) \ (fx \supset gx) \cdot (Ex)fx] \supset (Ex)gx.$$

This law, which we shall call the *Law of Application,* is a basic logical assumption. It is also assumed by the laws of contradictories given in the last chapter, which say that what must hold for every x cannot fail to hold for an existing, individual x.

Since the singular proposition further identifies the individual of the more general particular proposition, the Law of Application also holds for the identified individual designated by the singular quantifier. We may say equally well that what holds universally for every x will hold for one, specified, existing x.

35.2 A Form for Valid Inferences

The Law of Application, since it contains an implication, is a basis for valid inference. Let us now return to our sample inference; let us consider its functions, Sx and Px, as values of the universal symbols for *any* functions, fx and gx. We may then substitute gx and fx for Sx and Px in the form of the inference, and we thus obtain the symbolization of the Law of Application. This law is a true implication, and our inference is valid.

Let us note that this form of valid inference between propositional functions is analogous to the form of *modus ponens* between propositions.

Let us take another example:

No purely armchair theories will solve the problems involved, and some theory solved the problems. Hence, it could not be a purely armchair theory.

Let us symbolize "x is a purely armchair theory" by Ax, and "x cannot solve the problems" by $\sim Sx$. The form is:

$$[(x) \ (Ax \supset \sim Sx) \cdot (Ex) \ Sx] \supset (Ex) \sim Ax.$$

When we substitute general for specific symbols, fx for Ax and gx for $\sim Sx$, we have:

$$[(x) \ (fx \supset gx) \cdot (Ex) \sim gx] \supset (Ex) \sim fx.$$

This is a valid form. It reduces to the previous form when, for $(fx \supset gx)$, we substitute its counterimplication. Our inference, therefore, is valid. It is, as should be noted, analogous to *modus tollens* between propositions.

35.3 Invalid Inferences

These forms, and their extension in the next chapter, are the basic valid forms for the application of a universal to a special case. Any inference of this type which does not have one of these forms will be, so far as we know, invalid. Two common invalid forms will be illustrated.

Consider the inference:

If a person looks hard, he will find the place; and, since someone found it, I surmise he looked hard.

Symbolizing "x is a person who looks hard" by Lx, and "x is a person who finds it" by Fx, we have:

$$[(x) \ (Lx \supset Fx] \cdot (Ex) \ Fx] \supset (Ex)Lx.$$

Again, if we substitute the general for the specific symbols, we have:

$$[(x) \ (fx \supset gx) \cdot (Ex)gx] \supset (Ex) \ fx.$$

This inference is invalid. For it is not the application of a universal to a specific case. The existing x for which gx holds is certainly not a special case of the x's of which fx (and hence gx) holds. We recognize this form as analogous to the invalid form called *affirming the consequent*.

Again, let us consider the inference:

> If a man is in a place different from that where a crime is committed, he is not guilty. Now this man was on the scene of the crime, and hence must be guilty.

Let us symbolize "x is a man in a place different from that where a crime is committed" by Dx, and "x is not guilty" by $\sim Gx$. The form is:

$$[(x) \ (Dx \supset \sim Gx) \cdot (Ei) \sim Dx] \supset (Ei)Gx.$$

If we substitute fx for Dx and gx for $\sim Gx$, we have:

$$[(x) \ (fx \supset gx) \cdot (Ei) \sim fx] \supset (Ei) \sim gx.$$

This inference is not based on the Law of Application. For the existing x for which $\sim fx$ holds is certainly not a special case of the x's for which fx (and hence gx) holds. Hence the inference is invalid. We recognize the form as analogous to that of *denying the antecedent*. Any inference having this form will be invalid.

In quantified inferences, there may be a fallacy of *improper quantification*. Since these inferences all apply universal propositions to specific instances, they must all contain a universal proposition as a premise. The implicative premise must have a universal scope in order to apply to any x of the existential premise. If the implicative premise is only particularly or singularly quantified, it will not extend to other particular instances which exist. Hence, when the implicative premise is not universal, the inference is invalid.

This form of invalid inference is very common in the inferences we make. We often assume, hastily and wrongly, that what applies to one person will apply to another. We assume that since John gets good grades when he studies, Jim will, too. We assume that what is true of one Russian is also true of another. This illicit generalization is at the bottom of many invalid inferences.

Consider, for example, the inference:

> If some scientists work hard, they will be recognized; and, since this scientist works hard, he will be recognized.

Symbolizing "x is a scientist who works hard" by Wx, and "x is a scientist who will be recognized" by Rx, we have:

$$[(Ex) \ (Wx \supset Rx) \cdot (Ei) \ Wx] \supset (Ei)Rx.$$

The inference is invalid, since the first implicative premise is not universally quantified. What holds of some, more fortunate scientists may not apply to this scientist.

In summary, our two valid forms are:

$$[(x) \ (fx \supset gx) \cdot (Ex) \ fx] \supset (Ex)gx;$$
$$[(x) \ (fx \supset gx) \cdot (Ex) \sim gx] \supset (Ex) \sim fx.$$

Three common invalid forms are:

$$[(x) \ (fx \supset gx) \cdot (Ex) \ gx] \supset (Ex) \ fx;$$
$$[(x) \ (fx \supset gx) \cdot (Ex) \sim fx] \supset (Ex) \sim gx;$$
$$[(Ex) \ (fx \supset gx) \cdot (Ex) \ fx] \supset (Ex)gx.$$

EXERCISES

In the following inferences, designate the conclusion, and symbolize the component propositions by quantified propositional functions. Then symbolize the inferences, stating which forms they illustrate.

Example: Inference 1.

    Concl.: Some people are to be found in the Coffee House.
    $Dx = x$ is a person who likes a discussion.
    $Cx = x$ goes to the Coffee House after the play.

$$[(x) \ (Dx \supset Cx) \cdot (Ex)Dx] \supset (Ex)Cx$$

$$[\quad (p \supset q) \cdot \quad p \ ] \supset \quad q$$

Theoretically, we should replace the specific by the general propositional functions. However, since this method is rather cumbersome, the student may find it easier to follow this approximate check. He may replace the antecedent and consequent by p and q, remembering that the implication must be universally quantified.

1. Those who like a lively discussion go to the Coffee House after the play. So, since some people like the interchange of ideas, they are to be found at the Coffee House after the play.
2. If a person is at the door, he will knock. Since I heard a knock, someone must be at the door.*
3. No people who grow mentally keep the same ideas through the years. Some people always have the same ideas. Hence, they do not grow in mental stature.
4. No true politician makes many enemies. Some politicians offend many people, and so are not true politicians.
5. Unless a check is signed, it has no value. So I fear that this check is valueless, since it is unsigned.
6. He knows that if some people buy lottery tickets, they get big prizes. Since he is always buying lottery tickets, he will surely win a big prize.
7. If a person is arrested for picketing, he must live in a city with an antipicketing ordinance. Since some people were arrested for picketing, their city must have an antipicketing ordinance.*
8. Unless people object beforehand, they will have no right to complain about the results. Since there are some who objected beforehand, they can complain about the results.

9. If a man is a communist, he will not answer questions about his affiliations. There are those who do not answer questions about their affiliations. Hence they are communists.

10. This triangle has equal sides, since its base angles are equal. And a triangle with equal base angles has equal sides.

11. Some people do not believe in democracy, since some people can tolerate these slum conditions. And no one who believes in democracy can tolerate these slums.

12. A sound from the right side strikes the right ear with more force than it strikes the left. Some sounds strike the right ear with more force than they strike the left. Hence, they are from the right side.

13. That man is carrying a small leather bag, and those who carry bags like that are doctors. Hence, he must be a doctor.

14. When some people fish there, they always catch fish. So, since you are going to fish there, you will catch some fish.

15. No pleasures in what destroys society should be encouraged. Some pleasures are destructive of human values. Hence, they should not be encouraged.*

16. Aristotle said that if a man develops good moral qualities he must practice them. This man has developed a fine character, so he must have practiced his good qualities.

17. He also said that no man is really just who does not enjoy being just. This man doesn't enjoy being just, and so he is not really just.

18. Those who do not believe in white supremacy will not vote for Smith. There is a vote for Smith. Hence, at least one person believes in white supremacy.*

19. If a man leaves footprints going up to and stopping at the window, he must have climbed through it. Someone left such footprints and must have entered the window.

20. If a man has lived in Tibet, he will understand what was meant. There is a man here who has lived in Tibet, so he will understand what was meant.

21. Unless a person has great determination, he will not become a

concert artist. Many people fail to become concert artists, and so presumably don't have great determination.

22. No one who has heard this recording would be satisfied with any other one. Since many people are satisfied with other recordings, they could not have heard this one.

36 OTHER INFERENCES CONTAINING EXISTENTIAL PROPOSITIONS

36.1 Another Qualification

Suppose Sherlock Holmes's inference at the beginning of the last chapter had read:

> "If a man can stride four-and-a-half feet without effort he is in the prime of life. The murderer strode four-and-a-half feet without effort, and so the murderer is in the prime of life."

This inference, instead of applying the universal to "someone," applies it to "someone who was the murderer." The existent x has an additional qualification, that of being the murderer. To symbolize this inference, we need another function, "x is the murderer," which we shall call Mx. As before, let us use Sx for "x is a man who can stride four-and-a-half feet without effort" and Px for "x is in the prime of life." The inference becomes:

$$[(x) \ (Sx \supset Px) \cdot (Ex) \ (Mx \cdot Sx)] \supset (Ex) \ (Mx \cdot Px).$$

Now this inference is really just an expansion of the valid form presented in the last chapter. Here, replacing our specific by general symbols, Sx by fx, Px by gx, and Mx by hx, we have:

$$[(x)\ (fx \supset gx)\cdot(Ex)\ (hx\cdot fx)] \supset (Ex)\ (hx\cdot gx).$$

We have added to the last form only that the existing x for which fx, and hence gx, holds is also defined by a third qualification, hx. Now the universal proposition, $(x)\ (fx \supset gx)$, must apply to *every* existent instance for which fx holds, no matter how many additional qualifications it has. Since this application is valid for an x limited by one function, it must also be valid for an x limited by two or more functions in conjunction. Its form is analogous to that developed for propositions in Chapter 21:

$$[(p \supset q)\cdot r\cdot p] \supset r\cdot q.$$

The additional qualification of the special case, here symbolized by hx, may be written either before or after its first qualification, here symbolized by fx. For, by the commutative law, the order of a conjunction makes no difference.

Let us consider another example:

> If anything is a proposition, it may be true or false. This question may be neither true nor false, and so it is not a proposition.

Let us symbolize "x is a proposition" by Px, "x may be true or false" by Tx, and "x is a question" by Qx. We have:

$$[(x)\ (Px \supset Tx)\cdot(Ei)\ (Qx\cdot{\sim}Tx)] \supset (Ei)\ (Qx\cdot{\sim}Px).$$

Replacing the specific by the general symbols for functions, the form is:

$$[(x)\ (fx \supset gx)\cdot(Ei)\ (hx\cdot{\sim}gx)] \supset (Ei)\ (hx\cdot{\sim}fx).$$

This form is equivalent to the last, as may be shown by substituting for $(fx \supset gx)$ its counterimplication, $({\sim}gx \supset {\sim}fx)$. The inference is valid.

Thus, the same types of inferences, but with an added qualification of the existent x to which the universal applies, are valid as those we found valid in the preceding chapter.

36.2 Invalid Inferences

Any inferences which do not have these forms, or are not derivable from them, are to be considered invalid. The same forms which were called invalid in the last chapter are still invalid when the individual instances have an added qualification. Inferences cannot *affirm the consequent* or *deny the antecedent*. And, as before, the implicative premise must be universal in order to apply to the special instance.

Another fallacy is possible when there is an additional qualification. In a valid inference, the special instance to which the antecedent applies must be the same special instance to which the consequent is shown to apply. This means that the additional qualification, usually symbolized by hx or $\sim hx$, must be the same in the premise and the conclusion. Otherwise the inference will be invalid. Consider the example:

> No watches can go without repairs, and some watches do not keep good time. So some watches that keep good time cannot go without repairs.

Let us symbolize "x is a watch" by Wx, "x can go without repairs" by Gx, and "x is a watch that can keep good time" by Tx. The inference is:

$$[(x)\ (Wx \supset \sim Gx) \cdot (Ex)\ (Wx \cdot \sim Tx)] \supset (Ex)\ (\sim Gx \cdot Tx).$$

In this inference, the third qualification, $\sim Tx$, occurs as Tx in the conclusion. Consequently, the implication is invalid.

EXERCISES

In the following inferences, designate the conclusion. Then symbolize the propositional functions by specific variables, and give the form of the inference, indicating whether it is valid.

1. If a person is a real friend, he will help another person in time of trouble. Consequently, since Mr. Jones helped another person when he was down and out, Mr. Jones is a real friend.

2. The president cannot be lonely, since he is constantly meeting people. And if a person meets no people, he is lonely.
3. If a man has an alibi, he is not the burglar. Smith has an alibi, and so he can't be suspected of the burglary.
4. Socrates insisted that he would remain in prison. For a man who escapes from prison violates the laws, and Socrates always followed the laws of Athens.*
5. If a person doesn't honk his horn before an accident he is to blame. But no one would consider Bob to blame, since he honked his horn very loudly.
6. If a judge makes an important decision, he must cite a precedent. But Judge Brown makes only trivial decisions; so he need cite no precedents.
7. If a man goes to a university he has a chance to develop his natural intelligence. But Mr. Jones never went beyond high school, so he had no chance to develop his natural intelligence.
8. If a man has a very inquiring mind, he wants to inquire further at a university. Mr. Smith never wanted to waste time at a university, so he did not have a very inquiring mind.*
9. Unless a man has courage, he will not state opinions to which everyone is opposed. Since Mr. Smith states opinions with which everyone agrees, he is not courageous.
10. Angle 1 and angle 2 are equal, since they are both equal to angle 3. And things equal to the same thing are equal to each other.
11. If a body is acted upon by equal and opposite forces, no motion results. The earth moves. Hence it must be acted on by unequal forces.
12. All the members of society use the same conventions in language, and so each member can tell his fellows what he has experienced. My dog cannot tell his companions what he has experienced. Hence he is not a member of society.
13. Distance receptors receive stimuli from sources not in contact with the organism. Some senses receive only those stimuli which are in contact with the organism. Hence they are not distance receptors.

14. A wise person knows that he does not know everything; some sophomores think they know it all, and so are not wise.

15. Opposite interior angles made by a line intersecting parallel lines are equal. These angles are opposite interior angles made by a line intersection parallel lines, and so they are equal.

16. Since no rocks exhibit an age of over two billion years and since the solid crust of our earth is basically rock, the crust must have been formed from previously molten material not more than two billion years ago.

17. If some books, not enjoyed at first, are reread, they are enjoyed. You did not enjoy this book. Hence you did not reread it.

18. Most of our beliefs consist in the tacit acceptance of current attitudes, and since such tacit acceptance is unreflective, most of our beliefs are unreflective.

19. Mill claims that if everything they ought to know is to be accessible to the leaders of mankind, everything they ought to know must be free to be written and published without restraint. But, since some heretical opinions are suppressed, some things they ought to know are unknowable to the leaders of mankind.

20. Galileo assumed that if a ball slid down a perfectly smooth inclined plane, it behaved like a freely falling body (when allowance had been made for the slope of the plane). A brass ball was rolled down a smooth inclined plane. Hence, it obeyed the laws of falling bodies.

37 INFERENCES COMPOSED OF UNIVERSAL PROPOSITIONS

37.1 Valid Inferences

Not all inferences combine a universal with a particular proposition in their premises. Some inferences combine two universal propositions in their premises. Then the conclusion, too, must be universal. Such an inference follows:

> Since true statesmen must make farseeing judgments of the consequences of every act and since those who make such judgments must base them on reason, true statesmen must base their judgments on reason.

Let us symbolize "x is a true statesman" by Sx, "x makes a farseeing judgment" by Jx, and "x bases his judgments on reason" by Rx. The form is:

$$[(x) (Sx \supset Jx) \cdot (x) (Jx \supset Rx)] \supset (x) (Sx \supset Rx).$$

We may write the quantifier only once, putting it first, since it quantifies every proposition. Also, let us replace the specific by the general variables, thus:

$$(x) [(fx \supset gx) \cdot (gx \supset hx)] \supset (fx \supset hx).$$

Actually, this form may be easily shown to be equivalent to the valid form of an inference with a particular conclusion, which was given in the last chapter. That it is valid may also be shown from its correspondence to an implicative series. Like the series, this valid form obeys three rules. They are:

(1) The antecedent of the first premise is the antecedent of the conclusion.

(2) The consequent of the last premise is the consequent of the conclusion.

(3) The consequent of the first premise is the same as the antecedent of the second.

A fourth rule, added here, is that all of the propositions must be universally quantified. Any inference which obeys all four of these rules is valid.

Often, we must rearrange the propositions to show the form of a valid series. Consider Socrates' argument:

> No man acting voluntarily would choose the lesser instead of the greater good. The evil-doer chooses the lesser good; hence the evil-doer does not act voluntarily.

Let us symbolize "x is a man acting voluntarily by Vx," "x chooses the lesser good" by Lx, and "x is an evil-doer" by Ex. We have:

$$(x)\ [(Vx \supset \sim Lx)\cdot(Ex \supset Lx)] \supset (Ex \supset \sim Vx).$$

Is this inference valid?

By substituting its counterimplication in the first premise, and putting it second, we have the form of an implicative series. The inference is valid.

Whenever the form of an inference may be shown to have the form of an implicative series, one which obeys all four of its rules, the inference is valid. The form (and its variations) is the only known form which combines universal propositions into an inference of this type. It will be our basic form for valid inferences composed of universally quantified propositions.

37.2 Invalid Inferences

If any inference composed of universal propositions of this type cannot be shown to have or to be based on the form of the implicative series it is to be considered invalid. As we have said, our knowledge of validity is relative to our knowledge of what forms are valid; and, in inferences of this type, the implicative series is adequate to apply to the inferences of our knowledge. Let us consider an example of an invalid inference:

Since all scientists make philosophic assumptions and since a lawyer is not a scientist, a lawyer makes no philosophic assumptions.

Let us symbolize "x is a scientist" by Sx, "x makes philosophic assumptions" by Px, and "x is a lawyer" by Lx. We have:

$$(x) [(Sx \supset Px) \cdot (Lx \supset {\sim}Sx)] \supset (Lx \supset {\sim}Px).$$

Is this inference valid?

We may manipulate this inference as much as we please, but we cannot get from it an implicative series which obeys all of the rules. If, to obey the first rule, we put the second premise first, we cannot satisfy the third rule, where the consequent of the first premise, here ${\sim}Sx$, is the antecedent of the second premise. Hence, the premises do not imply the conclusion, and the inference is invalid.

EXERCISES

In the following inferences, designate the conclusion. Then symbolize the component propositions with capital letters, give the form, and say whether it is valid or not.

1. In order to be eligible to play on the football team, a student must keep up in his studies. But no student who flunks economics can keep up in his studies. Hence a student who flunks economics is not eligible for the team.*
2. No one who saw all the difficulties involved in the task would volunteer to do it. Strangers in town were oblivious of the difficulties; and hence we could conclude that anyone who volunteered for the job was a stranger in town.
3. The laws for propositions hold for propositional functions. The implicative series is a valid form for propositions, and hence also for propositional functions.
4. If two sides of a triangle are equal, its opposite angles are equal. Since an isosceles triangle has two equal sides, its angles opposite them are equal.*
5. Karl Pearson says that if a scientist discovers a law from which a

group of facts is seen to flow, he must have great powers of disciplined imagination. Newton discovered the law of gravitation, the basis of many predictions; hence he must have had great powers of disciplined imagination.

6. Croce argues that art is not a physical fact; for a physical fact is an abstraction, and art is immediately experienced.

7. Works of art make serious demands upon powers of imagination and invention. The construction of scientific theories makes such demands, and so scientific theories are works of art.

8. Since any freely falling body has uniform acceleration and since this stone is falling freely, this stone has uniform acceleration.

9. Every mathematician can think in abstract terms, but that is just what a politician can't do. So no mathematician is a politician.

10. Imprudent people do not protect themselves against future hazards, while those who take out health insurance are protecting themselves against the future. So we may conclude that imprudent people do not take out health insurance.

11. If a man ever succeeds in reaching Mars, he will be subjected to the same atmospheric conditions as an airplane pilot would encounter at extremely high altitudes. A man subjected to such atmospheric conditions must use some means of maintaining air pressure around him, so anyone reaching Mars must use some means of maintaining air pressure around him.

12. Socrates claimed that those who knew what was good would do it. Many men do not do what is good, and hence are ignorant of it.

13. When an excess of the solid is added to a saturated solution, it remains in the solid state. Now, since this salt dissolves in the solution, the solution must not be saturated.

14. The Sophists claimed that what seemed true to any individual *was* true. Since the theory that might is right seemed true, it *was* true.*

15. Since the sum of the angles of a Euclidean triangle is equal to the sum of two right angles, and since the sum of the angles of a physical triangle is more or less than the sum of two right angles, a physical triangle is not Euclidean. So space is not Euclidean!*

16. Whoever can give his undivided attention to any enterprise can succeed in it, and no one who is uninterested in an enterprise can give it his undivided attention. Hence, no one who is uninterested in an enterprise can succeed in it.

17. James Thurber wrote: A student who passed botany had to spend several hours a week looking through a microscope. I could never see through a microscope, and so I could never pass botany.

18. He also wrote that if one sees plant cells through a microscope, one sees a variegated constellation of flecks, specks, and dots. These he saw. Hence he saw plant cells through the microscope.

19. When the solute is an electrolyte, its molecules tend to split up into ions. Since the molecules of this solute do not split up into ions, it is not an electrolyte.

20. Bergson argues that art has no other aim than to brush aside the conventional and social accepted generalities in order to bring us face to face with reality. Comedy accepts these generalities as ways of organizing laughter. Hence, comedy is not really art.*

21. When wires are heated to incandescence they produce light. A current of electricity passing through a wire heats it to incandescence, and hence it produces light.

22. Peirce reasons that if a theory explains phenomena which would otherwise be left unexplained, it should be accepted. Now the theory of fallibilism explains the variety in nature, which would be otherwise unexplained. Hence, it should be accepted.

38 OTHER INFERENCES

38.1 Inferences Based on Implication-in-Reverse

So far we have studied only those inferences containing a universal (implicative) proposition which applies to a special instance or which links with other implicative propositions. Yet, inferences containing quantified propositions, just as those containing unquantified propositions, may be validly based on all the other relations between propositions.

Consider the following inference:

> Kant said that only if an action is done from respect for the moral law does it have moral worth. This man refuses to shoplift because he's afraid he'll be caught. Hence, his refusal to shoplift has no moral worth.

Let us symbolize "x is an action done from respect for the moral law" by Lx, "x has moral worth" by Mx, and "x is this man's refusal to shoplift" by Rx. We have:

$$[(x) (Mx \supset Lx) \cdot (Ei) (Rx \cdot \sim Lx)] \supset (Ei) (Rx \cdot \sim Mx).$$

In the first premise, since it contains an implication-in-reverse, *only if* introduces the consequent. We see that this is a valid form, that of *modus tollens* applied to a special instance. The inference is valid. Again,

> Since only verifiable hypotheses are scientific and since no hypothesis which cannot be tested by observation is verifiable, only hypotheses which can be tested by observation are scientific.

Let us symbolize "x is a verifiable hypothesis" by Vx, "x is scientific" by Sx, and "x can be tested by observation" by Ox. We then have:

$$(x) [(Sx \supset Vx) \cdot (\sim Ox \supset \sim Vx)] \supset (Sx \supset Ox).$$

By substitution of its counter implication for the second premise, we find the form of the valid implicative series.

38.2 Inferences Based on Disjunction

Many disjunctive inferences apply the disjunction to a special instance. Consider the following inference:

> Mentally ill offenders should be cured or they should not be returned to society. This mentally ill offender is not cured and hence should not be returned to society.

Symbolizing "x is a mentally ill offender who is cured" by Cx, and "x should be returned to society" by Rx, we have:

$$[(x)\ (Cx \vee \sim Rx) \cdot (Ei) \sim Cx] \supset (Ei) \sim Rx.$$

The validity of this inference may be shown in two ways. If we keep to the use of the relation of implication, we may substitute for the disjunctive premise its implicative equivalent, $(x)\ (\sim Cx \supset \sim Rx.)$ We would then have a valid implicative inference with the form of *modus ponens,* applying a universal to a special instance.

Alternatively, we may say that a universal disjunction applies to any existent instance of any of its disjuncts. Hence, the same valid forms which held for disjunctive inferences between propositions will hold for the application of a disjunction to a special instance. So we may say directly that the above form is valid. Any disjunctive inference having that form, analogous to that of a valid disjunctive inference between propositions, is valid.

38.3 Inferences Based on Incompatibility

Again, consider the inference containing an incompatibility:

> It is impossible for a man to smoke a cigarette with another and remain a stranger to him. So, after the Russian soldier had smoked a cigarette with the man, the Russian soldier was no longer a stranger.

Let us symbolize "x is a man who smokes a cigarette with another" by Cx, "x remains a stranger to him" by Sx, and "x is a Russian soldier" by Rx. The form of the inference is:

$$[(x) \sim (Cx \cdot Sx) \cdot (Ei)\ (Rx \cdot Cx)] \supset (Ei)\ (Rx \cdot \sim Sx).$$

If we substitute for the incompatibility the equivalent implication

$Cx \supset \sim Sx$ we see that we have the form of *modus ponens* applied to a special instance, (Ei) (Rx). The inference is valid.

Here, again, we may say that a universal incompatibility applies to any existent instances of the incompatible propositions. The same valid forms which held for inferences based on the incompatibility of two propositions will also hold here. We may say directly that the above inference is valid.

Thus we may say that any of the forms analogous to those for valid inferences which held for unquantified propositions also hold for the inferences between quantified propositions in which a universal relation is applied to a special instance. The scope of the inferences we can symbolize has been greatly broadened.

EXERCISES

In the following inferences, designate the conclusion. Then symbolize the propositional functions with capital letters, and show whether the conclusion follows from the premises.

1. Either a business fails or it competes with others. Since the new store is doing a big business, it is competing.
2. If anything is desired, it is good. Some things disliked by some people are desired by others. Hence they are good.
3. You can't always rush from one activity to another and also do much thinking. Since Mr. Smith does nothing at all, he must do a lot of thinking.*
4. Granted that one either does a thing or has no desire to do it; since Mary finally went on the trip, she must have desired to go.*
5. Only those who can park parallel to the curb can pass their driver's test. Since these boys can park parallel to the curb, they can pass their test.
6. Since it is not possible that there is life on a planet and that the planet has no atmosphere and since Jupiter has no atmosphere, Jupiter has no life.
7. Since only what is right should be enforced by law, and since

keeping one's place in line is right, there should be a law enforcing the keeping of one's place in line.

8. Reichenbach says that all arguments are either logical or psychological. Moral arguments are not logical, and hence they are psychological.

9. Only if a thing can be compared with a standard unit can it be measured. There is no standard unit with which to compare the value of a smile, which, consequently, cannot be measured.

10. A country cannot have freedom and fail to guarantee a fair trial to everyone. That country guarantees a fair trial to law-breakers, and hence that country is free.

11. Either the speaker does not read his speech or he loses direct contact with the audience. The famous man who spoke at commencement did not read his speech. Hence his appeal was direct.

12. There are several pawnbroker's numbers scratched on this watch. Only a watch which has been pawned has such numbers scratched on it. Hence this watch has been pawned.*

13. It is impossible to be a dictator and to be happy. Consequently, although Alexander the Great commanded many countries, he did not command happiness.

14. Only taxes can pay for public improvements. And all taxes are opposed by some taxpayers. So public improvements are always opposed by some taxpayers.

15. If a defendant won't talk, he is afraid to incriminate either himself or others. John Brown, the defendant, won't talk, and he never is afraid to incriminate others when he himself is not involved. Hence, he is afraid to incriminate himself.

16. Assuming that a work cannot have been written by a man and fail to have his characteristic style, since this so-called Platonic dialogue does not have Plato's style, it is spurious.

17. Only those who are allowed equal opportunities are treated as though they had the same human worth as others. But racial minorities are not allowed equal opportunities. Therefore they are treated as though they did not have the same human worth as others.

18. If a person pursues the wrong ends in life, either he does not know what the right aims are, or he is weak-willed and cannot guide his actions by them. Smith, who is very strong-willed, pursues wrong aims. Hence he does not know what the right aims are.*

19. Hobbes believed that people could not live peaceably together and fail to have a strong government. Since the citizens of Utopia live peaceably together, they must have a strong government.

20. Croce says that a work of art is truly artistic only when it has a vital principle which unifies it. But mechanical drawings are without feeling and so are not united by a vital principal. Hence they are not art.*

39 TELESCOPED INFERENCES

39.1 The Missing Generalization

Throughout most of this book, we have been examining inferences in order to see whether their conclusions, which are given, follow validly from the given premises. Yet we found, in the last Part, that the premises or conclusions of our inferences are often not all given. A premise is often silently presupposed, and the inference is then incomplete. It is a *telescoped* inference, or, in traditional language, an *enthymeme*. In dealing with such an inference, we must find the missing premise so that we can bring it into the open, examine it, and know what we are presupposing.

This logical enterprise, then, is different from the usual one. The problem is not, given certain premises and the conclusion of an inference, to find whether or not the inference is valid. The problem is, given only some proposition of an inference and assuming that *it is valid,* to find the missing proposition which must be presupposed if the inference is valid. And this logical enterprise, though different from the former one, may be very important.

Let us take an example. The inspector, condemning a building after an earthquake, may say:

> This wall may crumble any time, for its supports have been torn loose.

The inspector was making an inference, drawing the conclusion "This wall may crumble any time," from the premise "its supports have been torn loose." Yet this inference, by itself, is invalid in formal logic, for the conclusion is justified not by the stated premise alone, but also by another unstated premise. The inference is incomplete, or telescoped.

Our problem is to find the missing premise, the only one which will result in a valid inference. To do so, we will first symbolize the inference. Then we will see what form of premise, when added, will complete a form for a valid inference.

Symbolizing "x is a wall with its supports torn loose" by Lx, and "x is a wall which may crumble anytime" by Cx, the telescoped inference is:

$$(Ei)\ Lx \supset (Ei)Cx.$$

We see that the complete form with this premise and conclusion is:

$$[(x)\ (Lx \supset Cx)\cdot(Ei)\ Lx] \supset (Ei)Cx.$$

The missing premise, which completes the form, is:

$$(x)\ (Lx \supset Cx).$$

If a wall has its supports torn loose, it may crumble any time. This missing premise must be universal, being derived from the inspector's acquaintance with walls and construction generally—not with this individual wall, which he is condemning—though he may say that what applies to any wall may apply to this one.

Thus, we often silently presuppose the universal premise which is needed to give validity to an inference. Our inferences are full of— or, rather, have presupposed and omitted to mention—many of the generalizations with which our language deals. When these generalizations are obvious or well-known, or when their truth is intended to be concealed, they are usually unstated.

Similarly, the scientific worker assumes the established, general laws of his field. He reasons:

> Since this object is immersed in water, it has lost weight equal to the weight of the water displaced.

Symbolizing "x is an object immersed in water" by Ix, and "x has lost weight equal to the weight of the water displaced" by Lx, the telescoped inference is:

$$(Ei)\ Ix \supset (Ei)Lx.$$

This becomes a valid inference when it is prefixed by the premise:

$$(x)\ (Ix \supset Lx).$$

> Any body immersed in water loses weight equal to the weight of the water displaced.

This general law, known by the name of its discoverer, Archimedes, is presupposed if the scientist's incomplete and telescoped inference is valid.

39.2 Telescoped Inferences with Universal Conclusions

Sometimes the premise and conclusion of the telescoped inference are both universal, thus calling for a different form into which the missing premise can fit. Consider the inference:

> Since vice and virtue do not belong to the physical descriptions of any human acts, they are fictions made by man for his convenience.

Let us symbolize "x is a vice or virtue" by Vx, "x belongs to the physical description of an act" by Px, and "x is a fiction" by Fx.

The telescoped inference is:

$$(x) \ [(Vx \supset \sim Px) \supset (Vx \supset Fx)]$$

If we complete the inference to make it an implicative series, the second premise, which is the missing one, is:

$$(x) \ (\sim Px \supset Fx)$$

> What does not belong to the physical description of an act is a fiction made by man for his convenience.

In this example, the missing premise, when stated and brought out into the open, is seen to be false or at least debatable. Certainly, its truth is not accepted by all philosophers. Although considerations of the factual truth of this premise take us beyond the field of formal logic, it is a logical problem to formulate the missing premise, so that its factual truth may be evaluated.

EXERCISES

A. Find an argument in your reading that is telescoped, as are most arguments you read or hear. Symbolize the argument, and supply the missing premise which will result in a valid argument.

B. In the following inferences, find the conclusions, symbolize the propositions, and supply the premise which will make each inference valid.

1. This is good varnish, for it dries quickly to a hard finish.
2. Something must be wrong with this radio, for it has a persistent hum.
3. John has not fulfilled his language requirement; so he cannot graduate.
4. This law cannot pass, since only those laws are passed which the public demands.
5. "You have been reasoning with me," sobbed David's child-wife, "and a man can't reason with his wife and love her, too."

6. All general propositions are false, it is said, since no general propositions can be observed to hold in all instances.

7. Since the judge ruled that Brown was guilty, he could not have known Brown's character.

8. These angles are equal, since they are the opposite interior angles made by intersecting parallel lines.

9. All human beings act as they must act so Jones could not have refrained from stealing.

10. How can John be guilty of the robbery? He was a good friend of the man who was robbed.

11. Inference and implication cannot be the same, for the inference can be mistaken, but not the implication.

12. At least one of the witnesses must be lying, since their stories are contradictory.

13. Only if languages can express the logical connections between ideas are they developed. So primitive languages are not developed.

14. According to the paper, several smart shops have forgotten communism, since they have started selling top hats and canes.

15. Clive Bell wrote: Great art remains stable and unobscure, because the feelings it awakens are independent of time and space.

16. Since either a person doesn't want to do a thing or he doesn't forget, John must not have wanted to go to the meeting.

17. Since the Copernican hypothesis completely explained the motion of the planets by fewer and less complicated hypotheses, it was accepted.

18. Since Copernicus knew that previous astronomers had hypothesized whatever orbits they thought would explain the motion of the planets, he concluded that he should be allowed to hypothesize orbits to explain their motion.

19. Galileo showed that since the hypothesis that a glassy substance fills out the mountainous surface of the moon to form a perfect sphere was unverifiable, it could not be accepted.

20. Kepler stated the hypothesis that a planet describes an ellipse with the sun for one focus, for this hypothesis entirely explained his observations of the motion of the planets.

40 REVIEW

We have seen how many of our inferences are elliptical, silently presupposing a generalization which makes them valid arguments. Many arguments which seem inductive thus turn out to be deductive, though the justification of the truth of the assumed generalization goes beyond formal logic. At this point, let us pause and look back over what this Part has added to the analysis of valid deductive reasoning.

Here we have used the symbolism of quantified propositional functions to indicate the extent of reference, or the generality of propositions. We distinguished universal, particular, and singular propositions. When they were symbolized, the relations between them were made clear, and new kinds of inference involving them could be justified. These new kinds of propositions and the inferences based on them were founded on the same relations and laws which hold between unquantified propositions. But these inferences have a greater scope and flexibility than the former.

First, we considered the simple application of a universal statement to its special instances, such as the application of "A freely falling body has a velocity independent of its mass" to falling sticks and stones. Moreover, we saw how universally quantified propositions could be linked to yield other universals. We thereby could symbolize arguments which would include the traditional syllogisms, but which would be closer to a natural expression of our thought than many—though not all—syllogistically stated inferences. In addition, we could symbolize arguments in which the relations of disjunction or incompatibility occurring in universal propositions could be applied to special instances.

Here we must stop. In order to consider further types of inference, we would have to extend the symbolism of propositional functions to those containing more than one variable. This would extend the type of inferences we could analyze, but such an extension would take us beyond an introduction to logic.

However, we have seen how even complex arguments have a logical form which is relatively simple and which may be found and symbolically stated. It is this form which shows them to be valid. It shows that the premises are so related to the conclusion that if they are true then the conclusion is true. When, and only when, we have found this logical form can we say that the conclusion is true. We cannot base its truth on its attractiveness, urgency, or other emotional force.

The exercises which follow may all be analyzed by methods we have used and symbolized by propositional functions with only one variable. Many of them are paraphrased from arguments which have actually occurred. The exercises may serve for review and for further practice in applying logic to the inferences we use.

EXERCISES

In the following inferences, designate the conclusion. Then symbolize the propositional functions by capital letters from important words in the functions, and show whether the inference is valid.

1. If a solution is made increasingly dilute by adding water, there is an increase in the percentage of dissociation of molecules. Since an equal amount of water has been added to this solution, it has more dissociation of molecules.
2. No one who believes in democracy can also believe in authoritarianism. Some people who call themselves democrats believe in authoritarianism, and so do not really believe in democracy.
3. Mill believes that no act which does not harm others should be interfered with by society. Refusing to be vaccinated harms others. Therefore there should be compulsory vaccination.
4. Mill also believed that unless people have become capable of being improved by free and equal discussion, they should not

have democracy. We have always been told that we should have democracy. Hence, it is assumed that we may be improved by free and equal discussion.

5. He also said that if acts do not harm others, they should not be restrained by society. Most tastes and pursuits, even though foolish, wrong, or perverse, do not do real injury to others. Hence, they should not be restrained.

6. If men were perfectly unjust, they could not act together in harmony to carry out a plan. Robbers work together to perpetrate a robbery. Hence, not even robbers are perfectly unjust.

7. Since those who think clearly trust their own thinking and since radicals trust their thinking, radicals think clearly.

8. A well-managed business shows planning and a directing intelligence. Since there exist many well-managed businesses, there is evidence of a planning and directing intelligence.

9. If craters are formed from volcanic action, they are—judging from terrestrial volcanoes—only a few miles across and are not uniform in structure. But some lunar craters are over a hundred miles across and are uniform in structure. Hence, so far as we can judge, the lunar craters are not extinct volcanoes.

10. No moral theories which place too much emphasis on intelligence alone explain human conduct. But, so our professor claims, John Dewey's theory explains human conduct. Hence, it does not place too much emphasis on intelligence alone.

11. There is a conception, Dewey claims, that moral issues can be settled within the inner life (apart from knowledge of actual conditions). Consequently, according to that theory, since the practical problems of the world cannot be settled within the inner life, they are not moral issues.

12. Socrates argued that the soul was immortal, thus: On the approach of death, that which has its opposite, life, must either perish or withdraw. But the soul, having life, cannot perish. Hence, it must withdraw.

13. In the *Apology,* Meletus admitted that a man could not believe in spiritual or divine agencies and fail to believe in spirits or demigods. Since, as he swore in his affidavit, Socrates believed

in a spiritual agency, Meletus had to conclude that Socrates believed in spirits or demigods.

14. Boyle's Law states that if the volume of a gas increases, its pressure at the same temperature will decrease. When some air in the tire is released, it expands into the outside air. Hence, when some air is released from the tire, its pressure will decrease.

15. I will agree only to reform legislation which can be enforced. Since I do not consider that the prohibition of the sale of liquor can be enforced, I will not agree to it.

16. The same number cannot be both odd and even. Since 5 is an odd number, it cannot be an even one.

17. Only a person with a great desire for accuracy would have taken note of such a small deviation; since the young physiologist noted the deviation, he must have had a passion for accuracy.

18. Freud said that our actions are directed by either conscious or unconscious wishes. Mary did not know why she went to concerts. Hence her concert-going was motivated by an unconscious wish.

19. If the probability of each face of the die turning up corresponded only to human ignorance, there would be no law that each face of the die will turn up about one-sixth of the throws. Since there is such a law of probability, probability is not due to ignorance alone.

20. Either a person would enjoy the speech or he is hypercritical. Since the heckler in the back row was too critical, he did not enjoy the speech.

21. Hobbes argued that people could not have security and still govern themselves. Some people, living in a state of nature, insist on governing their own lives. Hence, they are insecure.

22. Cardozo believed that in some cases courts must add to the laws and rulings of the past; for, if a case has no exact precedent, it must be decided on the basis of an added ruling, and Cardozo cited some cases with no exact precedents.

23. Another reason why in some cases courts must change past law

is the conflict of past decisions. Some judges have reversed other decisions, and where past law is contradictory, it cannot be cited without change.

24. It is impossible for a person to use propaganda to attain his ends and not to sacrifice ends to means. Since these political speakers use propaganda to attain their ends, they sacrifice ends to means.

25. Every member either prepares a written speech or appears in person at the meetings. Since these members, who just joined, will not be present, they are preparing written statements.

26. Lincoln said that no one who spent his time in personal contention could make the most of himself. Since some politicians spend their time in personal contention, they can't make the most of themselves.

27. Some fish bite in deep water; since no fish bite in this water, this water is not deep.

28. Augustine and the Council of Carthage had said that divorce might be granted on the ground of adultery. Hence, since idolatry and apostasy were "spiritual adultery," for hundreds of years divorces were granted for idolatry and apostasy.

29. Iago argued: Who steals my purse steals trash; but, since my good name is not my purse, he who filches from me my good name does not steal trash.

30. The lawyer for the defense argued that if Mr. Smith had learned the defendant's past habits, he must have been plotting to frame the defendant. The witness testified that Mr. Smith had questioned her concerning the defendant's habits. So the lawyer concluded that Mr. Smith had been plotting to frame the defendant.

31. Either a man keeps to his principles or he can't complain about others who violate their principles. Now some businessmen keep to their principles. So they can complain about others violating theirs.

32. Kant said that to treat a man as a mere means is immoral. To buy and sell slaves is to treat people as mere means. Hence, slavery is immoral.

33. Kant emphasized that a treaty of peace after victory never ends the conditions of wars. And what does not end the conditions of

war does not end war. Hence, he claimed that a peace treaty after war can never end war.

34. He maintained that the right to make war can never be granted by a law of nations. For the right to make war is the right to decide by force what is just, a right which can never be granted by a law of nations.

35. Kant concluded that only a federation of nations could insure peace. For only a federation of nations could settle disputes by a consideration of rights rather than force, and only what settled disputes by a consideration of rights rather than force could insure peace.

36. Thomas Aquinas reasoned that no man endeavors toward an aim unless it be previously known to him. Since man aims at a higher good than can be attained in this life, he must know something higher than those things to which our reason can attain in this present life.

37. Just punishment should result in reforming the offenders, but much punishment of juvenile delinquents results in producing hardened criminals. Hence, much punishment of juvenile delinquents is unjust.

38. Either a person's actions should not be interfered with by society, or they affect others. What a man believes affects only himself. Hence, his beliefs should not be restrained by society.

39. Socrates argued that if a man's offenses were supposed due to nature, no one would rebuke or be angry with the offender. But the offenses of some are blamed and rebuked; hence, they cannot be supposed natural faults beyond the offender's control.

40. Kant said that if there is quarrelling about anything, there is a hope of mutual reconciliation and consequently grounds for judgment which are not merely subjective. There is quarreling about what is judged beautiful; hence, there must be grounds for judging what is beautiful which are not merely subjective.

41. The first law of motion is that every body continues in its state of rest or uniform motion unless it is compelled to change its state by the action of impressed forces. Since the planet Uranus

deviated from its orbit, it must have been attracted by another force.

42. A person who believes in democracy must believe in the ability of people to choose good leaders and policies, and whoever believes in this ability must believe that the people can be reasonably appealed to. Hence, whoever believes in democracy must believe that people may be reasonably appealed to.

43. Jefferson wrote that that government is best which provides the most effectively for the most able and virtuous people to fill its offices. In order to do this, the government must provide a general system of education from which the ablest people will emerge. Hence, that government is best which provides such a system.

44. If a place has a high temperature and a low humidity, high-frequency sound waves are absorbed by the air in it. The concert hall was hot and dry. Hence, it lost the higher violin tones.

45. Aristotle argued that natural occurrences either happen by chance or are due to an end. Now, observed adaptations happen regularly and so are not the result of chance. Hence, they are due to ends.

46. Hume reasoned that since all of our knowledge comes from experience and since no knowledge of necessary causality comes from experience, there is no knowledge of necessary causality.

47. Kant countered—in effect—that since no knowledge of necessary causality comes from experience and since there is knowledge of necessary causality, not all of our knowledge comes from experience.

48. Sherlock Holmes (in the *Sign of Four*) concluded, after observing Dr. Watson's watch, that Watson's brother, its former owner, was careless. The lower part of the watchcase was not only dented in one or two places but was cut and marred all over from the habit of keeping other hard objects, such as coins or keys, in the same pocket. "And, surely," Holmes ended, "it is no great feat to assume that a man who treats his watch so cavalierly must be a careless man."

49. If a patient suffers damage to certain portions of the auditory area of the brain, he is able to hear but not understand spoken words. This man can understand everything he hears. Therefore those portions of the auditory area of the brain were not damaged.

50. If the mass per unit volume of the fluid is assumed to remain constant, the volume of the fluid passing every section of a given tube per unit time must then also be the same. Now, at a given temperature, the mass density of this water does not change. Hence the rate of flow of the water through the tube must be equal.

51. The success of the artist depends upon imaginative sympathy with his fellow men. But one who has no experience of the emotions of life could not have sympathy with his fellow men. Hence the successful artist must have experience of the emotions of life.

52. Mill wrote that whenever the omission of certain acts would harm others, those acts might rightfully be compelled. Many acts, such as sharing in the common defense, would harm society if they were omitted. Hence, many acts may be enforced by law.

53. If a satellite of a planet comes too close to the planet's surface, it is shattered into many small bodies and forms a "ring" around the planet. Our moon, in the far distant future, will come too close to the earth's surface. Hence, in the far distant future our moon will be shattered and will form a "ring" around the earth.

54. If a planet supports life, its temperatures do not always go above boiling or below freezing. Mercury is so close to the sun that the temperature on its daylight side rises high enough to melt lead, and the temperature on its opposite side (which is eternal night) is far below the freezing point of water. Hence, life cannot exist on Mercury.

55. A person cannot be a great artist and have no love for art. Since Plato was a great literary artist, he must have had a love for art.

56. Disraeli said: No government can be long secure without a formidable opposition. The present American government contains a large opposition. Hence, it is secure.

57. The logical positivists say that all factual knowledge is reducible

to propositions about observable objects of experience. But no religious theory is reducible to statements about what is observed. Hence, no religious theory is factual knowledge.

58. A country cannot consistently maintain nationalism and believe in the rights of the workers of all countries. Now, Russia has nationalistic ideals, and so cannot believe in international communism.

59. Only intelligent beings possessing a high degree of culture could have constructed irrigation canals of such geometrically perfect regularity. And the landmarks of Mars, he believed, were canals constructed by its inhabitants. Hence, there were intelligent inhabitants with a high degree of culture on Mars.

60. If a planet has any type of vegetation on its surface, it will have a noticeable concentration of oxygen in its atmosphere. Spectroscopic analysis of the atmosphere of Venus fails to indicate free oxygen. This leads us to conclude that there is no extensive vegetation on the surface of Venus.

PART IV

LOGIC OF CLASSES

41 SYMBOLIZATION OF CLASSES

The history of modern symbolic logic, in its systematic form, begins with the construction of a logic of classes. This is perfectly understandable, because the traditional logic of Aristotle lent itself readily to an interpretation in terms of classes. Aristotle had dealt mainly with propositions in which a property or attribute is predicated of some given subject: "All men are mortal," "Socrates is wise," "No Greeks are barbarians," and so on. From these it is but a step to an interpretation not only of the subject terms, but also of properties or attributes, as denoting classes of things. Thus "All men are mortal" may be restated: "The class of men is included in the class of mortal beings," or "Socrates is wise" paraphrased as "Socrates is a member of the class of wise men," or "No Greeks are barbarians" as "The class of Greeks is excluded from the class of barbarians."

This and the following two chapters will present the basic notions of a logic of classes, and succeeding chapters will expand these basic notions to an extent sufficient to comprehend Aristotelian and a great many other types of inference.

Before undertaking this study, however, it should perhaps be mentioned that the Aristotelian logic, with its central topic of "syllogistic" inference, still appears to constitute the body of most introductory courses in formal logic. Students in such courses learn a formidable vocabulary of logical names and principles. Hearing of this imposing terminology of the classical logic, the reader of this textbook might suspect that his education in elementary logic was deficient in some respects. But this is not at all the case. Rather, just the opposite might be said to be true. For the machinery of modern symbolic logic has a more basic and general application than that of Aristotelian logic, thereby rendering superfluous much of the classical terminology. If all syllogistic and other Aristotelian inferences can be treated more systematically and rigorously by the symbolic logic of classes, then it seems clear that there is no practical, non-academic need for learning the ancient and medieval terminology, sanctioned though it may be by tradition.

41.1 Class Variables

We may adopt the usual convention of representing *class variables* by lower-case letters beginning with *a*:

$$a, b, c, \ldots$$

These letters stand for actual variables, in that they may designate any class whatever—classes of things, properties, events, relationships, and so forth. We will find it convenient to use class variables whenever we wish to state a law or a general form of inference in the class logic, or when our purpose is to designate a class the specific membership of which does not concern us.

41.2 Class Abbreviations

On the other hand, when we wish to designate some specifically named class, we use upper-case letters:

$$A, B, C, \ldots$$

It will prove helpful to use the first letter of a class name as its abbreviated designation. The class of "men" might in this way be represented by the abbreviation *M*, the class of "wise men" by *W*, and the class of "wise Greeks" by either *W* or *G*.

A class abbreviation may thus be taken as expressing a *value*—that is, a specifically named instance—of a class variable. Any given variable *a* has an indefinite number of such values or specified instances, and it is distinguished from any other variable *b* only by the fact that *b* (if it is not asserted to be identical with *a*) has an indefinite number of different values.

41.3 Singular Variables and Abbreviations

The individual members of a class must be treated differently from the class of which they are a part. It was thought formerly that each of the singular members of a class could itself be considered a peculiar kind of class. For example, Socrates, Plato, and Aristotle were individual members of the class of Greek philosophers, but they themselves could be treated logically as classes composed of only one member. This interpretation, however, produced so many paradoxical consequences that present-day logicians have been forced to abandon the traditional view and to treat members of classes as of a different logical order from the classes they constitute. Accordingly, let us represent singular or individual members of a class by the variables:

$$s, t, \ldots$$

To avoid confusion with class abbreviations, the same lower-case letters may be used both for singular variables and their abbreviated values. Thus, the *variable s* will represent any individual member of a class, while the *abbreviation s* will stand for any person or thing indicated by a proper name or by demonstrative or possessive adjectives: "Socrates," "Mary Jones," "the Woolworth Building," "the Atlantic Ocean," "this man," "that building," "your father," "his book," and so forth. In the exceptional case requiring another singular variable, we may use the letter t.

41.4 Complementary Classes

To refer to any class is tacitly to assume a second class, representing everything within a *universe of discourse* which the designated class does *not* include. The notion of a universe of discourse will be treated more fully in subsequent chapters, but for the time being it may be considered the linguistic context in which a term functions or, in a denotative sense, the class under which any given class is subsumed. For example, if we refer to the class of red things, we assume ordinarily as our universe of discourse or linguistic context the entire class of colors. Thus the class of all colors which are *not* red is called the *complementary* class of the class of red things.

The complementary class of any given class may be symbolized by drawing a bar over the variable or abbreviation:

$$\bar{a},\ \bar{b},\ \bar{c},\ \ldots \qquad \bar{A},\ \bar{B},\ \bar{C},\ \ldots$$

and may be read, for the sake of brevity, "not *a*," "not *b*," and "not *c*."

The relationship of a class to its complementary class may be diagramed in the following way:

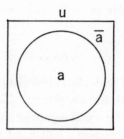

FIGURE 41–1

This diagram shows graphically that the class $\bar{a}$ is the complementary class of *a*, and includes everything in the universe of discourse *u* which is not *a*. In addition, *a* is the complementary class of $\bar{a}$, since it includes everything in the universe of discourse that is not comprehended under $\bar{a}$. If *a* stands for "universities," and the universe of discourse is "schools," then $\bar{a}$ stands for "high schools," "elementary schools," "trade schools," and all other schools that are not universities.

A diagram such as the one above is called a *Venn diagram* after its inventor, John Venn, a British logician of the last century. In the following chapters we will find Venn diagrams exceedingly useful in depicting class relationships and in performing operations in the logic of classes.

EXERCISES

Symbolize each of the following classes or singular members of a class, using *only* the abbreviation F for "Frenchmen," or *s* for a singular member:

1. Frenchmen.
2. This Frenchman.
3. People who are citizens of France.
4. Non-Frenchmen.
5. Napoleon Bonaparte.
6. The Eiffel Tower.
7. People who are not Frenchmen.
8. The Frenchman who wrote *Les Misérables*.
9. Foreigners to France.
10. The nation defeated in the Franco-Prussian War.

42 CLASS PRODUCTS AND SUMS

Thus far we have learned how to identify a class both symbolically and diagrammatically and, with the help of the concept of a universe of discourse, to symbolize and diagram a complementary class. We must now devise a means of identifying the various classes that result when more than one class is contained in the same universe of discourse.

42.1 Class Products

Since any class has a corresponding complementary class, a universe of discourse composed of *two* classes will contain *four* possible subclasses. The Venn diagram for two classes, *a* and *b*, will therefore always look like this:

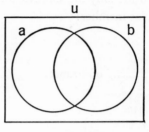

FIGURE 42–1

The class of members possessed in common by two classes, that is, the overlapping class in the above diagram, is called the *class product* or *conjunctive class* of those two classes. Class products are symbolized, like mathematical products, by a simple union of variables. Thus the product or conjunctive class of *a* and *b* is written:

$$ab$$

and is read: "*a* and *b*" or "*a* times *b*" or simply "*ab*."

The remaining three subclasses in a universe of discourse containing two classes may be named in a similar manner. The class of members which are in *a* but outside *b* is the product of *a* and $\bar{b}$, and consequently is symbolized $a\bar{b}$. In the following diagram, it may easily be seen that, just as the class *ab* contains only membership possessed conjointly by *a* and *b*, so the class $a\bar{b}$ contains membership possessed conjointly by *a* and the complementary class of *b*:

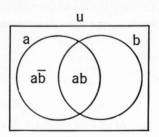

FIGURE 42–2

Thus, for example, if *a* stands for the class of lawyers, and *b* for women, the class *ab* represents the class of women lawyers. The class *ab̄*, on the other hand, since it contains membership possessed in common by *a* and *b̄*—that is, lawyers and men (or nonwomen)—is the class of men lawyers.

Similar considerations hold for the remaining two classes. The class of members outside *a* but in *b* is the product of *ā* and *b*, and so may be symbolized *āb*. And the class of members outside both *a* and *b* is the product of *ā* and *b̄* or *ab̄*:

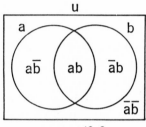

u

a   b

ab̄   ab   āb

āb̄

FIGURE 42–3

In the above diagram, if *a* and *b* stand once more for lawyers and women, then *āb* represents women who are not lawyers, while *ab̄* represents men who are not lawyers.

It should be noted that the complementary class of *a*, when another class *b* is involved, includes both that part of the universe of discourse which is outside *a* but in *b*, and that part which is outside *a* and also outside *b*. In our example, the complementary class of "lawyers" includes both men and women who are not lawyers. Similarly, the complementary class of *b*, (*b̄*,) includes both *ab̄* and *ab̄*. The complementary class of women, in other words, includes both men who are, and who are not, lawyers.

Extreme care must be taken that $-(ab)$ is clearly distinguished from *ab̄*. The parentheses in $-(ab)$ serve as punctuation marks to indicate that we are naming the *complementary class of a product,* rather than, as in *ab̄*, a *product of two complementary classes.* The complementary class of *ab*, that is, $-(ab)$, includes everything in the universe of discourse which is not *ab*, thus comprehending

$\overline{ab}$, $\overline{a}b$, and $\overline{ab}$. The class product of $\overline{a}$ and $\overline{b}$, on the other hand, denotes that which $\overline{a}$ and $\overline{b}$ have in common. Thus, if $\overline{a}$ includes $\overline{a}b$ and $\overline{ab}$, while $\overline{b}$ includes $a\overline{b}$ and $\overline{ab}$, then what $\overline{a}$ and $\overline{b}$ have in common is only the class $\overline{ab}$. Once more referring back to our example, the complementary class of women lawyers includes men lawyers, women who are not lawyers, and men who are not lawyers. This clearly is different from a product of the complementary classes of lawyers and women, since that which nonlawyers and nonwomen have in common is only the class of men who are not lawyers.

One final caution. The notion of a class product must not be confused with a mathematical product. It is perhaps unfortunate that the early symbolic logicians used mathematical terms to denote the new notions of logic. But the reason for their doing so is understandable, since they were attempting to systematize logic according to mathematical models. Their usage has now become so general that it would be futile to attempt a change. The student of logic must therefore always bear in mind that the mathematical-sounding terms he encounters are nonquantitative in meaning. Thus, a, b, and c are not number variables, but class variables. A bar before the expression (ab) does not indicate the operation of subtraction, but a complementary class. And ab itself does not signify a multiplication of two quantities, but the class product of a and b.

42.2 Class Sums

We will sometimes be required to designate, not the common membership, but the *total* membership of two classes, whether common to both classes or not. This may be accomplished by using the notion of a *class sum,* or *disjunctive class*—that is, the class which includes all members of either class or both classes. The class sum of a and b may be symbolized:

$$a + b$$

and read "a plus b" or better (to avoid confusion with mathematics) "a or b."

On the diagram in Figure 42.3, $a + b$ is the class composed of all members in $a\bar{b}$, ab, and $\bar{a}b$, while the complementary class of $a + b$ —that is, $-(a + b)$—since it includes whatever remains in the universe of discourse, is synonymous with $\overline{ab}$. Using for the purpose of comparison our same example of lawyers and women, the sum of these two classes contains men lawyers, women lawyers, and women who are not lawyers, and the complementary class of the same class sum contains only men who are not lawyers.

The underlying principles are exactly the same if, for example, a is added to the complementary class of b—that is, $a + \bar{b}$. Here we are designating the total membership of a, or lawyers, and $\bar{b}$, or men. Thus $a + \bar{b}$ contains men lawyers, women lawyers, and men who are not lawyers. And the complementary class of this sum, $-(a + \bar{b})$, refers then simply to women who are not lawyers.

Once more, we must be careful not to confuse $-(a + b)$ with $\bar{a} + \bar{b}$, the complementary class of a sum with the sum of two complementary classes. For $-(a + b)$ refers only to the class $\overline{ab}$, but $\bar{a} + \bar{b}$ includes $\bar{a}b$, $\overline{ab}$, and $a\bar{b}$. This may be seen by reference to Figure 42.3.

The same rules and terminology that apply to two classes may now be extended to three classes. Consider the following diagram:

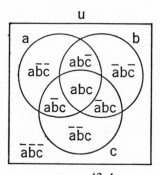

FIGURE 42–4

Rather than four subclasses, we now have eight, each of which is identified as a product of three classes or complementary classes. Suppose a and b still stand for lawyers and women, while c represents the class of smokers. Then, $\overline{abc}$ denotes the class of men lawyers who do not smoke, $a\bar{b}\bar{c}$ the class of women lawyers who do not smoke, $a\bar{b}c$ the class of men lawyers who do smoke. The product of all three classes is abc, standing for women lawyers who smoke; the sum of all three classes is $a + b + c$, which includes all lawyers, women, and smokers, and the complementary class of such disjunction, $-(a + b + c)$, refers only to $\overline{abc}$—that is, to nonsmoking men who are not lawyers.

When products or sums of more than three classes must be taken into account, the Venn diagram technique of representing classes will no longer suffice, because, as the reader may verify for himself, the sixteen possible products of four classes cannot be diagramed by means of overlapping circles. However, the products or sums of any number of classes may always be *symbolized* in the same manner as before. If, for example, we take into account along with our previous classes of women, lawyers, and smokers, the class of attractive persons, d, and that of industrious persons, e, then the class $abcde$ represents the class of attractive, industrious women lawyers who smoke, and so on for the other thirty-two possible conjunctive classes.

EXERCISES

Assuming that the universe of discourse is the class of men, draw a Venn diagram for the three classes: doctors (D), young men (Y), and married men (M). Then, referring to your diagram when in doubt, symbolize each of the following classes, using no more than three abbreviations: D, Y, and M:

1. Doctors.
2. Young doctors.*
3. Male doctors.
4. Married doctors.
5. Married men.
6. Men who are not doctors.*

7. Young married doctors.
8. Married doctors who are not young.
9. Eligible young doctors.
10. Uneducated young men.*
11. Old married men.
12. Well-confirmed bachelors.
13. All doctors and all married men.
14. Men who are not young doctors.
15. Men who are not young bachelors.
16. Men who are either young or married.*
17. High-school students.
18. Doctors who are neither young nor married.
19. Men who are neither young nor married.
20. Both men who are not young and men who are not married.

43 CLASS PROPOSITIONS

All of our efforts so far in Part Four have been devoted to the symbolizing and diagraming of classes and individual members of classes. To name or identify a class or a product or sum of classes, however, is still not to say anything about that class. We must now contrive some means of asserting *propositions*, or descriptive statements, in the class logic.

43.1 Class Identity

One type of proposition that we will find useful is the assertion of a logical identity, or coextensiveness, holding between two classes. To say that class a is identical, or coextensive, with b means that these two classes have the same boundaries, so to speak, and that if there is any membership in either *a* or *b*, it is held in common by both classes. This assertion of identity may be symbolized:

$$a = b, \text{ (read: "}a\text{ is identical with }b\text{").}$$

If we adopt the convention of lining out on a Venn diagram those classes which have no membership, the proposition *a* = *b* may be diagramed like this:

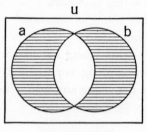

FIGURE 43–1

The interpretation of this diagram is as follows: If *a* is identical with *b*, then there can be no members of *a* that are not also members of *b*—which is to say that the class *a* outside *b*, or *ab̄*, is empty of membership. Nor can there be any membership in *b* outside of *a*, so that the class *āb* is also empty of membership. And this is precisely what has been indicated on the diagram, that the classes *ab̄* and *āb* are empty.

If, for example, *a* stands for the class of Persians and *b* for the class of Iranians, then *a* = *b* is a true proposition. The Venn diagram portrays this statement by lining out class *ab̄* (Persians who are not Iranians) and class *āb* (Iranians who are not Persians), showing in this way that these two classes are empty, and that if there are any Persians or any Iranians, they are in the same class *ab*.

43.2 Class Nonidentity

Our logical notation will also require a symbol relating two classes that are *not* identical—that is, two classes the membership of which is not possessed in common. Once more adopting a mathematical symbol, but reinterpreting it in terms of classes, we may indicate the nonidentity of two classes *a* and *b* in the following manner:

$a \neq b$ (read: "*a* is not identical, or not coextensive, with *b*,"
Do *not* read: "*a* is not equal to *b*").

A proposition expressing the nonidentity of two classes, *a* and *b*, cannot be represented by means of only one Venn diagram. For the assertion that *a* is not identical with *b* may mean (i) that *a* has membership outside of *b*, or (ii) that *b* has membership outside of *a*, or (iii) that *a* and *b* both have membership that is not held in common—that is, that both (i) and (ii) are true.

Nor can the nonidentity of two classes be represented by lining out classes on a Venn diagram. We are permitted to line out classes on a diagram of the proposition $a = b$, because this assertion of identity means, first, that there is *no membership* in class *a* outside *b* or in class *b* outside *a*, and second, that *if* there is any actual membership in *a* or *b*, such membership will be possessed conjointly by both classes. The proposition $a \neq b$ is not a hypothetical assertion of membership, but an assertion that actual membership exists in *a* outside *b* or in *b* outside *a*. What is required then, in diagraming $a \neq b$, is a new device for portraying actual membership in a class.

Suppose we adopt the convention of using a cross to indicate on a diagram that the class in which this mark is contained is *not* empty, but possesses at least one unspecified member. The proposition $a \neq b$ may then be considered true if any one of the propositions depicted by the following diagrams is true:

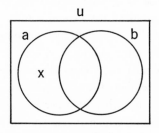

FIGURE 43–2

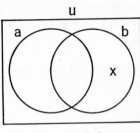

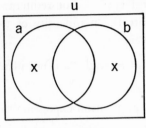

FIGURE 43–3   FIGURE 43–4

In other words, if *a* stands for the class of Persians and *b* for Moslems, then the proposition $a \neq b$ is true when there is at least one Persian who in not a Moslem or at least one Moslem who is not a Persian, or both.

We should note that each of the above diagrams, any one of which is sufficient to ensure the truth of $a \neq b$, may itself be symbolized as a specific proposition. Figure 43.2 shows not only that *a* is not identical with *b*, but more specifically that *a* is not identical with the class *ab*; the diagramed proposition may therefore be symbolized $a \neq ab$. In a like manner, the proposition depicted in Figure 43.3 may be symbolized $b \neq ab$, and that in Figure 43.4 may be symbolized as a joint assertion of the two propositions portrayed in Figures 43.2 and 43.3.

43.3 Singular Membership

The symbols representing identity or nonidentity, however, can only be used to assert a relationship between classes. If a *singular member* of a class is related by one of these symbols to a class or to another singular member (as in $s = a$ or $s = t$), a meaningless assertion has been made, since a singular member cannot be said to have the same membership as, or be coextensive with, a class or another singular member of a class. Even when a class contains only one identified member, the class and the member are of different logical orders, and this member must therefore be distinguished from the class of which it happens to be the sole instance.

This means that a new symbol is required when we wish to

assert singular membership in a class. Let us use for this purpose the Greek letter ε (epsilon) and symbolize the proposition that some individual *s* is a member of some class *a* like this:

$$s \; \epsilon \; a, \; (\text{read: "}s\text{ is a member of }a\text{").}$$

We may diagram this proposition by showing, not the cross of unspecified membership, but the *s* of a specifically named member of *a*:

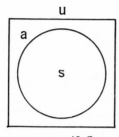

FIGURE 43–5

It might be thought that a new symbol is required for the *denial* of singular membership, just as a symbol for nonidentity was required in order to express the denial of a proposition asserting identity. Such a symbol, however, is not required. For the denial that *s* is a member of the class *a* amounts to saying that *s* is a member of the *complementary* class of *a*. The proposition *s* ε *a*, in other words, is denied by asserting the proposition *s* ε *ā*, as may easily be seen by inspecting a Venn diagram.

EXERCISES

(1) Symbolize each of the following expressions in the logic of classes, distinguishing carefully between classes, singular members, and propositions. (2) Draw a corresponding diagram for each proposition asserting class-identity or singular membership in a class:

1. Dictionary.
2. A lexicon is a dictionary.*
3. A biographical dictionary.*
4. This is a dictionary.
5. This is a biographical dictionary.*
6. His biographical dictionary.
7. This is not a lexicon.
8. A lexicographer is the author of a dictionary.
9. Bibliographers are not lexicographers.*
10. Noah Webster was a lexicographer.
11. Daniel Webster was not a lexicographer.
12. A bibliographer need not be a bibliophile.
13. He is both a bibliographer and a bibliophile.
14. Either bibliographers or bibliophiles.
15. His bibliography.
16. Biographies are different from bibliographies.
17. Boswell was a biographer, but not a bibliographer.
18. Samuel Johnson was neither a bibliographer nor a biographer, but he was a lexicographer.
19. Samuel Johnson's Dictionary.
20. That is a Webster's Dictionary.

44 THE UNIVERSE CLASS AND THE NULL CLASS

44.1 The Universe Class

To explain the nature of complementary classes, we were required to introduce the notion of a *universe of discourse*, or broader class under which any given class is subsumed. The universe of discourse is a class itself—we may call it the *universe class*—and it corresponds roughly to what was referred to in Part One as the the genus of an Aristotelian definition. This comparison is suggestive, since placing the name of a class in its universe of discourse or linguistic context serves to fix its meaning.

The universe class may be represented by a lower-case letter *u*, and on a Venn diagram by the rectangular box we have already used to enclose circles standing for subsumed classes. Thus, we may precisely characterize the universe class in the following way:

$$u = a + \bar{a}.$$

The universe class, in other words, is identical with the sum of any class and its complementary class. That this characterization of the universe class is correct may be seen on any Venn diagram.

The relationship either of identity or nonidentity may be said to hold between the universe and any other class, and it thereby will express either a true or a false statement. If, for example, the universe of discourse is the class of American Presidents, and the abbreviation *C* stands for Commanders in Chief of the American Armed Forces, then the following identity and corresponding diagram represent true propositions:

$$C = u.$$

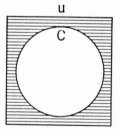

FIGURE 44–1

That is, there is no member of the universe class of American Presidents who is not also a member of the class of Commanders in

Chief. The class of Presidents who are *not* Commanders in Chief is empty of membership.

False propositions, of course, may just as easily be symbolized and diagramed. If the universe class once more stands for American Presidents and if R represents the subsumed class of Republican Presidents, then $R = u$ is a false proposition. Since it is a false proposition, the following nonidentity and diagram stand for true propositions:

$$R \neq u.$$

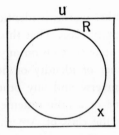

FIGURE 44–2

In other words, there is membership in the universe class of American Presidents who are or were not Republicans.

In symbolizing such propositions as "There are American Presidents who were not Republicans," it is better, as we shall see in later chapters, to treat American Presidents and Republicans as ordinary classes, both of which are contained in some broader universe class, say, the class of politicians or statesmen or Americans. In every case, however, circles representing classes on a Venn diagram must be enclosed in a universe class. Certain applications of Venn diagrams will not be possible unless this is done.

The extent, or range, of a universe class very often is not precisely known. The term "lawyers" may have for its universe of discourse "professional people," "Americans," "human beings," even "carnivorous primates." Ordinarily, of course, the context in which a term is used will roughly determine its universe of discourse. But when it does not do so, we may ourselves stipulate what we take to be the most plausible universe class. In any event, the actual manipulation of the class logic will not be affected by the extent of the universe class, provided it is at least as large as its subsumed classes.

44.2 The Null Class

We saw previously that every class must be assumed to have a complementary class. The universe class is not excepted from this rule. Its complementary class is called the *null class* and is symbolized by a zero: 0. The notion of a null class is rather difficult to explain, but the class perhaps is best described as *the class of all classes having no members*. Either of the following identities, therefore, is a true proposition and may be considered a definition of the null class:

$$(i)\ 0 = \bar{u} \qquad\qquad (ii)\ 0 = a\bar{a}$$

The first proposition states that the null class is identical with the complementary class of the universe, and since the universe class already contains all relevant classes having membership, the null class is therefore identical with nothing. The second proposition, $0 = a\bar{a}$, states that the null class is identical with a product of any class and its own complementary class; but that which is common to any class and its own complementary class is nothing, and so we arrive at the same meaning as before.

It may perhaps be asked at this point why we must bother with so tenuous a notion as this of the null class—a class which seems the very epitome of empty "nothingness," since it is an abstraction stemming from a generalization of all classes in which nothing is contained. However, subsequent chapters will reveal the central importance of a null class in manipulating the class logic, and even now we can see how useful the concept of a null class is in symbolizing many elementary propositions. Suppose, for example, we wish to assert the proposition "There are no mermaids." Using the abbreviation M for mermaids, our symbolization and diagram will be as follows:

$$M = 0 \text{ (read: } M \text{ is empty).}$$

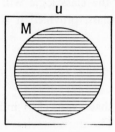

FIGURE 44–3

Since our symbolism must be capable of representing fantasy as well as fact, the null-class concept might be used in the following way:

$$M \neq 0 \text{ (read: } M \text{ is not empty).}$$

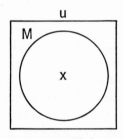

FIGURE 44–4

We are saying here, if M stands for mermaids, that the class of mermaids is not identical with the null class, in other words that it is not empty or—with the same meaning—that it has membership. Just as a lined-out class is characteristic of a diagram in which we portray a proposition asserting identity with the null class, so a cross standing for indefinite membership will always appear on the diagram of a nonidentity with the null class.

44.3 Interchangeability of Null and Universe Classes

Since 0 is the complementary class of u, any proposition in which a class is asserted to be identical with the universe class may also be expressed by using the sign or the concept of the null class. An inspection of the appropriate diagrams will show that the proposition $a = u$, for example, may be rephrased: $\bar{a} = 0$, while the proposition $a \neq u$ may be expressed: $\bar{a} \neq 0$. Indeed, we shall find it an easier and more straightforward way of expressing ourselves to say that some given class is or is not empty than to say that it does or does not comprehend the universe of discourse. For this reason, we shall incorporate the null class into most of the propositions requiring symbolization in later chapters.

EXERCISES

Symbolize and diagram each of the following propositions in the logic of classes. Assume that the universe of discourse in each case is the class of men, and use only the abbreviations H (honest), S (sociable), A (ambitious), s (Alexander), and t (Diogenes):

1. Diogenes was honest.
2. Diogenes was an honest man.
3. There are no honest men.*
4. Alexander was sociable and ambitious.*
5. There are many ambitious, sociable men.
6. The class of honest, sociable men is empty.
7. Diogenes was not a sociable man.
8. To be sociable is to be ambitious.
9. There are some honest men.
10. An ambitious man is a sociable man.
11. Some men are dishonest.*
12. Diogenes was honest but unsociable.*
13. The class of honest, unsociable men has membership.
14. Diogenes was neither sociable nor ambitious.
15. To be honest is to be ambitious.
16. There are no honest men, nor are there any men who are not ambitious.
17. Unsociable, unambitious, but honest—that was Diogenes!

18. Some men are lacking in ambition, honesty, and sociability.
19. No man lives who is sociable, ambitious, and yet is honest.
20. All men are sociable.

45 SOME ELEMENTARY LAWS

45.1 Validity and Truth

The careful reader might have remarked, in the last chapter, that the notions of a universe and null class were explained by using two apparently different kinds of proposition. A universe class first was said to be identical with any class plus its complementary class $(u = a + \bar{a})$, and then examples were given of the identity of actual classes with the universe class $(a = u, C = u)$. The null class, similarly, was said to be identical with $\bar{u}$ or with $a\bar{a}$, and then was explained by reference to sample propositions. We must now examine the very important difference between propositions such as $u = a + \bar{a}$, on the one hand, and $u = a$, on the other.

Observe, first, that the proposition $u = a + \bar{a}$ cannot be diagramed in the same way as can $u = a$ or $u \neq a$. These latter propositions are diagramed by lining out the appropriate class or inserting a cross. But no lined-out class or cross will indicate what is asserted by $u = a + \bar{a}$. This is because the *necessary truth* of $u = a + \bar{a}$ is already established when the blank form of a Venn diagram is given. If we know what is *meant* by drawing a box for the universe of discourse and a circle for a subsumed class, then we cannot help but admit that what is inside the circle and what is outside (class and complementary class) together exhaust the universe of discourse, and that $u = a + \bar{a}$ is therefore incapable of being falsified, no matter what the actual state of membership in a or in $\bar{a}$.

Let us refer to a proposition such as $u = a + \bar{a}$ as a *valid* (or "tautological") proposition, meaning that, whatever values are substituted for the variables, the proposition is always true. A universe class, in other words, is coextensive with $A + \bar{A}$, $B + \bar{B}$, $C + \bar{C}$, or any other actual class in disjunction with its complementary class, regardless of whether or not these classes contain membership. Validity, then, is a special kind of truth, and attaches only to propositions the truth of which can be ascertained merely by examining what is meant by the proposition.

A proposition of the type $u = a$, on the other hand, is not necessarily, but only *contingently*, true. That is, the truth of such a proposition cannot be determined merely by consulting the meanings involved, but must be determined by means of further observation or testing—a requirement that might conceivably always result in finding the proposition false.

45.2 Laws of the Class Logic

Any valid proposition in the logic of classes may, for our purposes, be called a *principle* or *law* of the class logic. It is true that the term "validity" is ordinarily used to characterize an inference or argument and that the term "law" is usually reserved for a more general proposition asserting an identity or nonidentity between classes. Nevertheless, a law of logic is always a valid inference, in the broad sense of a proposition the necessary truth of which is based upon meanings of terms. At the same time, a valid inference is always a logical law, once more in the broad sense of a proposition that is capable of interpretation as a general principle in the deductive framework of the class logic.

Any proposition, then, that follows necessarily from the conceptual structure we have so far erected is a law of the class logic. Not only $u = a + \bar{a}$, but propositions such as $0 = \bar{u}$, $0 = a\bar{a}$, $a = a$, $a = a(u)$ (that which any class has in common with the universe class is only the class itself), $a = a + 0$ (no increase in membership results from disjoining the null class to any class), and any other proposition that is verifiable by reference to meanings alone, either symbolized or diagramed, may be called a law in the logic of classes. In contrast, propositions of the general type $s \, \epsilon \, a$ or $a = b$ or $a \neq 0$, to be called true, require more than mere knowledge of what is meant; hence, they are contingent, possibly false, propositions.

The remainder of this chapter will be devoted to a brief explanation of several laws that will prove useful in elaborating and applying the class logic.

45.3 Law of Double Negation

Any class is identical with the complementary class of its own complementary class:

$$a = \bar{\bar{a}}.$$

For example, people who are educated are people who are not uneducated, and happy people are those who are not unhappy. The student will be reminded of the grammatical rule concerning double negation with which he wrestled in grade school.

45.4 Laws of Commutation

The order in which the variables or abbreviations occur in class products or sums has no effect upon their meaning—that is, class products and sums are commutative:

$$ab = ba,$$

$$a + b = b + a.$$

The class of neurotic Eskimos is identical with the class of Eskimo neurotics and the class composed of neurotic people or Eskimos is identical with the class of Eskimos or neurotic people. The commutative laws, like many of the elementary laws of logic, are so obvious and occupy so basic a position in our reasoning and use of language that we are likely never to become consciously aware of them if they are not, as here, deliberately brought to our attention.

45.5 Laws of Association

Class products and sums are associative, which is to say that the grouping or association of the members of a conjunction or disjunction of classes does not alter the meaning:

$$a(bc) = (ab)c,$$
$$a + (b + c) = (a + b) + c.$$

In other words, a product of a and bc is identical with a product of ab and c. And the sum of a and $b + c$ is identical with the sum of $a + b$ and c. The class of educated persons who are neurotic Eskimos is no different from the class of educated neurotics who are Eskimos. And the class of all educated people, along with all neurotics and all Eskimos, is coextensive with the class of educated persons or neurotics along with the class of Eskimos. The associative laws therefore mean, in effect, that parentheses can be omitted from any class symbolization which is purely conjunctive or disjunctive.

45.6 DeMorgan's Laws

The logician Augustus DeMorgan drew our attention to a pair of laws that permit us always to express a class product as a sum, or vice versa:

$$-(ab) = \bar{a} + \bar{b},$$
$$-(a + b) = \overline{ab}.$$

The complementary class of a product is identical with a sum of complementary classes, and the complementary class of a sum is identical with a product of complementary classes. For example, the complementary class of educated intelligent people, $-(EI)$, as we may easily see on a Venn diagram, is composed of educated unintelligent people $(E\bar{I})$, uneducated intelligent people $(\bar{E}I)$, and uneducated unintelligent people $(\overline{EI})$. But this is exactly the same as the class sum of uneducated and unintelligent people $(\bar{E} + \bar{I})$, since uneducated people are either intelligent or unintelligent, while unintelligent people are either educated or uneducated. In brief, the only class not comprehended by either $-(EI)$ or $\bar{E} + \bar{I}$ is the class EI, or educated intelligent persons.

45.7 Laws of Distribution

Another, rather more complex pair of laws that, like DeMorgan's Laws, are useful in transforming propositions from conjunction to disjunction and vice versa are as follows:

$$a(b + c) = ab + ac,$$

$$a + (bc) = (a + b)(a + c).$$

It will be noted that the first law, distributing a product over a sum, is a law of ordinary algebra, while the second law, distributing a sum over a product, does not hold in mathematics—an indication of the confusion to which a mathematical interpretation of logical propositions might lead. Examples of the laws of distribution are too detailed and too lengthy to be included here. But their validity may be seen by looking at a three-class Venn diagram.

45.8 Rule of Replacement

The application of the above logical laws is obvious. Any class term (variable or abbreviation) may be replaced by any other term denoting an identical class without changing the validity or invalidity, or the truth or falsity, of any proposition. If $s \in a$ is true, then, by the law of double negation and rule of replacement, the proposition $s \in \bar{\bar{a}}$ is equally true. And if $-(ab) = \bar{a} + \bar{b}$ is valid, then by the two laws of commutation and the rule of replacement $-(ba) = \bar{b} + \bar{a}$ is also valid.

EXERCISES

A. Each of the classes listed in Column I is logically identical with one and only one of the classes listed in Column II. Fill in the blank parentheses in Column I with the number of the identical class in Column II. (Most, but not all, of the class-identities are based on the logical laws presented in this chapter.)

Column I	Column II
( ) (a) 0	1. $b + a$
( ) (b) u	2. $\bar{b} + \bar{a} + \bar{c}$
( ) (c) a	3. $\bar{u}$
( ) (d) ab	4. $-(a + b)$
( ) (e) $a + b$	5. $b + 0$
( ) (f) $\bar{a}$	6. $a + \bar{a}$
( ) (g) $\bar{a}(b)$	7. $cb + ab$
( ) (h) $-(abc)$	8. $\bar{\bar{a}}$
( ) (i) $\overline{ab}$	9. ba
( ) (j) $a\bar{b}$	10. $-(\bar{a} + b)$
( ) (k) $b(a + c)$	11. $b(\bar{a})$
( ) (l) b	12. $\bar{a}(u)$

B. Each of the propositions listed in Column I is equivalent to one and only one of the propositions in Column II. Fill in the blank parentheses in Column I with the number of the corresponding proposition in Column II:

Column I	Column II
( ) (a) $s \,\epsilon\, a$	1. $b(u) = \bar{\bar{a}}$
( ) (b) $a = 0$	2. $\bar{a} \neq u$
( ) (c) $a \neq 0$	3. $s \,\epsilon\, b(b)$
( ) (d) $a = b$	4. $s \,\epsilon\, -(\overline{ab})$
( ) (e) $a = u$	5. $\bar{\bar{a}} = a\bar{a}$
( ) (f) $a \neq b$	6. $s \,\epsilon\, -(\bar{a} + \bar{b})$
( ) (g) $s \,\epsilon\, b$	7. $s \,\epsilon\, a + 0$
( ) (h) $s \,\epsilon\, ab$	8. $s \,\epsilon\, (a + b)\,(a + c)$
( ) (i) $s \,\epsilon\, a + b$	9. $\bar{a} = 0$
( ) (j) $s \,\epsilon\, a + (bc)$	10. $a + 0 \neq 0 + b$

46 CLASSIFICATION OF PROPOSITIONS

Before proceeding any further in our study of validity and the laws of logic, we must examine more fully and systematically the types of *contingent* propositions that are capable of being symbolized in the class logic. This task of symbolizing common types of propositions, surprisingly enough, is more difficult than the highly abstract job of determining validity and manipulating symbolized propositions according to logical laws. For the task of symbolizing from ordinary language requires that we capture as nearly as possible the meaning of statements which, as used in practice, are never so clear and precise as their symbolized counterparts.

However, it will simplify matters considerably if we can organize the bewildering variety of common propositions in such a way that they can be paraphrased in terms of a limited number of *standard form propositions,* as we may call them. The task of symbolizing and diagraming these standard forms will then be comparatively easy.

46.1 Complexity: Simple, Compound, and Conjunctive Propositions

A distinction first can be made regarding the degree of *complexity* exhibited by a proposition. It is convenient to distinguish three degrees of complexity: simple, compound, and conjunctive. A *simple proposition* is one which contains only a single class variable or abbreviation (excluding the null or universe class). A *compound proposition* is one containing a product or sum of classes (once more excluding the universe or null class). A *conjunctive proposition* in the class logic is one in which two or more simple or compound propositions are jointly asserted—that is, said to be true together. This last type of proposition, the conjunctive, must be not confused with a conjunctive *class*, but rather is to be interpreted (as in the logic of propositions) as a conjunction of two or more propositions.

Examples of simple propositions are: $a = 0$, $A = 0$, $a \neq 0$, $s \,\epsilon\, a$, $s \,\epsilon\, \bar{a}$, $s \,\epsilon\, A$, and so on. Compound propositions are of this type: $ab = 0$, $abc \neq 0$, $A\bar{B} = 0$, $s \,\epsilon\, ab$, and $s \,\epsilon\, a + b$. A joint assertion of any combination of these propositions, whether simple or compound, will be called a conjunctive proposition. In symbolizing conjunctive propositions, we adopt the convention (from the propositional logic) of using the dot to signify conjunction: $ab = 0 \cdot a \neq 0$, $s \,\epsilon\, a \cdot b = 0$, $a\bar{b} = 0 \cdot a = c \cdot c \neq 0$, and so on. The first of these examples can be read "*ab* is empty *and* a is not empty," meaning that both propositions are asserted jointly to be true.

In the illustrations just given of simple and compound propositions, no mention was made of an identity with the universe class. The reason for this omission has already been suggested in a previous chapter, in which it was pointed out that the null class may always be substituted for the universe class in any proposition asserting identity or nonidentity with a given class a, provided that $\bar{a}$ is also substituted for a. The proposition $a = u$, for example, is equivalent to $\bar{a} = 0$, while $a \neq u$ is equivalent to $\bar{a} \neq 0$. Since using an identity with the null class permits a more direct rendering of propositions capable of treatment in the class logic, we shall use the null class ordinarily in preference to the universe class.

46.2 Quantity: Universal, Particular, and Singular Propositions

Already assumed and symbolized in the class logic is the distinction between propositions asserting identity with the null class, propositions asserting nonidentity with the null class, and propositions asserting singular membership in some class. Let us adopt the conventional terminology, speaking of these as universal, particular, and singular propositions, and refer to this distinction as one of *quantity*.

In the logic of classes, a *universal* proposition is one in which some class is asserted to be coextensive with the null class—is asserted, that is, to be empty. The term "universal" connotes the fact that a generalization has been made about a class—namely, that it is entirely lacking in membership. A simple proposition such as $a = 0$ and a compound proposition like $ab = 0$ both assert something about the whole of a class, and hence are universal in quantity.

In contrast to these generalizations, a *particular* proposition asserts only that a class contains some unspecified membership—that it is not identical with the null class. Whether the class contains only one member or whether it contains many, the proposition asserting such fact will be particular, since nothing concerning the total membership is implied. Propositions such as $a \neq 0$ or $ab \neq 0$ imply only that membership in the classes a or ab is not lacking.

Singular propositions possess characteristics both of universal and of particular propositions. To say, for example, that $s \varepsilon a$ is to assert that s as a whole is a member of class a, and at the same time that class a has membership. Nevertheless, or perhaps because of their dual aspects of universality and particularity, singular propositions are unique and cannot be identified either as universal or particular. The membership asserted by a singular proposition nullifies its universality and the specification of such membership nullifies its particularity.

46.3 Quality: Affirmative and Negative Propositions

Whatever the complexity or quantity of a proposition, it may still be expressed in an affirmative or negative way. This traditional distinction of *quality,* however, applies mainly to the manner in which a proposition is asserted in language rather than to the way it is symbolized. In the process of symbolizing, as we shall see in a later chapter, the difference between affirmative and negative propositions is often undermined, so that the symbolic phrasing of either type of proposition is the same. Once the proposition has been symbolized, it may always be rephrased either affirmatively or negatively in ordinary language.

However, since our primary concern at present is with a systematic classification of the most common propositions used in ordinary language in order more easily to symbolize and diagram them, we will find it convenient to distinguish between affirmatively and negatively stated propositions.

EXERCISES

Symbolize, diagram, and classify the following propositions as to (i) complexity, (ii) quantity, and (iii) quality. Use the abbreviations P for politicians and I for cultured people, and consider the universe of discourse to be the class of Americans:

1. There are some cultured Americans.
2. He is a cultured person.
3. He is not a politician.
4. There are no cultured politicians.
5. Thomas Jefferson was a cultured politician.
6. The class of uncultured politicians has membership.
7. That person is neither cultured nor a politician.
8. There are some cultured politicians and Thomas Jefferson is one of them.
9. Jefferson and Franklin were both cultured.
10. There are many American politicians, but Americans are not cultured.
11. No uncultured politicians exist.
12. No politicians are uncultured.
13. All politicians are cultured.
14. The terms "politician" and "cultured person" are synonymous.
15. Uncultured politicians are common, although a few of the other kind may be found.

47 UNIVERSAL PROPOSITIONS

Any proposition in which a class is asserted to be empty of membership may, as we have seen, be called universal. Simple propositions of this type will cause us no trouble, since they are easily identified, symbolized, and diagramed. Compound universal propositions, however, as they appear in ordinary language, are much more diversified in form and hence will require further study.

47.1 Universal Affirmative Propositions

An exceedingly common type of universal proposition is that in which one class is asserted to be included in another. A simple phrasing of class-inclusion propositions, and one which we may adopt as the standard form for all such propositions, is:

All *a* are *b*.

To say that the class *a* is included in class *b* is the same as saying that there is no membership in *a* that is not also in *b*. The class *a* outside of *b*, in other words, is empty, and so a class-inclusion proposition may be symbolized and diagramed in the following manner:

$$a\overline{b} = 0$$

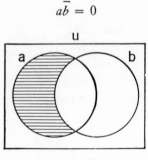

FIGURE 47–1

If, for example, *a* stands for the class of chimpanzees and *b* for primates, the proposition "All chimpanzees are primates" can be diagramed by lining out $a\bar{b}$, the class of chimpanzees who are not primates, and symbolized by asserting the identity of this class with the null class. Propositions asserting class-inclusion, then, are universal and affirmative, since by asserting the absence of membership in one class that is not in another class, they affirm that any membership in the first class is also included in the second.

Among possible variations of the standard form "All *a* are *b*" are the following, each of which is universal in quantity and affirmative in quality:

(i) Every man must bear arms. (All men are persons who must bear arms.)

(ii) Each individual is unique. (All individuals are unique.)

(iii) Brave are the Trojans. (All Trojans are brave. Note that this proposition may *not* be paraphrased: All brave persons are Trojans.)

(iv) An adult is responsible for his actions. (All adults are persons responsible for their actions.)

(v) One who runs away is one who fights again. (All persons who run away are persons who fight again.)

(vi) Any trespasser will be prosecuted. (All trespassers are persons who will be prosecuted.)

(vii) All Mozart's music was written in a hurry. (All compositions by Mozart are compositions which were written in a hurry.)

(viii) Armenians are shrewd. (All Armenians are shrewd.)

Propositions (vi) and (vii) indicate that the relationship of class-inclusion is tenseless—that is, that past, present, and future tenses are alike insofar as the form of a proposition is concerned. If the time element is essential in a proposition, then one of the class terms must be rephrased so as to give evidence of the appropriate tense. Should the student of logic be annoyed by the awkwardness of such paraphrasing, he must remember that we are here concerned with clear thinking, not with literary artistry.

The last proposition in the list, "Armenians are shrewd," also deserves special attention. When a proposition contains only class terms, with no quantifying term such as "all," "every," "any," it must still be treated as a universal proposition. Some people, of course, after they have asserted that "Mexicans are illiterate" or that "College graduates are highly intelligent," and after exceptions are pointed out to them, attempt to qualify their generalizations by stating that what they really meant was "*Most* Mexicans" or "*Almost all* college graduates." But this is not at all what they meant, if they were using the English language carefully. Any class-inclusion proposition, even though lacking a quantifying term, must be assumed to be a generalization.

47.2 Universal Negative Propositions

We often deny that two classes have any membership in common or, in other words, assert that the membership of one class is entirely excluded from another class. These class-exclusion or *universal negative* propositions, as we may call them, are of the general form:

No *a* are *b*.

Since to say that "No *a* are *b*" is to assert that the class of members held in common by *a* and *b* is empty, we may symbolize and diagram a universal negative proposition in the following way:

$$ab = 0$$

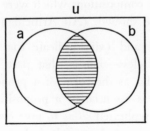

FIGURE 47-2

To illustrate, the universal negative proposition "No chimpanzees are stupid," since it asserts that the class of chimpanzees is entirely excluded from the class of stupid animals, may be symbolized and diagramed by indicating that the class of stupid chimpanzees is empty.

Examples of alternative phrasings of the same standard form proposition are:

(i) Nobody is perfect. (No human beings are perfect.)
(ii) Nothing suits him. (No things are suitable to him.)
(iii) An alligator is not a domestic animal. (No alligators are domestic animals.)
(iv) None of them escaped. (No persons among them are persons who escaped.)
(v) No profanity will be permitted. (No profane language is language that will be permitted.)

47.3 Exclusive Propositions

One very common type of universal proposition is called *exclusive*, because it asserts that the membership of one class exclusively makes up the membership of another class. Variations of this kind of proposition are:

(i) Only lawyers are shysters.
(ii) None but lawyers are shysters.
(iii) Lawyers alone are shysters.

It is clear that these three propositions all make the same assertion and that this assertion is true. But no matter how many painful legal encounters the reader may have had or have heard about, he will probably grant that the proposition "All lawyers are shysters" is *not* true. Exclusive propositions cannot be paraphrased then, as one might at first suppose, as ordinary universal affirmative propositions. Nor can they be paraphrased as ordinary universal negative propositions. For they are exclusive not in the sense of one class excluding another, but in the sense of one class exclusively constituting the membership of another class.

In order to arrive at the proper symbolization of an exclusive proposition, we must first note that "Only *a* are *b*" may be paraphrased "Nothing that is not a member of *a* is a member of *b*," or more briefly "No *ā* are *b*." The statement "Only lawyers are shysters," then, may be paraphrased as a universal negative proposition "No nonlawyers are shysters."

Turning now to symbolizing and diagraming, we see that if "No *a* are *b*" is symbolized $ab = 0$, "No *ā* are *b*" must be symbolized in the following way, and diagramed accordingly:

$$\bar{a}b = 0$$

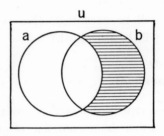

FIGURE 47–3

This diagram suggests that an exclusive proposition might be expressed also as a universal affirmative proposition with the two terms reversed. If a diagram in which *a* outside of *b* is empty may be read "All *a* are *b*," then it would seem that a diagram in which *b* outside of *a* is empty may be read "All *b* are *a*." This possibility is true, as shown in the symbolized version of an exclusive proposition (Fig. 47–3). The proposition $\bar{a}b = 0$, by applying the law of commutation, becomes $b\bar{a} = 0$, which is read "All *b* are *a*."

In brief, then, the exclusive proposition "Only *a* are *b*" should be paraphrased either as a universal negative proposition: "No *b̄* are *a*" or as a universal affirmative proposition with reversed sequence of terms: "All *b* are *a*." Our example "Only lawyers are shysters" means "No nonlawyers are shysters" or, what amounts to the same thing, "All shysters are lawyers."

EXERCISES

Each of the following propositions should (if necessary) be paraphrased into standard form, then symbolized and diagramed. Although the propositions are all universal, they may be simple or compound, affirmative or negative:

1. There are no ghosts.
2. There are no observable ghosts.
3. Unobservable things do not exist.
4. All ignorant people are superstitious.
5. None but ignorant people are superstitious.
6. Every criminal is a psychiatric case.
7. Criminals are to be pitied.*
8. There are no justified crimes.*
9. Laws are made to be obeyed.
10. The judiciary is not exempt from the law.
11. Pacifists alone are relieved from military service.*
12. Wars are always tragic.
13. Nobody likes to die.
14. Only heroes are decorated.
15. Might makes right.*
16. A penny saved is a penny earned.
17. A rolling stone gathers no moss.
18. Taxpayers are not paupers.
19. The only people who cheat on their income tax are people who think they can get away with it.
20. The velocity and locus of a subatomic particle cannot simultaneously be determined by any means known to physicists.

48 PARTICULAR AND SINGULAR PROPOSITIONS

Unlike universal propositions, particular and singular propositions assert that some class has membership, either indefinite or specific. If the extent of the membership is not known or not individually named, the proposition is particular, and all we can say of the class containing such membership is that it is not identical with the null class, which is to say that it is not empty. If the membership is singular—that is, capable of being identified as an individual in some way—we may use the epsilon-relationship (the ϵ) to assert singular membership. The quality of particular or singular propositions, in contrast to their quantity, may be expressed in ordinary language as affirmative or negative.

48.1 Particular Affirmative Propositions

We often assert that an indefinite number of members of one class are also contained in another class. A simple variation of this type of proposition, and one which we adopt as our standard form, is:

Some a are b.

We have here a particular affirmative proposition of the compound variety, since it affirms that a part of the membership contained in a is also contained in b. This amounts to saying that membership is possessed by a and b in common; hence, the following symbolization and diagram is appropriate:

$$ab \neq 0$$

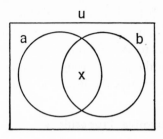

FIGURE 48–1

To say, for example, that "Some berries are edible" is essentially to affirm that the class of edible berries is not empty. Thus the quantifying word *some* has a special connotation in logic. "Some *a* are *b*" means "At least one and possibly all *a* are *b*." The proposition "Some berries are edible" is true if only one kind of berry is edible or if all berries are edible. It may seem that so unspecific a denotation of the word "some" (or of a "nonempty class") in particular affirmative propositions might seriously hinder the application of a class logic. Indeed, more sensitive logics have had to be devised for certain special applications. For ordinary, nontechnical purposes, however, a more specific connotation of "some" is not required.

Each of the following types of proposition may be paraphrased into the standard form "Some *a* are *b*:"

  (i) At least one of the great philosophers was insane.
 (ii) A few politicians are dishonest.
(iii) Several items are missing.
 (iv) Many former luxuries are now necessities.
  (v) Most good things in life are free.

The last proposition in this list, "*Most* good things in life are free," and perhaps one or two of the others, are sometimes used in contexts in which their meaning is not exhausted by symbolizing or diagraming as a particular affirmative proposition. Thus if, when we say "Most good things in life are free," we mean not only that some good things are free, but also that a few good things are *not* free, then the proposition must be treated as a conjunctive one, the nature of which will be described in the next chapter. If, on the other hand, the person stating that "Most good things in life are free" does not mean to exclude the possibility that *all* good things in life are free, then the paraphrasing "Some good things in life are free" is sufficient to express the intended meaning.

48.2 Particular Negative Propositions

A compound particular proposition which is negative *denies* that the entire membership of one class *a* is contained in another class *b*. The standard form is:

Some *a* are not *b*.

Since we are here stating that there is membership in that part of *a* which is outside *b*—that is, that the class *ab̄* is not empty—the proposition is symbolized and diagramed:

$$a\bar{b} \neq 0$$

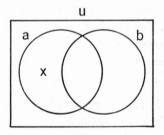

FIGURE 48–2

The proposition "Some paintings are not works of art," for instance, is readily diagramed by showing that the class of paintings which are not works of art possesses particular membership and is symbolized by stating that such class is not identical with the null class.

Like other standard form propositions, the particular negative proposition may be expressed in several alternative ways:

(i) At least one of Plato's *Dialogues* is not genuine.
(ii) Many men are not happy in their work.

(iii) Few politicians are dishonest.

(iv) Everything is not lost.

(v) All women are not gossips.

(vi) Not all people like golf.

The third proposition in this list, "Few politicians are dishonest," should be compared with the particular affirmative proposition "A few politicians are dishonest." Clearly both these propositions are particular, since unspecified (but existing) membership is assumed to occupy the class of politicians. The latter proposition, beginning with "A few," is ordinarily *affirmative,* not only because of its immediate connotation, but also because it can be used to deny the negative proposition "No politicians are dishonest." On the other hand, the proposition "Few politicians are dishonest" must usually be interpreted as *negative.* Very often, when asserting a proposition of this form, we tend to stress the first word, "few," meaning thereby that "*Most* politicians are *not* dishonest." This proposition also is the one we might use in denying the affirmative proposition "All politicians are dishonest."

The last three propositions on the above list—(iv), (v), and (vi)—also merit careful consideration. They are all of the same basic form: "Every *a* is not *b*," "All *a* are not *b*," and "Not all *a* are *b*." "An incautious student of logic is usually tempted to reduce these to the universal negative proposition "No *a* are *b*," because "All *a* are *not b*" would seem to indicate universality and negativity. This, of course, is a faulty analysis. "All *a* are not *b*," in its various forms, means "*Some a* are not *b*," a particular negative proposition. To say that "All men will not reach fifty years" clearly does not mean that no men will reach fifty, but rather that *some* men will not reach that age.

48.3 Singular Propositions

The proper symbolizing and diagraming of *simple* singular propositions has already been suggested in Chapter 43, where the epsilon-relationship was explained. The assertion that *s* is a member of *a* is symbolized $s \epsilon a$ and diagramed by placing s inside the circle representing class a. To *deny* that s is a member of a is equivalent to asserting that $s \epsilon \bar{a}$, and the s accordingly is entered on a diagram outside the circle representing a.

Nor is any particular difficulty encountered in treating *compound* singular propositions. That s is a singular member both of a and b is expressed:

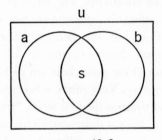

FIGURE 48-3

For example, the proposition "Sputnik is a Russian satellite" means simply that Sputnik is a singular member of the class both of satellites and Russian-made or -owned things. However, the negative form of a compound singular proposition is not always so easily diagramed. We can symbolize the proposition "The moon is *not* a Russian satellite" as $s \epsilon -(RS)$, but the diagram for such a proposition would have to show the moon to be a member either of Russian things which are not satellites, of satellites which are not Russian, or of objects which are neither Russian nor satellites. Of course, we have no diagrammatic technique for representing this disjunction of possibilities. Only when a singular negative proposition of the compound type is more specific, as in the proposition "The moon is a non-Russian satellite," may we profitably use a Venn diagram.

It is worth mentioning, at this point, that singular members of a class are not always designated by proper names. We very often use demonstrative or personal pronouns, and sometimes demonstrative or possessive adjectives, to indicate singular membership in a class:

(i) I am his friend.
(ii) This party is lively.
(iii) This is a lively party.
(iv) That drink must be highly intoxicating.
(v) Mine is a martini.
(vi) Your taste is different from mine.

Each of these propositions is distinguished as singular by its reference to a single, specifically designated member of a class. However, the same kind of pronoun or adjectival expression is often used to denote more than one object, as in the propositions: "We are his friends," "These are lively parties," "This type of party is lively," "Ours are martinis," "Your preferences are different from mine." Propositions such as these do not assert singular membership but rather class-inclusion, and therefore they must be symbolized and diagramed as universal propositions.

EXERCISES

The following list includes universal, particular, and singular propositions. A. Classify each proposition as to complexity, quantity, and quality. B. Paraphrase each proposition that is not already in standard form. C. Symbolize and diagram each proposition.

1. All scientists are methodical.
2. Some scientists are not objective.
3. Many scientific theories will become obsolete.
4. Biology is one of the natural sciences.*
5. Some biologists are botanists.*
6. All zoologists are not microbiologists.*
7. The amoeba is a species of protozoan.*
8. Not all protozoa are microscopic.

9. This looks to me like a paramecium.
10. It is not a parasitic protozoan.
11. Darwin was not among the first evolutionists.
12. Some biologists still accept the Lamarckian theory of evolution.
13. Lysenko is one of the biologists who reject Darwinism.
14. He is a Russian botanist.
15. Every biologist now accepts a theory of evolution.
16. Not every physicist accepts relativity theory.
17. A few prominent physicists have thought that quantum mechanics provided an argument for freedom of will.
18. Other physicists have rejected this interpretation of quantum mechanics.
19. Mathematical physics is a branch of applied mathematics.
20. Only the social sciences are concerned primarily with human behavior.

49 PURE CONJUNCTIVE PROPOSITIONS

Certain common types of proposition cannot be adequately represented by any one of the simple or compound propositions we have so far learned to symbolize and diagram. They require paraphrasing as a joint assertion of at least two of the propositions which we have studied, and hence they are classified as *conjunctive* propositions.

49.1 Conjunctive Particular Propositions

It has already been pointed out, in the discussion of particular propositions, that the assertion of a particular affirmative proposition, "Some *a* are *b*," does not exclude the possibility that a particular negative proposition, "Some *a* are not *b*," may also be asserted as true. Indeed, more often than not, when a statement of particular membership is appropriate, both the affirmative and negative forms of such statement are true together.

Among the various ways in which a conjunction of particular propositions may be asserted are the following:

(i) Almost all criminals are maladjusted.
(ii) Nearly all criminals are maladjusted.
(iii) Not quite all criminals are maladjusted.
(iv) All but a few criminals are maladjusted.
(v) All criminals, with certain exceptions, are maladjusted.
(vi) About fifty percent of criminals are maladjusted.
(vii) Only a few criminals are maladjusted.

Statements such as these are not universal, because they explicitly assert that some, but not all, criminals are maladjusted. Since the logical meaning of "some" covers the range from "at least one" to "possibly all," we may express a part of the meaning by a particular affirmative proposition: "Some criminals are maladjusted." But that this does not capture the whole meaning is apparent when we consider, once more, that *not all* criminals are said to be maladjusted. We have already learned that propositions of the form "Not all *a* are *b*" must be interpreted as particular negative, and hence we may add to the statement that "Some criminals are maladjusted" the supplementary statement that "Some criminals are *not* maladjusted." This paraphrasing, to be sure, fails to express the fact that more (or fewer) criminals are maladjusted than not. But this is a subtlety that cannot be expressed in an elementary system of class logic.

Using the dot to represent a conjunction or joint assertion of two or more propositions, the symbolization and diagram of a conjunctive particular proposition is easily accomplished:

$$ab \neq 0 \cdot a\bar{b} \neq 0 \text{ (read: } ab \text{ is}$$
$$\text{not empty } and \ a\bar{b} \text{ is not empty.)}$$

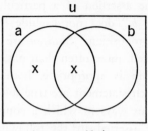

FIGURE 49–1

(The dot in the above conjunctive proposition is to be interpreted not as a symbol to be incorporated and explicated in the class logic, but only as an abbreviation of the word "and" or of any other term that might be used to connect propositions jointly asserted. This relationship of joint assertion has been symbolized and incorporated into the system of propositional logic presented in Part Two of this text.)

49.2 Coextensive-Class Propositions

Propositions of the general form "*a* is *b*" or "*a* are *b*" sometimes must be taken as asserting not only that the class *a* is included in *b*, but also that the class *b* is included in *a*. Consider the following propositions, each of which must be interpreted as affirming a relationship of reciprocal class-inclusion:

(i) Hellenes are Greeks.
(ii) Hellenes are the same as Greeks.
(iii) Hellenes and Greeks are identical.
(iv) All Greeks and only Greeks are Hellenes.
(v) Greeks and Greeks alone are Hellenes.
(vi) To be a Hellene is to be a Greek.

These variations of the same proposition make it clear that a statement such as "Hellenes are Greeks," is of the same form as "Athenians are Greeks" but is not equivalent in meaning. To say that "Hellenes are Greeks" means not merely that every Hellene is a Greek, but also that every Greek is a Hellene, or, in other words, that the class of Hellenes is identical with the class of Greeks. We have already learned that this type of proposition may be expressed symbolically by inserting the symbol for class-identity between the two classes in question. However, since coextensive-class propositions are universal, and since in our system of classification universal propositions are expressed as identities with the null class, we shall interpret class-identity as mutual class-inclusion. Thus, the proposition "*a* and *a* alone are *b*" should be expressed as a conjunction of two propositions, one asserting that *a* is included in *b*, and the other, an exclusive proposition, that *b* is included in *a*:

$$a\bar{b} = 0 \cdot \bar{a}b = 0$$

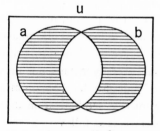

FIGURE 49–2

An alternative symbolization of coextensive-class propositions may be achieved by using the symbol for a class sum: $a\bar{b} + \bar{a}b = 0$. This symbolization, since it empties both the classes $a\bar{b}$ and $\bar{a}b$, accomplishes the same effect as a joint assertion of the emptiness of each class. However, caution must be exercised in using this alternative rendering of coextensive-class propositions, for the principle involved cannot be extended to conjunctive propositions in which particular membership is asserted. The proposition $ab + a\bar{b} \neq 0$, for example, is *not* equivalent to $ab \neq 0 \cdot a\bar{b} \neq 0$. The first proposition asserts membership in either ab or $a\bar{b}$ or both, while the second definitely asserts membership in both ab and $a\bar{b}$.

49.3 Exceptive Propositions

A more difficult type of proposition to analyze is called "exceptive," because in this type one class alone is excepted from inclusion in some other class. Some examples are:

(i) All except philosophers are practical.
(ii) All but philosophers are practical.
(iii) Philosophers alone are not practical.
(iv) Only philosophers are not practical.
(v) None but philosophers are impractical.

The proposition "All except philosophers are practical" means basically that "All nonphilosophers are practical," which is a proposition of the general form "All $\bar{a}$ are b." If "All a are b" is symbolized $a\bar{b} = 0$, then "All $\bar{a}$ are b" is symbolized $\overline{ab} = 0$. Thus, our example of an exceptive proposition means at least this, that the class of people who are not philosophers and also not practical is empty.

Ordinarily, however, the person using this exceptive type of statement, "All except a are b," means also to assert a universal negative proposition, "No a are b." The proposition "All except philosophers are practical" usually means not only that "All nonphilosophers are practical," but also that "No philosophers are practical." The appropriate conjunctive symbolization and diagram of exceptive propositions, therefore, is as follows:

$$\overline{ab} = 0 \cdot ab = 0$$
$$(\text{or, } \overline{ab} + ab = 0)$$

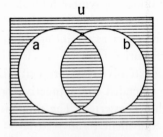

FIGURE 49–3

In other words, the exceptive type of proposition usually assigns each member of a universe class to one or the other of two mutually exclusive classes. If, in our example, the universe of discourse consists simply of "people," then the proposition "All except philosophers are practical" means that everyone is either a philosopher or a practical person, but not both.

It should be pointed out, however, that logicians do not agree about the advisability of supplementing the universal affirmative with a universal negative proposition in the analysis of exceptive propositions. Certain statements of the exceptive type—for example, "All except good swimmers are afraid to use the lake"—seem not to imply that a negative proposition—"No good swimmers are afraid to use the lake"—is true. Other exceptive propositions—for instance, "All except children will be admitted to the theater"—do appear to require the conjunctive interpretation. Exceptive propositions, therefore, are equivocal as they stand and should really be paraphrased into standard form according to their individual meaning and context.

EXERCISES

The following list includes conjunctive, as well as simple and compound, propositions. Classify, paraphrase, symbolize, and diagram each proposition.

1. Not all the great poets were learned men.
2. Many poets were poor.
3. Robert Burns was a spendthrift.*
4. Scotchmen are not always thrifty.*
5. Almost all of Shakespeare's comedies have tragic undertones.*
6. Only Shakespeare's greatest tragedies are lacking in poetic justice.
7. The majority of tragedies contain comic relief.
8. Wordsworth and Coleridge were greatly influenced by Spinoza.
9. The poems of Keats and Shelley reflect the influence of Plato.
10. All except free verse is metrical.*
11. Blank verse is the same as unrhymed iambic pentameter.*
12. *Paradise Lost* is written in blank verse.
13. No epic poem is light reading.
14. All but a few Greek dramatists observed the three unities.
15. Only fragments of Aristotle's *Poetics* have been discovered.
16. The *Iliad* is not a product of any one author.
17. There are several Homers.

18. All great books and only great books are worth a second reading.
19. Almost all poetry is both expressive and informative.
20. Only the poorest of poetry is not in some way instructive.

50 MIXED CONJUNCTIVE PROPOSITIONS

The conjunctive propositions we have so far examined may be called *pure,* in the sense that the two standard-form propositions into which they were analyzed in each example were either both universal or both particular. The conjunctive particular proposition was paraphrased as a joint assertion of two particular propositions, while the coextensive-class and exceptive types of proposition were paraphrased as joint assertions of universal propositions. Now, however, we must examine an important type of conjunctive proposition in which a universal and a particular proposition are jointly asserted, and which therefore may be called a *mixed* conjunctive proposition.

50.1 Existential Affirmative Propositions

The discerning student may already have noted, with some misgivings, that our symbolizations and diagrams of universal propositions are only partial representations of what is ordinarily meant by such propositions. We have thus far interpreted universal propositions as meaning only that some given class is empty of membership. But, one might object, do not propositions such as "All firearms are dangerous" or "No infants are legally responsible," in addition to asserting that the classes of safe firearms and legally responsible infants are empty, also assert that there is membership in the class of firearms or in that of infants?

The older logicians assumed, without question, that universal propositions carried an implication of membership. But this interpretation is not always correct, for some universal propositions appear not to assert membership in any class. Consider the statement posted in some supermarkets: "All shoplifters in this store will be prosecuted to the fullest extent of the law." This proposition clearly does not claim that there is membership in the class of "shoplifters in this store." On the contrary, the store manager hopes, by his warning, to keep the class of shoplifters in his market an empty class. Our diagram and symbolization of this universal proposition, therefore, will be perfectly appropriate and complete if we simply indicate, as we have learned to do, the emptiness of the class of shoplifters who will not be prosecuted.

We are left, then, with two types of universal affirmative proposition. Both types affirm the emptiness of some given class. But one type is *hypothetical,* in the sense that the question of membership is left open. In this type, the proposition "All *a* are *b*" means that *if* there is membership in the class *a*, it must also be in *b*. The *existential* type of universal proposition, although linguistically expressed in exactly the same way as the hypothetical type, "All *a* are *b*," asserts not only that the class $a\bar{b}$ is empty, but also that the class *a* has membership. Since this membership cannot exist in the empty class $a\bar{b}$, it must be located in *ab*. The symbolization and diagram of an existential affirmative proposition, accordingly, will take this general form:

$$a\bar{b} = 0 \cdot a \neq 0$$

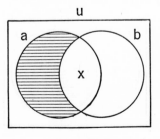

FIGURE 50–1

Whether a universal affirmative proposition should be considered existential or hypothetical must be decided on factual, nonlogical grounds. When symbolizing or diagraming a proposition of the general form "All *a* are *b*," we must ask if, as a matter of fact, we can assume membership in the class *a*. Ordinarily, we can assume such membership, and the proposition may be treated as existential. Of course, an existential universal is basically a hypothetical proposition that has been supplemented by a statement of membership. Hence, in most of the topics to be discussed in the following pages, it will make no difference whether universal propositions are treated as existential or as hypothetical. But at certain crucial points thereafter, as we shall see, this distinction will make all the difference between good and bad reasoning. For the time being, however, we will treat all universal propositions as hypothetical, except those in which an *inference* must be made from a universal to a particular proposition.

50.2 Existential Negative Propositions

The symbolizing and diagraming of universal *negative* propositions of the existential type is complicated somewhat by the fact that membership may be located in either one or both of the two classes involved. In general, however, membership exists in both classes and so the symbolization of an existential negative proposition requires the joint assertion of three standard-form propositions:

$$ab = 0 \cdot a \neq 0 \cdot b \neq 0$$

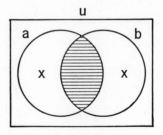

FIGURE 50–2

The proposition "No men are perfect," for example, interpreted hypothetically, asserts merely that there are no perfect men, and leaves open the question of membership in the class of imperfect men and in the class of perfect beings who are not men. If, on the other hand, a more specific interpretation is required (as it is in making an inference to a particular conclusion), the proposition would ordinarily be construed as asserting existence both in the class of men and in the class of perfect beings, and the type of symbolization and diagram above would then be appropriate. The possibility remains, of course, that a person who uses the proposition "No men are perfect" means to assert membership in the class of men but to withhold his judgment concerning membership in the class of perfect beings. The proper symbolization in this case is $MP = 0 \cdot M \neq 0$, and the corresponding diagram will show membership only in the class of men.

50.3 Summary Classification of Propositions

We are now ready to return to the topic of valid inference and the application of logical laws. This, the study of pure deductive logic, perhaps is the most interesting (and probably the easiest) topic in an elementary logic of classes. Nevertheless, if the class logic is not to be a relatively empty deductive exercise, a close study of the ways in which propositions in ordinary language are symbolized and diagramed is essential. Should this be disregarded, a student of logic may easily find himself becoming proficient at manipulating symbols without ever knowing whether or not he is treating actual inferences.

As an aid in studying symbolizations and diagrams, a systematic classification of the propositions described in this and the preceding four chapters is listed in the following table. This list should *not* be memorized. Rather, what should be learned is the comparatively limited number of underlying principles and distinctions. Only in this way can one acquire the knack of symbolizing and, in general, of making logical sense out of the extraordinary variety of ways in which something can be said in ordinary language. In other words, the *reason* for each symbolization must be clearly understood. If it is not, and the symbolization is merely committed to memory, one of the main purposes in studying logic and logical methods of reasoning is defeated.

Type	Standard Form	Symbolization	Diagram
I. *Simple Propositions*			
A. Universal	"There are no *a*."	$a = 0$	Fig. 44.3
B. Particular	"There are some *a*."	$a \neq 0$	Fig. 44.4
C. Singular			
1. Affirmative	"*s* is an *a*."	$s \in a$	Fig. 43.5
2. Negative	"*s* is not an *a*."	$s \in \bar{a}$	
II. *Compound Propositions*			
A. (Hypothetical) Universal			
1. Affirmative	"All *a* are *b*."	$a\bar{b} = 0$	Fig. 47.1
2. Negative	"No *a* are *b*."	$ab = 0$	Fig. 47.2
3. Exclusive	"All *b* are *a*."	$\bar{a}b = 0$	Fig. 47.3
	(*e.g.* "Only *a* are *b*.")		
B. Particular			
1. Affirmative	"Some *a* are *b*."	$ab \neq 0$	Fig. 48.1
2. Negative	"Some *a* are not *b*."	$a\bar{b} \neq 0$	Fig. 48.2
C. Singular			
1. Affirmative	"*s* is an *ab*."	$s \in ab$	Fig. 48.3
2. Negative	"*s* is not an *ab*."	$s \in -(ab)$	(no single diagram)
III. *Conjunctive Propositions*			
A. Particular	"Some *a* are *b* and some *a* are not *b*."	$ab \neq 0 \cdot a\bar{b} \neq 0$	Fig. 49.1
	(*e.g.* "All but a few *a* are *b*.")		
B. Coextensive-Class	"All *a* are *b* and all *b* are *a*."	$a\bar{b} = 0 \cdot \bar{a}b = 0$	Fig. 49.2
	(*e.g.* "*a* is identical with *b*.")		
C. Exceptive	"All *ā* are *b* and no *a* are *b*."	$\overline{ab} = 0 \cdot ab = 0$	Fig. 49.3
	(*e.g.* "All except *a* are *b*.")		
D. (Existential) Universal			
1. Affirmative	"All *a* are *b* (and there are some *a*)."	$a\bar{b} = 0 \cdot a \neq 0$	Fig. 50.1
2. Negative	"No *a* are *b* (and there are some *a* and some *b*)."	$ab = 0 \cdot a \neq 0 \cdot b \neq 0$	Fig. 50.2

EXERCISES

Classify, paraphrase, symbolize, and diagram each of the

following propositions, determining from your factual knowledge whether the universal propositions are existential or hypothetical:

1. Nearly all football players are heavy.
2. A few college quarterbacks weigh less than 150 pounds.
3. None but tall men are basketball players.
4. Runners who can do the mile in three minutes are in excellent shape.
5. All sports except cricket are fun to watch.
6. Cricketers alone enjoy their game.
7. All but a few countries have a national game.
8. Chess is the Russian national game.
9. Perfect chess games are rare events.
10. Capablanca never played a perfect game.
11. Only a few games are based entirely on skill.
12. Most card games involve the element of chance.
13. Poker is a game of skill.
14. This poker game is dishonest.
15. Five aces is a winning hand.
16. The best player always wins.
17. Few people make a living on horse racing.
18. Horses that win every race are worth a fortune.
19. Anyone accepting bets from minors will be charged with a felony.
20. All except children may place bets.

51 INFERENCE IN GENERAL

An inference or argument, as noted in the Introduction to this text, is composed of *conclusion* and *premises*—that is, of a proposition or propositions to be proved (conclusion), and the reasons or propositions offered in support of such conclusion (premises). A *deductive* or *formal* inference is one in which knowledge of the bare structure, or form, of the inference, together with meanings of certain logical terms involved, is sufficient to permit a pronouncement as to whether the conclusion does actually follow from the premises. As pointed out in our discussion of the laws of logic, an inference is *valid* when its conclusion necessarily follows from its premises. In other words, *if* the premises of a valid inference are true, then the conclusion necessarily is also true. On the other hand, if the conclusion of an inference containing true premises might possibly be false, then the inference is *invalid*.

51.1 Symbolization of Inferences

For the sake of a uniform symbolism, let us continue from Part Two the convention of using the symbol $\supset$ to represent the relationship between premises and conclusion. Thus the symbolization

$$(a = 0) \supset (ab = 0)$$

represents an inference in which $a = 0$ is a premise and $ab = 0$ is a conclusion. We may read this inference either "*a* is empty, *therefore ab* is empty," or "If there are no *a*, then no *a* are *b*." An instance of this type of argument is "There are no mermaids, therefore there are no beautiful mermaids."

An inference such as the one we are examining contains only two propositions, a premise and a conclusion, and therefore is called a *simple* inference. A *compound* inference is one in which either the premises or conclusion is conjunctive—that is, contains more than one proposition. Examples of valid compound inferences are:

$$[(a = 0) \cdot (b = 0)] \supset (a + b = 0),$$

$$(a + b = 0) \supset [(a = 0) \cdot (b = 0)].$$

If *a* were to stand once more for mermaids, and *b* for the class of sirens, then the first example of a compound inference would read "There are no mermaids and there are no sirens, hence the entire class of mermaids or sirens is empty." The second example would then be read in just the reverse order "The class of mermaids or sirens is empty, hence there are no mermaids and there are no sirens."

51.2 Reciprocal Inference: Equivalence

These last examples of inferences show that the role of premises and conclusion may sometimes be reversed, and that a relationship of *reciprocal inference* or *equivalence* may be said to hold between such propositions. An inference of this type may be represented, as in the propositional logic, by three bars:

$$[(a = 0) \cdot (b = 0)] \equiv (a + b = 0)$$

This reciprocal inference may be read " '*a* is empty and *b* is empty' is equivalent to '*a* + *b* is empty.' " Many of the laws of logic must be expressed in terms of such equivalences. That the law of commutation, for example, applies not only to logical products and sums, but also to class-identities, is formulated as an equivalence:

$$(a = b) \equiv (b = a).$$

It is clear, from these examples, that a distinction between premises and conclusion is not required in equivalent propositions. Either side of an equivalence will yield the other side. It is convenient, therefore, to use the term *equivalents* to designate such propositions. Thus, $a = b$ and $b = a$ are both equivalents in the equivalence $(a = b) \equiv (b = a)$.

51.3 Diagrammatic Test of an Inference

Any proposition or set of propositions containing up to three class terms (and any number of singular terms), if it can be symbolized in the logic of classes, can also be represented on a Venn diagram. This being true, we already have a method for testing the validity of inferences which contain no more than three class terms. For, as we have seen, an inference is valid if and only if its structure is such that the truth of its premises requires the truth of its conclusion. Thus, if we enter only the premises of a valid inference on a diagram, we should expect to find the conclusion already there. And if the argument is *not* valid, a diagram of the premises will fail to exhibit the conclusion.

The example of an inference symbolized on page 310, $(a = 0) \supset (ab = 0)$, contains two classes, and hence our test diagram must show the same number of classes. Entering the premise $a = 0$ on this diagram, we get:

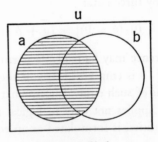

FIGURE 51–1

An inspection of this diagram reveals at once that the conclusion $ab = 0$ is already contained in the statement of the premise, and therefore the inference is *valid*.

If, however, we test the reverse of the above inference—that is, $(ab = 0) \supset (a = 0)$—we get the following diagram:

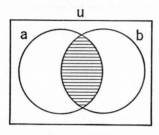

FIGURE 51–2

Here we see clearly that the conclusion, $a = 0$, is not necessarily implied by the premise, $ab = 0$, since the class $a\bar{b}$ may or may not have membership. This inference, therefore, is *invalid*.

It will be observed in Figure 51.1, showing a valid inference, that a part of the information conveyed by the premise was superfluous; it is not necessary to know the absence of membership in $a\bar{b}$ in order to deduce the conclusion $ab = 0$. A valid *reciprocal* inference, however, is one in which each of the equivalents is just sufficient to yield up the other, and therefore a diagram of either equivalent is at the same time a diagram of the other. The validity, for example, of the equivalence $[(a = 0) \cdot (b = 0)] \equiv (a + b = 0)$ is exhibited in the following diagram:

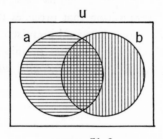

FIGURE 51–3

In contrast to this valid equivalence, a reciprocal inference such as $(a = 0) \equiv (ab = 0)$, as an inspection of either Figure 51.1 or 51.2 will show, is an invalid equivalence.

51.4 Detecting the Form of an Inference

Our first step in examining an inference as it appears in language should always be to distinguish between the premises and conclusion. This—like the question so often needed during a serious discussion, "What are you trying to prove?"—is of utmost importance. For it is impossible to test the validity of an argument until we know which statement is being proved and which statements are used as reasons in such proof. We have no assurance at all that the premises of an inference will appear first, before the conclusion. Indeed, it is more likely that the conclusion will precede the premises, since we very often assert a proposition first, and then find ourselves obliged to give reasons for it. But one cannot always depend even upon this likelihood. In general, we must assume that, in its natural context, the conclusion of an argument may appear before or after or even between the premises.

To distinguish between the premises and conclusion of an argument, we must rely mainly on the clues furnished by certain key words appearing in the argument. The logical connectives *therefore, hence, thus, so, consequently, it follows that* will always introduce a conclusion, permitting us to assume ordinarily that what precedes these words is a premise or set of premises. Where there are no key conclusion-words, we should look for certain words or expressions that always introduce a premise, such as *since, because, for, for the reason that;* and the proposition that precedes these words, if any, will usually be a conclusion. A second premise may often be identified by its conjunction with a known premise, such conjunction being effected by words like *and, but, while, although,* and *nevertheless.*

EXERCISES

A. Distinguish between the premises and conclusion in the following skeletal inferences:

1. *a* are *b*, since *a* are *c*.

2. a are b and it follows that a are c.

3. a are b, because a are c and c are b.

4. If a are b, then a are c.

5. a are b and therefore, since b are c, a are c.

6. a are b. For c are b and a are c.

7. a are b and so b are c, since a are c.

8. a are b and consequently a are c, since b are c.

9. Although a are b, a are c, because b are c.

10. a are b but a are c. Thus b are c.

    B. Test the validity of the following symbolized inferences and equivalences by means of Venn diagrams:

1. $(ab \neq 0) \supset (a \neq 0)$.

2. $(a \neq 0) \supset (ab \neq 0)$.*

3. $(a = 0) \supset (a + b = 0)$.

4. $(a + b = 0) \supset (a = 0)$.

5. $(ab = 0) \equiv (ba = 0)$.

6. $(a\bar{b} = 0) \equiv (b\bar{a} = 0)$.

7. $[(a\bar{b} = 0) \cdot (a \neq 0)] \supset (ab \neq 0)$.*

8. $(a \neq 0) \supset (u \neq 0)$.

9. $(a \neq 0) \equiv (u \neq 0)$.

10. $(a + \bar{b} = 0) \equiv (b + \bar{a} = 0)$.

    C. Symbolize the following inferences and then test them for validity by means of diagrams:

1. There are no b and therefore no a are b.*

2. No a are b since no b are a.

3. All a are b implies all b are a.*

4. Some a are b because all a are b.

5. a and a alone are b. Hence only a are b.*

6. Some a are not b. For some b are not a.

7. Some a are b. Therefore some a are not b.

8. All except a are b, consequently no b are a.

9. If none but a are b, then some b are a.

10. s is a member of ab, and thus is a member of b.

52 SIMPLE INFERENCES BASED ON DOUBLE NEGATION

In the previous chapter we saw how certain elementary inferences can be symbolized in the class logic and how their validity can be determined by means of Venn diagrams. We must now embark on a more systematic examination of inferences in this logic. A convenient starting point is furnished by a very common type of reciprocal inference based on the law of double negation: $a = \bar{\bar{a}}$. This type of inference, called *obversion* by classical logicians, permits us to express any affirmative proposition as negative, and vice versa.

52.1 Obversion of Universal Propositions

The term "obversion" refers specifically to the class of inferences in which, by a kind of double denial, the quality of a standard-form proposition may be changed. First, the quality of the proposition itself is changed, while the same quantity is retained. Second, the quality of the *second* term in the proposition is changed, the given class term being replaced by its complementary class term. Thus a universal affirmative proposition, when obverted, becomes universal negative, and a universal negative proposition becomes universal affirmative:

$$\text{All } a \text{ are } b \equiv \text{No } a \text{ are } \bar{b},$$

$$\text{No } a \text{ are } b \equiv \text{All } a \text{ are } \bar{b}.$$

Examples of these reciprocal inferences are:

All married people are happy $\equiv$ No married people are unhappy.

No married people are happy $\equiv$ All married people are unhappy.

The validity of such obversions may easily be tested either symbolically or diagrammatically. Symbolizing the above standard forms, we get:

$$(a\bar{b} = 0) \equiv (a\bar{b} = 0),$$

$$(ab = 0) \equiv (a\bar{\bar{b}} = 0).$$

Let us call any case in which a proposition is said to be equivalent to itself a *patent tautology*. Thus, the obversion of a universal affirmative proposition, when symbolized, turns out to be a patent tautology, but the obversion of a universal negative proposition is valid by the law of double negation. Of course, the validity of either reciprocal inference may also be established diagrammatically, since diagrams of $a\bar{b} = 0$ and $ab = 0$ are identical with diagrams of their stated equivalents.

We may assume, as an interesting consequence of this symbolic analysis of obversion, that the difference in quality of propositions in the class logic is not of the same basic importance as the difference in quantity. Although not all possibilities of obversion will be treated here, it will nevertheless become apparent that any proposition may theoretically be rephrased as a proposition of the opposite quality. With respect to quantity, however, no amount of rephrasing or symbolic manipulation permits us to express, for example, a universal proposition as particular or singular.

52.2 Obversion of Particular Propositions

The same procedure we used in obverting universal propositions —changing the quality of the proposition and substituting the complementary class of the second term—may be applied with equal success to particular propositions. If we change only the quality of the particular affirmative proposition "Some married people are happy," we get the negative proposition "Some married people are not happy." And now, substituting the complementary class of "happy people" for the second term, we are left with the obverse and an equivalent of the original proposition, "Some married people are not unhappy."

In obverting the particular negative proposition "Some married people are not happy," we simply omit the word "not," thereby achieving the required change in quality. Then, substituting once more the complementary class of the second term, we have the equivalent proposition "Some married people are unhappy."

Thus, expressed in terms of standard form propositions, the obversion of particular propositions may be outlined in the following way:

$$\text{Some } a \text{ are } b \equiv \text{Some } a \text{ are not } \bar{b}.$$

$$\text{Some } a \text{ are not } b \equiv \text{Some } a \text{ are } \bar{b}.$$

And when we symbolize these reciprocal inferences, we are left once more with an equivalence by the law of double negation and with a patent tautology:

$$(ab \neq 0) \equiv (a\bar{\bar{b}} \neq 0),$$

$$(a\bar{b} \neq 0) \equiv (a\bar{b} \neq 0).$$

This second equivalence, obverting a particular negative proposition, is so obvious when expressed in language that it is mentioned only for the sake of systematic presentation. The first equivalence, however, obverting a particular affirmative proposition, is used very widely in ordinary discourse to soften the impact of an otherwise startling or unconventional pronouncement. The statement, for example, "Some suicides are premeditated" might in certain circles be received with a little more reluctance than the equivalent statement "Some suicides are not unpremeditated." And we may easily imagine a situation in which we should hesitate to say that "Many improper jokes are humorous," but in which we might quietly suggest that "Many improper jokes are not lacking in humor."

52.3 Obversion of Singular Propositions

The singular affirmative proposition "He is happy" obverts to "He is not unhappy," while the singular negative "He is not happy" obverts to "He is unhappy." As before, the symbolization of these equivalences reflect their validity:

s is an a $\equiv$ s is not a $\bar{a}$. $(s \;\epsilon\; a) \equiv (s \;\epsilon\; \bar{\bar{a}})$

s is not an a $\equiv$ s is a $\bar{a}$. $(s \;\epsilon\; \bar{a}) \equiv (s \;\epsilon\; \bar{a})$

EXERCISES

The following simple inferences are based, either correctly or incorrectly, on the law of double negation. Paraphrase each inference, when necessary, into standard form, and then test for validity by symbolizing and/or diagraming:

1. Nobody is perfect, therefore every human being has his faults.
2. All unhappy people are maladjusted, because no person who has found happiness can be called maladjusted.
3. Many dentists are not unhappy about inflicting pain. Hence some dentists are sadistic.*
4. Only optimistic people are gamblers, and consequently there is no gambler who is not optimistic.
5. He must be a gentleman, for his behavior is never ungentlemanly.*
6. All men engaging in menial labor are not satisfied with their lot. It follows that no menial workers are satisfied.
7. All show girls except strip-teasers are decent people, and therefore no show girls who do not strip are indecent.
8. Since none but educated people are literate, no persons with an education are illiterate.
9. Nearly all men are fallible, and so we may truthfully say that no men are infallible.
10. No rational beings are nonhuman, for the reason that human beings and human beings alone are rational.

53 SIMPLE INFERENCES BASED ON COMMUTATION

Another very common type of simple reciprocal inference is one which permits us to interchange the two class terms in a compound proposition. This interchange, or inference, when it is based solely on the law of commutation ($ab = ba$) is called *conversion*. If, however, the law of commutation must be supplemented by the law of double negation in order to effect an interchange of terms, the inference is called *contraposition*. Let us examine these two kinds of simple reciprocal inference.

53.1 Conversion

Only two standard-form compound propositions, the universal negative and particular affirmative, can validly be converted:

No *a* are *b* ≡ No *b* are *a*. $(ab = 0) \equiv (ba = 0)$

Some *a* are *b* ≡ Some *b* are *a*. $(ab \neq 0) \equiv (ba \neq 0)$

Thus, the proposition "No reptiles are mammals" is equivalent to "No mammals are reptiles," and "Some organisms are microscopic" is equivalent to "Some microscopic objects are organisms." That these conversions are valid may easily be seen by reference either to diagrams or to the above symbolizations. Through symbolization, by the law of commutation applied to logical products, and by the rule of replacement, either equivalent can be deduced from the other.

Conversion of the universal affirmative or particular negative type of proposition is *invalid,* as both diagrams and symbolizations show. On a diagram, the proposition "All *a* are *b*" is indicated by lining out the class $a\bar{b}$, whereas the converse, "All *b* are *a*," is represented by lining out $\bar{a}b$. Similarly, if we apply the law of commutation to a symbolized universal affirmative proposition $a\bar{b} = 0$, we get the proposition $\bar{b}a = 0$, which might be read "No $\bar{b}$ are a," but which still does not give us "All b are a," or $b\bar{a} = 0$.

Nevertheless, the illicit conversion of universal affirmative propositions is a rather common form of bad reasoning. Many people find it tempting, for example, to draw the inference from a proposition such as "All communists are socialists" to the proposition "All socialists are communists." Fallacies such as this (if not deliberate) are probably due to a confusion between class-inclusion and coextensive-class propositions, since the general form "All a are b," in actual use, may be interpreted either way.

53.2 Contraposition

There is a way, however, in which we may interchange the two terms of a universal affirmative or particular negative proposition without changing either the meaning or the standard form. By a reciprocal inference called "contraposition," we may interchange the terms of these propositions, provided we substitute the complementary class of each term. Thus the following inferences are valid:

All a are b ≡ All $\bar{b}$ are $\bar{a}$.

Some a are not b ≡ Some $\bar{b}$ are not $\bar{a}$.

The proposition "All married people are happy" is equivalent by contraposition to "All unhappy people are unmarried." And the proposition "Some married people are not happy" is equivalent to "Some unhappy people are not unmarried." It will be observed that contraposition, like conversion, does not change the standard form of a proposition. The contrapositive of a universal affirmative proposition remains universal affirmative, and of a particular negative proposition remains particular negative.

When we examine contraposition symbolically, we see that the contrapositive in each case may be deduced in two steps, the first an equivalent by commutation, and the second an equivalent by double negation:

$(a\bar{b} = 0) \equiv (\bar{b}a = 0) \equiv (\bar{b}\bar{a} = 0)$ (Universal affirmative),

$(a\bar{b} \neq 0) \equiv (\bar{b}a \neq 0) \equiv (\bar{b}\bar{a} \neq 0)$ (Particular negative).

If it is not at once apparent that the final equivalent in each of these inferences is a contrapositive of the first equivalent, it may clarify matters to reason in this way: If $b\bar{a} = 0$ can be read "All b are a," then $\bar{b}\bar{a} = 0$ can be read "All $\bar{b}$ are $\bar{a}$." And if $b\bar{a} \neq 0$ can be read "Some b are not a," then $\bar{b}\bar{a} \neq 0$ can be read "Some $\bar{b}$ are not $\bar{a}$."

It is interesting that a contrapositive may be deduced linguistically by successive applications of the rules of obversion and conversion. If a universal affirmative or particular negative proposition is first obverted, then converted, and once more obverted, the contrapositive results:

All happy people are friendly.	(Universal affirmative)
No happy people are unfriendly.	(Obverse)
No unfriendly people are happy.	(Converted obverse)
All unfriendly people are unhappy.	(Obverse of converted obverse, *i.e.*, contrapositive)

EXERCISES

A. Deduce the contrapositive of "Some happy people are not friendly" by successive applications of obversion and conversion.

B. By means of symbolizations and diagrams, show whether each of the following propositions can or cannot be deduced from the given proposition "All healthy children are active."

1. All inactive children are unhealthy.*
2. No healthy children are inactive.
3. All active children are healthy.
4. No inactive children are healthy.

5. All unhealthy children are inactive.
6. No active children are unhealthy.
7. Only active children are healthy.
8. No unhealthy children are active.
9. None but healthy children are active.
10. A healthy child is the same as an active child.

    C. Proposition (1) above is the *contrapositive* of the given proposition, "All healthy children are active." Name the relationship of each of the remaining propositions in the above list to the given proposition.

54 INFERENCES BASED ON OPPOSITION

The inferences covered in the last two chapters, based on the laws of commutation and double negation, have all been reciprocal, in that if either proposition in the inference were true, then the other proposition must also have been true. Similarly, we must note, if either of the propositions in a valid reciprocal inference is false, the other proposition must also be false. Thus, for example, if the proposition "No murderers are sane" is false, then the class of sane murderers has membership, and we may deduce the falsity of the converse proposition "No sane persons are murderers," and of the obverse "All murderers are insane."

We must at this point examine a class of inferences in which the falsity of one proposition may be deduced from the truth of another, or the truth of one deduced from the falsity of the other. Pairs of propositions such as this are called *opposites,* and the relationship between them is one of *opposition.* The three kinds of opposition with which we shall be concerned are *contradiction, contrariety,* and *subcontrariety.* Propositions opposed to each other by contradiction —*contradictories,* as we may call them—are complete opposites, in the sense that they may be neither true together nor false together. *Contraries,* on the other hand, are only partial opposites, in that it is possible for both to be false together although, like contradictories, both cannot be true together. *Subcontraries* are also partial opposites, but in a different way, since both may be true together but cannot at the same time be false.

54.1 Contradiction

Since a pair of contradictory propositions will always have opposite truth-values, this relationship may be expressed by using the negation symbol ($\sim$), representing in the logic of propositions the *denial* of whatever propositions follows. Thus the opposition, for example, between the propositions "There are no *a*" and "There are some *a*," may be symbolized in the following manner:

$$(a = 0) \equiv \sim(a \neq 0).$$

This symbolization indicates that the assertion of $a = 0$ is equivalent to the denial of $a \neq 0$. If *a* is empty, in other words, then it is false that *a* is not empty, and vice versa. Such opposition could equally well have been written:

$$\sim(a = 0) \equiv (a \neq 0).$$

For, if the truth of one proposition is equivalent to the falsity of another, then a denial of the first proposition is equivalent to an affirmation of the second. In short, from either member of a pair of contradictory propositions, we may always deduce the opposite truth-value of the other member.

It is important to observe that the contradictory of a universal is always a particular proposition, and the contradictory of a particular is always a universal proposition. This is evident on a Venn diagram from the impossibility of both lining out a class and entering in that same class the x-mark for particular membership—that is, the impossibility of asserting that a class is both empty and not empty. It thus becomes apparent that the contradictory of a universal affirmative proposition, "All a are b," is not, as we might at first expect, the universal negative proposition, "No a are b," but the particular negative proposition "Some a are not b." (This, indeed, explains why the nonstandard form "Not all a are b" must be paraphrased as a particular, rather than as a universal, negative proposition.) And the contradictory of "No a are b" is a particular affirmative proposition, "Some a are b." The following equivalences therefore are valid, as the corresponding diagrams clearly indicate.

$$(a\bar{b} = 0) \equiv \sim(a\bar{b} \neq 0)$$

is the contradictory of:

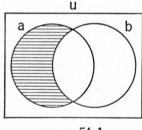

FIGURE 54–1a

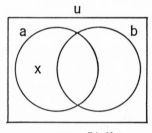

FIGURE 54–1b

$$(ab = 0) \equiv \sim(ab \neq 0)$$

is the contradictory of:

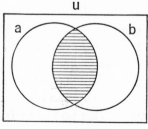

FIGURE 54–2a

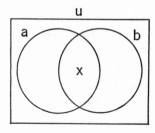

FIGURE 54–2b

One might, at this point, ask whether a *singular* proposition would not also serve as the contradictory of a universal proposition. However, while it is true that the assertion of singular membership in some class is not consistent with an assertion of nonmembership in that class, it is still possible that both these assertions are false. The propositions $a = 0$ and $s \,\epsilon\, a$, for example, cannot both be true, but if a has membership other than s, both propositions are false. Universal and singular propositions, therefore, cannot contradict each other.

A singular proposition may, however, be considered the contradictory of a singular proposition of the opposite quality. If we can assume that a singular member cannot both be included and not included in some class, and if we can further assume that the universe class is broad enough to contain the singular member in question, then the following equivalence is valid:

$$(s \,\epsilon\, a) \equiv \sim(s \,\epsilon\, \bar{a}).$$

54.2 Contrariety

Contrary propositions differ from contradictories in that, while both cannot be true, both may nevertheless be false. Such propositions as $a = 0$ and $s \,\epsilon\, a$, for reasons mentioned in the preceding section, are contraries, since the truth of one implies the falsity of the other but the falsity of one does *not* imply the truth of the other. This particular case of contrariety may be symbolized in the following manner:

$$(a = 0) \supset \sim (s \,\epsilon\, a) \quad \text{or} \quad (s \,\epsilon\, a) \supset \sim (a = 0).$$

It must be noticed that contrariety is symbolized not as an equivalence, but as a nonreciprocal inference. This is necessary because, even though the truth of a proposition implies the falsity of its contrary, the *falsity* of a proposition does *not* imply the truth of its contrary—which is simply another way of saying that contraries cannot both be true, although both may be false. Thus, if we assume the truth of the proposition "There are no flying saucers," we can deduce the falsity of the singular contrary "That up yonder is a flying saucer." But if we assume the *falsity* of "There are no flying saucers," we can only deduce the truth of its *contradictory,* "Flying saucers do exist," while the truth of "That up yonder is a flying saucer" remains an open question. In short, the inference between $a = 0$ and $\sim (s \in a)$, or between $s \in a$ and $\sim (a = 0)$, is not reciprocal, but is in one direction only, and hence these propositions are not equivalent.

The universal affirmative and negative propositions, "All *a* are *b*" and "No *a* are *b*," when given a hypothetical (nonexistential) interpretation, are not opposites of any kind. Both may clearly be false (when, for example, a conjunctive particular proposition is true), and both may also be true, since class *a* might be empty of membership. However, when these propositions are existential, implying membership in *a*, they become contraries, and the following inferences then are valid:

$$(a\bar{b} = 0 \cdot a \neq 0) \supset \sim(ab = 0),$$

$$(ab = 0 \cdot a \neq 0) \supset \sim(a\bar{b} = 0).$$

Thus, the propositions "All flying saucers are piloted" and "No flying saucers are piloted" may both be true (if we assume that the class of flying saucers might be empty), and hence these are not contrary propositions. On the other hand, certain propositions such as "All human beings are gullible" and "No human beings are gullible" are contraries, since there is membership in the class of "human beings," and consequently the falsity of either proposition may be deduced from the truth of the other.

54.3 Subcontrariety

Subcontraries are such that, while both may be true, both cannot at the same time be false. In other words, from the truth of a proposition we cannot deduce the falsity of its subcontrary, but from the *falsity* of a proposition we *can* deduce the truth of its subcontrary. Ordinarily, the two particular propositions "Some *a* are *b*" and "Some *a* are not *b*" are considered to be opposites of this type; subcontrariety does not hold between these two propositions, however, unless we assume membership in class *a*:

$$[\sim(ab \neq 0) \cdot a \neq 0] \supset (a\bar{b} \neq 0),$$

$$[\sim(a\bar{b} \neq 0) \cdot a \neq 0] \supset (ab \neq 0).$$

At first thought, it seems odd that the existential premise $a \neq 0$ must be conjoined to a *particular* proposition in order that an inference based on subcontrariety be valid. Since the proposition $ab \neq 0$ already asserts membership in the class a, it seems redundant to add that a is not empty. But the premise $a \neq 0$ must be introduced into this inference, for the particular proposition to which it is conjoined has been *denied*. To say that $ab \neq 0$ is *false* is equivalent by contradiction to saying that $ab = 0$ is true, in which case $a\bar{b} = 0$ might also be true; in this event the subcontrary $ab \neq 0$ would not follow. To illustrate, it would certainly be redundant to add the premise "Flying saucers exist" to the *assertion* of the premise "Some flying saucers are piloted," since this latter proposition already assigns membership to the class of flying saucers. But it is *not* redundant to add "Flying saucers exist" to the *denial* of "Some flying saucers are piloted," for such denial amounts to the assertion that "No flying saucers are piloted." And if this latter proposition is interpreted as hypothetical, then, as may easily be seen on a Venn diagram, membership must be asserted in the class of flying saucers before the inference based on subalternation (discussed below) is valid. This inference therefore may appropriately be rephrased: "*If* it is false that some flying saucers are piloted, and if flying saucers exist, then some flying saucers are *not* piloted."

54.4 Subalternation

An alternative (and perhaps a more useful) formulation of inference based on subcontrariety is one which takes advantage of the principle of contradiction. The denial of a particular affirmative or negative proposition is equivalent by contradiction to the assertion, respectively, of a universal negative or affirmative proposition. Thus, if the denials of the particular propositions in the two inferences based on subcontrariety are replaced by their equivalents, we get the following two inferences:

$$(ab = 0 \cdot a \neq 0) \supset (a\overline{b} \neq 0),$$

$$(a\overline{b} = 0 \cdot a \neq 0) \supset (ab \neq 0).$$

These same inferences, which we may refer to as inferences based on *subalternation,* could equally well have been derived from our formulation of inferences based on contrariety, simply by replacing the denied conclusions with their equivalents by contradiction. However they are derived, the inferences based on subalternation consist essentially in particularizing or weakening an existential universal proposition, and their validity may easily be seen by reference to Venn diagrams.

Before leaving the topic of subalternation, it should be mentioned that a rather widespread fallacy may be traced to the illicit use of subalternation as a *reciprocal* inference. Subalternation, however, is not reversible. From "Some *a* are *b*" we cannot deduce "All *a* are *b*," nor from "Some *a* are not *b*" can we deduce "No *a* are *b*." This type of fallacious reasoning, called *superalternation* or (in popular reference to fallacies) *hasty generalization,* when examined in the abstract seems so obvious as to be trivial. Yet most of us find it very tempting, if it suits our purpose, to reason from "some" or from "most" to "all." There are even persons who appear temperamentally incapable of thinking in terms of particular propositions, and whose prejudices, superstitions, or compulsive exaggerations may logically be explained in terms of the fallacy of superalternation.

EXERCISES

A. Assuming that the proposition "No fisherman is honest" is *true* and that the classes of "fishermen" and "honest people" are not empty, state whether each of the following propositions is *true, false,* or *doubtful* (that is, indeterminate).

1. All fishermen are honest.
2. Some fishermen are not honest.*
3. Some fishermen are honest.
4. All fishermen are dishonest.
5. No fishermen are dishonest.
6. Some honest people are fishermen.
7. No honest people are fishermen.
8. All dishonest people are fishermen.
9. All honest people are fishermen.
10. All honest people are nonfishermen.
11. Some honest people are not fishermen.
12. Some honest people are not nonfishermen.
13. There are no honest people.
14. Some fishermen are dishonest.
15. Nearly all fishermen are honest.
16. No dishonest person is a nonfisherman.
17. Only honest people are fishermen.
18. All dishonest people are nonfishermen.
19. All except fishermen are honest.
20. All fishermen are not honest.
21. Ted Williams is an honest fisherman.
22. Dishonest fishermen are rare.
23. Not every fisherman is honest.
24. None but dishonest people are fishermen.
25. Only a small percentage of fishermen are honest.

B. Proposition 1 above is the *contrary* of the given proposition, while Proposition 6 is its *converted contradictory*. Determine the relationship of the remaining propositions in the list to the given proposition.

C. Assuming that the given proposition "No fisherman is honest" is *false*, state whether each of the propositions listed above is *true*, *false*, or *doubtful*. (Remember that if the given proposition is false, its *contradictory* must be true.)

D. Assuming that the proposition "Some fishermen are not honest" is *true*, state whether each of the propositions listed above is *true, false,* or *doubtful*. Determine the relationship of each to the given proposition. Then, assuming that the given proposition is *false,* state the truth-value of each of the listed propositions.

E. Of the propositions listed in Exercise A that are true when the given proposition ("No fisherman is honest") is true, which are *equivalent* to the given proposition and which may only be *deduced from* the given proposition (without the relationship of reciprocal inference holding)?

55 PURE COMPOUND INFERENCES

The inferences based on opposition, when symbolized, are revealed as either simple or compound. Those involving contradiction (for example, $\sim(a = 0) \equiv (a \neq 0)$ are simple inferences, since neither the premises nor conclusions are conjunctive. Inferences involving contrariety, subcontrariety, and subalternation, on the other hand, since their premises are conjunctive, are compound inferences. It is now convenient to draw another distinction. We may refer to inferences containing propositions of different quantity as *mixed*, and to inferences containing propositions all of the same quantity as *pure*. Thus, the propositions appearing in inferences based on contrariety—for example, $(a\bar{b} = 0 \cdot a \neq 0) \supset \sim(ab = 0)$—are universal and particular, and therefore these inferences are mixed. The type of inference based on subcontrariety, however—for instance, $[\sim(a\bar{b} \neq 0) \cdot a \neq 0] \supset ab \neq 0$—is pure, since only particular propositions are involved. In the present chapter we shall consider several other types of pure compound inference, and in the following chapter we shall discuss mixed compound inferences.

Of the vast number of possible compound inference forms, we need treat only the more common. Among these will be the "syllogism," considered until recently of central importance in logic. However, we shall not distinguish the syllogism by name since, as traditionally defined, it lacks clarity and logical rigor, and in the context of modern logic, it does not have the pre-eminent status it formerly possessed.

55.1 Valid Inferences

In dealing with pure compound inferences, we need consider only those containing all universal propositions. This is not to say that inferences containing purely particular or singular propositions are not possible or not important, but only that these latter types of inference are less commonly found in ordinary argumentation.

Consider the following inference:

There are no true democracies, because utopias do not exist, and a true democracy is a utopia.

In evaluating an argument as it occurs in ordinary language the first step, always, is to distinguish the statement being proved from the reasons given for such statement. Here, the first proposition, "There are no true democracies," is the conclusion, as indicated by the logical connective *because,* and the propositions following are premises. Arranging these propositions, then, in the order in which they must be symbolized, and paraphrasing them into standard form, we get

All true democracies are utopias, and there are no utopias; therefore there are no true democracies.

The first premise is a compound proposition of the universal affirmative type, while the second premise and the conclusion are simple universal propositions. Using D for "true democracies" and U for "utopias," the symbolization of this inference is

$$(D\bar{U} = 0 \cdot U = 0) \supset D = 0.$$

We know that a *valid* inference is such that its conclusion is necessarily involved in the very statement of its premises. Hence, when we enter only the premises of the above argument on a Venn diagram, the conclusion, if the inference is valid, will also have been diagramed. The following diagram, therefore, in which only the premises have been entered, reveals that the conclusion is necessarily implied by these premises and that the argument is valid.

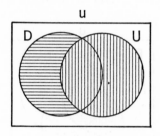

FIGURE 55–1

It will be observed that the two classes emptied of membership on this diagram have been lined out differently, one with horizontal and the other with vertical lines. This is to ensure that the information conveyed diagrammatically by the two premises can easily be distinguished. Thus, for example, we can see at a glance that both premises, $D\bar{U} = 0$ and $U = 0$, were required in order to deduce the conclusion $D = 0$.

Suppose the argument contains, not two, but three class terms, as in the following inference:

> No Republican is a Democrat, and therefore Republicans do not advocate a democratic form of government, since only Democrats believe in that type of government.

Something is obviously wrong with this argument. But we should not be misled into thinking that an inference with a patently false conclusion is therefore invalid; for an inference requires, to ensure the truth of its conclusion, not only valid reasoning but also true premises. Since in formal logic we cannot pronounce upon the truth of premises, but only upon validity, let us test the above argument, first by recasting it into logical order and paraphrasing the exclusive proposition into standard form, and then by symbolizing and diagraming.

> No Republicans (R) are Democrats (D), and all persons who advocate a democratic form of government (G) are Democrats. Therefore no Republicans advocate a democratic form of government.

$$(RD = 0 \cdot G\bar{D} = 0) \supset RG = 0.$$

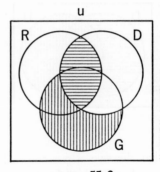

FIGURE 55–2

Now we see that after the premises have been entered on the diagram, the conclusion, $RG = 0$, is already there. The argument therefore is valid, and if something about it appears to be wrong, the error must be traced back to the premises themselves.

The soundness of the following inference might also be questioned:

> Marxists and Marxists alone are dialectical materialists. But to be a dialectical materialist is to be a communist. It follows that a Marxist and communist is one and the same.

Nevertheless, the argument is valid. For when it is symbolized (either into coextensive-class propositions or into equivalent universal affirmative propositions) and diagramed, we see that the conclusion is necessarily implied by the premises:

$$(M = D \cdot D = C) \supset M = C$$

or the equivalent symbolization

$$(M\bar{D} = 0 \cdot \bar{M}D = 0 \cdot D\bar{C} = 0 \cdot \bar{D}C = 0) \supset (M\bar{C} = 0 \cdot \bar{M}C = 0).$$

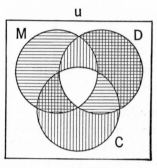

FIGURE 55–3

55.2 Invalid Inferences

Suppose that the second premise in the above argument, "To be a dialectical materialist is to be a communist," is interpreted not as a coextensive-class proposition, but as a class-inclusion proposition. The symbolization and diagram then become:

$$(M = D \cdot D\bar{C} = 0) \supset M = C.$$

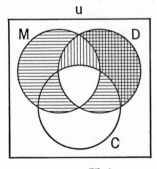

FIGURE 55–4

The inference now is invalid, because in order for the premises to yield the conclusion, $M = C$, the classes $M\bar{C}$ and $\bar{M}C$ both must be emptied of membership. We see on the diagram, however, that $\bar{M}C$ is only partly emptied by the premises, and that the class $\overline{MDC}$ *might* contain membership. This possibility renders the argument invalid, since its premises may be true while its conclusion is false.

EXERCISES

Symbolize each of the following inferences and test them for validity by means of Venn diagrams.

1. All Frenchmen are Europeans, but no American is a European. Therefore no American is a Frenchman.
2. All Frenchmen are Europeans, and therefore no Americans are Europeans, since no American is a Frenchman.*
3. No Americans are Europeans, because all Europeans are Frenchmen, and no American is a Frenchman.*
4. Women who are beautiful, intelligent, personable, and wealthy are women who make ideal wives. But the ideal wife does not exist, and consequently there is no woman who is beautiful, intelligent, personable, and wealthy.
5. Good dancers are popular with the girls, and so are millionaires. A millionaire must therefore be a good dancer.
6. All learning is painful and thus to be avoided, since that which is painful must be avoided.
7. All public figures are without privacy, and therefore it is safe to say that any person whose privacy is respected is not a public figure.
8. No logicians are free from error, but only persons who are free from error are superhuman. It follows that no superhuman beings are logicians.
9. All good psychiatrists have a first-hand knowledge of mental disorders. But anyone who has such knowledge is or has been a mental case himself, and therefore a good psychiatrist must be, or at least have been, a mental case.

10. Every antifraternal organization is guilty of discrimination. However college fraternities clearly are not antifraternal organizations, and hence are not guilty of discrimination.

11. Only motion pictures that exert a bad moral influence are denounced by public-decency organizations. But any picture so denounced attracts large audiences. It follows therefore that morally bad pictures attract large audiences.

12. No Floridians have money, since they cannot be called winter visitors, and the latter alone have money.

13. All except happily married couples are poor parents. Selfish people are unhappily married, and, hence, are poor parents.

14. A virus is capable of reproducing itself, and so must be a living organism, since these are all reproductive.

15. Spinoza concludes his *Ethics* with a famous statement: "But all things excellent are as difficult as they are rare." From this statement we may deduce that all rare things are difficult.

56 MIXED COMPOUND INFERENCES

56.1 Inferences Containing Singular Propositions

The following is a very common form of mixed inference:

Doctor Smith is a psychiatrist, because he is a psychoanalyst. And psychoanalysts are psychiatrists.

The first proposition is a conclusion and must, therefore, come last in our symbolization of this inference. Representing the singular member "Doctor Smith" by *s*, the class of "psychiatrists" by *P*, and the class of "psychoanalysts" by A, we get the following symbolization:

$$(s \in A \cdot A\bar{P} = 0) \supset s \in P.$$

Diagraming only the premises of this inference gives:

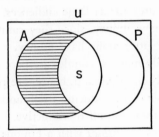

FIGURE 56–1

We see that the inference is valid, since the conclusion is clearly represented on the diagram when the premises are entered. In diagraming mixed inferences, the universal proposition should be entered before a singular or particular proposition, because otherwise the mark of membership might have to be relocated.

Suppose the above inference had read:

Doctor Smith is a psychoanalyst, because he is a psychiatrist.
And all psychoanalysts are psychiatrists.

Symbolizing and diagraming this revised inference, we get:

$$(s \in P \cdot A\bar{P} = 0) \supset s \in A.$$

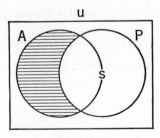

FIGURE 56–2

The *s* has been entered on the line between AP and $\bar{A}P$, indicating that, based on the information furnished us, the singular member might be in either class. It is possible, therefore, that *s* be a member of $\bar{A}$, which possibility requires us to pronounce the argument *invalid*. In general, whenever we do not know in which of two classes singular or particular membership belongs, the appropriate mark must be located on the line between the two classes.

As shown by the following inference, propositions asserting singular membership may occur in the context of an inference containing three classes.

> Doctor Smith is a psychoanalyst, and therefore he is a doctor of medicine, since any psychoanalyst is a psychiatrist and these latter are all doctors of medicine.

The principles involved in testing such an inference are the same as before, the only difference being that our Venn diagram must show three classes. After paraphrasing the inference into standard-form propositions, rearranging these propositions in logical order, and symbolizing and diagraming, we find that the inference is valid.

> All psychoanalysts (A) are psychiatrists (P), and all psychiatrists are doctors of medicine (M), and Doctor Smith (s) is a psychoanalyst. Therefore, Doctor Smith is a doctor of medicine.

$$(A\bar{P} = 0 \cdot P\bar{M} = 0 \cdot s \in A) \supset s \in M.$$

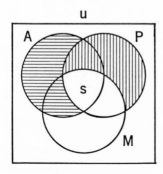

FIGURE 56–3

56.2 Inferences Containing Particular Propositions

No difficulty will be encountered now in evaluating mixed inferences containing universal and particular propositions. Suppose that we are asked to pronounce upon the validity of an inference such as this:

> Some Unitarians are not Christians, because some are freethinkers. And no Christian is a freethinker.

The first proposition in this inference is clearly the conclusion, while the second proposition, "some are freethinkers," refers back to "Some Unitarians." The proper paraphrase, symbolization, and diagram then reveal the validity of the argument:

> No Christians (C) are freethinkers (F), and some Unitarians (U) are freethinkers. Therefore some Unitarians are not Christians.

$$(CF = 0 \cdot UF \neq 0) \supset U\bar{C} \neq 0.$$

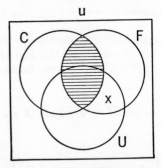

FIGURE 56–4

A somewhat different procedure must be adopted for any inference in which a particular conclusion is deduced from purely universal premises. Such an inference cannot really be tested unless we first determine whether or not the universal premises are existential. Consider the following argument:

> Lutherans are Protestants, and they are also Christians. Hence some Christians are Protestants.

This argument appears to be valid. But if we interpret the universal premises as hypothetical (nonexistential), the conclusion will obviously not follow. Stated simply, no cross for particular membership appears on a diagram containing only lined-out classes. Since, however, the assumption that there is membership in the class of "Lutherans" will undoubtedly be granted, the premises must be symbolized and diagramed as existential:

$$(L\bar{P} = 0 \cdot L\bar{C} = 0 \cdot L \neq 0) \supset CP \neq 0.$$

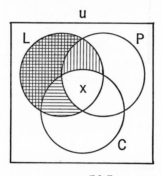

FIGURE 56-5

We see, as we had suspected, that the argument is valid. And as a general rule, if an argument contains purely universal premises and a particular conclusion, we must try assuming membership in each of the classes involved (when justified by our factual knowledge), and then see whether or not the conclusion follows. In the argument above, only one existential premise was added, because this premise happened to assign membership to all three classes in question. But when this is not so, each of the universal premises must be given an existential interpretation, if this is factually permissible, even though only one of these interpretations proves necessary.

Of course, adding existential premises to the type of inference we are discussing will not guarantee validity. The following argument, for example, as the accompanying symbolization and diagram will show, is invalid.

All Lutherans and Fundamentalists are Protestants, and consequently some Lutherans are Fundamentalists.

$$(L\bar{P} = 0 \cdot F\bar{P} = 0 \cdot L \neq 0 \cdot F \neq 0) \supset LF \neq 0.$$

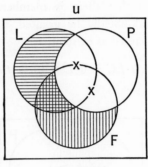

FIGURE 56–6

EXERCISES

Symbolize and diagrammatically test each of the following inferences for validity.

1. All football players are helped financially, and Tom Jones is a football player. It follows that Tom is helped financially.
2. Since all football players are helped financially, and Tom Jones receives financial help, he must therefore be a football player.
3. Anyone who associates with communists is a communist himself. And since many FBI men associate with communists, they themselves must be communists.*
4. Some degraded creatures are noble. For man is both degraded and noble.*
5. No girl who uses Liquid Velvet Bath Salts will fail to become engaged. But Dorothy doesn't use Liquid Velvet Bath Salts, and so will not be able to get a man.
6. Some men are primates, since men and primates both are mammals.
7. The Milwaukee Braves can't win the pennant, because the team

must drink a lot of beer. After all, beer drinkers can't play really good baseball and only a good team can win a pennant.

8. Many best-selling novels are not worth buying, since they are books that need be read only once. And no book that requires only one reading is worth buying.

9. Nearly all best-selling novels are not worth buying, since all but a few are books that require only one reading. And no such book is worth buying.

10. Cubans are Latin-Americans and hence speak Spanish. For all Latin-Americans speak Spanish.

11. Newton was a scientist and, therefore, he was an absent-minded thinker. For scientists are thinkers and these are always absent-minded.

12. From Spinoza's statement that "all things excellent are as difficult as they are rare" may be deduced the statement, "Some rare things are difficult."

13. Not all psychotics are unhappy and so not all are to be pitied. For no man who is happy need be pitied.

14. Any man who lies to his wife is a man who insults her intelligence. But any man who tells his wife the truth is a man who insults her vanity. And, of course, men who insult their wives land in the doghouse. I lie to my wife and you tell your wife the truth. The result is that we both insult our wives and find ourselves in the doghouse.

15. Anyone with both a door key and the combination of the safe is a suspect in this burglary. Jones has a key but not the combination. However, Taylor has both the key and the combination, while Smith has only the combination. No person without the key, nor anybody without the combination, can have committed the burglary. We may conclude, therefore, that neither Jones nor Smith, but only Taylor, is a suspect.

57 PURE TELESCOPED INFERENCES

57.1 Telescoped Inference in General

Arguments appearing in ordinary discourse are almost always *telescoped*—that is, abbreviated by omitting either a premise or conclusion. Telescoped inferences, or *enthymemes,* as such inferences are called in Aristotelian logic, are much more natural-sounding than the arguments we have so far examined in Part Four. The complete, formal statement of an inference, for most purposes, seems artificial and pedantic, and so is seldom used in common argumentation. We ordinarily omit a premise because it is sufficiently evident without explicit statement. And when we omit a conclusion, it is usually for rhetorical effect, the implication being that everybody should be able to draw so obvious a conclusion.

Before a telescoped inference can be evaluated by the techniques we have learned, the missing, or *suppressed,* proposition must be brought into the argument. Clearly, the ability to detect suppressed propositions, especially if they are premises, has great practical value. Human reasoning is shot through with unexpressed assumptions and presuppositions that must be understood and formulated if the reasoning is to be critically examined. Most telescoped inferences can be made valid, if one adds the appropriate premise. But more than validity is at issue here. For, as we know, to be assured of the truth of a conclusion not only valid reasoning is required, but also true premises. In a study of formal logic we cannot, of course, learn to distinguish between true and false premises. But before a start can be made toward determining such truth or falsity, we must know *what* the premises are. Proficiency in bringing suppressed premises to light, so that the question of truth at least may arise, is a skill that can be acquired during the study of formal logic.

57.2 Requirements of a Suppressed Premise

Little difficulty will be encountered in treating inferences with a suppressed *conclusion*. The suppressed proposition is usually quite apparent, and may readily be supplied. If the intended conclusion is in doubt, however, a Venn diagram on which the premises have been entered will reveal, if not the intended conclusion, at least some plausible conclusion.

Suppressed *premises* are often more difficult to detect. If the statement of a suppressed premise is seen immediately upon inspection of a telescoped inference, then, of course, this premise should be introduced into the inference at once and, if necessary, the usual testing techniques applied. However, when the suppressed premise is not immediately evident, instead of adopting a hit-and-miss procedure, we might better apply the knowledge of logic we have so far acquired to find systematically the appropriate premise. Take, for example, the following inference:

> Organized religions may be examined scientifically, because they are social institutions.

We see that each of the propositions in this inference is universal affirmative, and that the first proposition, as indicated by the term "because," is a conclusion, while the second proposition is a premise. Hence, we may rephrase the inference:

> All organized religions are social institutions. Therefore, all organized religions are objects of scientific examination.

As now stated, the inference is clearly telescoped, for the conclusion refers to "objects of scientific examination," a class which is not even mentioned in the premise. Before the inference can be evaluated, then, either for the truth of its premises or for validity, we must supply the premise that has been suppressed. We may begin by eliminating any premise which does not satisfy the following two conditions:

(i) No premise may be chosen that will make the argument invalid when there is available some alternative premise that will yield a valid argument. The inference must be held innocent of purely logical error, so to speak, until proven guilty.

(ii) No premise may be chosen that renders any given premise superfluous in drawing the given conclusion. In other words, we must assume that the word "therefore" connecting premise and conclusion in the telescoped inference above is meaningful, and that the proposition represented as a premise is a necessary element of the inference. Thus, for example, the obverse of the conclusion, "No organized religions are outside the scope of scientific examination," cannot be supplied as the intended premise because, even though a valid inference results, no use is made of the premise already furnished.

57.3 Diagrammatic Discovery of a Suppressed Premise

These two conditions narrow the choice of premises enough so that the missing premise is probably evident at this point and may be introduced into the argument. If the completed inference is still not apparent, however, or if we wish to confirm our notion as to what premise is required, we may continue the process of elimination by referring to a Venn diagram. This must be a special diagram, picturing not only the given premise but also the conclusion. In this way, we can more easily see what is needed for drawing the conclusion, together with what is supplied by the given premise. However, to ensure that this preliminary diagram is not mistaken for a test of validity, we must represent the conclusion in a special way, thus permitting us to distinguish it from the premise. Using the abbreviations R for "organized religions," I for "social institutions," and S for "objects of scientific examination," we may symbolize and diagram the telescoped argument above as in Fig. 57-1.

$$R\bar{I} = 0 \supset R\bar{S} = 0$$

On this diagram the given premise, $R\bar{I} = 0$, has been entered, and the conclusion, $R\bar{S} = 0$, has been depicted by means of slanted lines, indicating that it is not a premise but a proposition to be reached or yielded by the premises. The given premise, represented by hori-

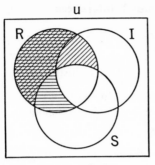

FIGURE 57-1

zontal shading, accomplishes part of what is demanded by the conclusion, since it empties the class $R\overline{IS}$. The suppressed premise, then,
need empty only the class $RI\overline{S}$. This can be done by any one of three
premises: "All R are S" ($R\overline{S} = 0$), "No R are I" ($RI = 0$), or "All
I are S" ($I\overline{S} = 0$). However, the first is the same proposition as the
conclusion and, since it makes no use of the given premise, is unsatisfactory; so too is the second, because taken in conjunction with
the given premise, it would empty the entire class R ("organized
religions") and thus prevent the conclusion from being interpreted
as existential. We are left, therefore, with the third possibility, "All
I are S," which proposition, when entered on the diagram, is seen to
satisfy the conditions we have imposed and to render the inference
valid:

$$(I\overline{S} = 0 \cdot R\overline{I} = 0) \supset R\overline{S} = 0$$

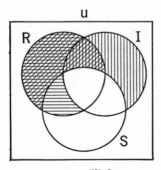

FIGURE 57-2

57.4 Invalid Telescoped Inferences

The diagrammatic technique of uncovering suppressed premises is especially useful in detecting the *invalidity* of a telescoped inference. Suppose that the previous illustration had read

> All fundamentalist churches (*C*) are organized religions (*R*), and therefore all organized religions are objects of scientific examination (*S*).

The symbolization and diagram now are as follows:

$$C\bar{R} = 0 \supset R\bar{S} = 0$$

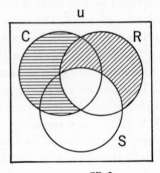

FIGURE 57-3

An inspection of this diagram makes it clear that no other premise *in conjunction with* the given premise will yield the required conclusion. The given premise, in other words, does not even empty a part of the class $R\bar{S}$, and therefore can be of no use whatever in deducing the proposition $R\bar{S} = 0$. But the inference is stated in such a way that $C\bar{R} = 0$ is given as a *reason* for $R\bar{S} = 0$. Hence, since there actually is no logical connection between these two propositions, the inference may be pronounced invalid.

EXERCISES

Introduce the suppressed premise or conclusion into each

of the following inferences, when necessary, and test the inferences for validity.

1. All European movies are realistic, and, therefore, all French movies are the same.

2. Health insurance programs are socialistic. It follows, therefore, that socialistic measures are to be condemned.

3. Democrats are socialists in disguise, because they are working for a welfare state.

4. Since no politicians have entirely blameless records, every politician has something to hide.

5. People who read *Das Kapital* are Marxists, and every professor of economics reads the book.

6. Babies, since they are naturally cunning, are always spoiled.

7. Whales are mammals because they are warm-blooded.

8. Every warm-blooded animal is a vertebrate, hence jellyfish are not vertebrates.

9. Doing whatever is not our duty is always a pleasant kind of activity, for only duties are unpleasant.

10. Whatever we desire is pleasant; hence whatever we find pleasant is good.

11. Smoking causes an irritation of lung tissue, and this produces lung cancer.

12. All smokers are risking lung cancer, because smoking irritates the lungs.

13. Military men are trained for war and thus are not experts in social legislation.

14. Cinderella-type characters are products of immature female dreams and therefore do not exist.

15. "Our ideas reach no farther than our experience. We have no experience of divine attributes and operations: I need not conclude my syllogism. You can draw the inference yourself." (Hume's *Dialogues*.)

58 MIXED TELESCOPED INFERENCES

58.1 Pure and Mixed Telescoped Inferences

The inferences examined in the last chapter, since they involve only universal premises and conclusions, may be called *pure* telescoped inferences. In general, any telescoped inference containing a universal conclusion requires a universal proposition as its suppressed premise, for only a universal proposition will empty the appropriate class of membership.

Similarly, the complete statement of a telescoped inference with a particular or singular conclusion will require at least one premise asserting the same kind of membership. This sort of telescoped inference will ordinarily be *mixed,* because the singular or particular premise must be supplemented by a *universal* premise that forces the given membership into the proper class. Only when the conclusion is a *conjunctive* particular or singular proposition will we have to consider the possibility that the inference is pure. Since particular or singular inferences of the pure type are rare in ordinary argumentation, we may restrict our attention in this chapter to mixed telescoped inferences.

58.2 Telescoped Inferences With Particular Conclusions

The following represents a very common form of telescoped inference:

> Some wrestling matches are not fixed, because professional wrestlers are often seriously injured.

It is clear that the conclusion, "Some wrestling matches are not fixed," cannot be deduced from the single given premise. But we see that this argument, like most inferences, is telescoped, and that a suppressed premise must be added before a pronouncement as to validity can be made. If the suppressed premise is not at once apparent, we may paraphrase, symbolize, and draw the special diagram we have devised for treating telescoped inferences.

Some professional wrestling matches (W) are sporting events in which the participants are seriously injured (I). Therefore some professional wrestling matches are not fixed (F).

$$WI \neq 0 \supset W\bar{F} \neq 0$$

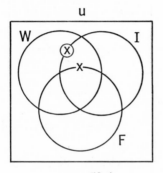

FIGURE 58–1

The conclusion is pictured on this diagram by means of a circled cross so that it will not be confused with the particular premise. We see now that the suppressed premise in order to make use of the given premise must force the membership on the line between WIF and $WI\bar{F}$ into the latter class, $WI\bar{F}$, thus ensuring the membership in $W\bar{F}$ demanded by the conclusion. Either of two premises will accomplish this: "No W are F" ($WF = 0$), or "No I are F" ($IF = 0$). The first will not do, however, because it yields the conclusion by subalternation, and thus does not, as at first appears, make use of the given premise. (In other words, the conclusion, "Some wrestling matches are not fixed," follows by subalternation from the presumably existential premise "No wrestling matches are fixed.") The only satisfactory alternative, then, is the premise "No I are F"—"No sporting events in which the participants are injured are fixed events." And this premise, as we see by entering it on the diagram, renders the argument valid without violating the conditions we have imposed upon suppressed premises:

$$(IF = 0 \cdot WI \neq 0) \supset W\bar{F} \neq 0$$

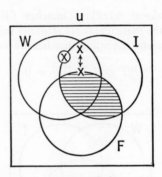

FIGURE 58–2

Perhaps the cynical observer of professional wrestling will feel that there is still something wrong with this argument. But this feeling, since the inference is clearly valid, must be traced to doubt of the truth of the supplied premise. Thus, as previously suggested, even though most telescoped inferences may be made valid, in supplying premises we are often permitted to detect a dubious presupposition of the inference.

It is always possible, of course, that a telescoped inference will turn out to be invalid. Suppose that our cynic with respect to wrestling matches were to deny the premise introduced into the above argument, and conclude that some wrestling matches only appear to involve serious injury to the participants, but do not really do so. His argument then would be stated and tested in the following way:

> Some sporting events involving injury to the participants (I) are fixed (F). Therefore, some wrestling matches (W) are not events involving injury to the participants.

$$IF \neq 0 \supset W\bar{I} \neq 0$$

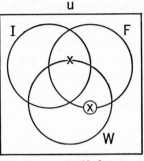

FIGURE 58–3

A glance at the diagram reveals that a suppressed premise might push the membership in *IF* into *IFW*, but no premise can move the membership entirely out of *I*, as required by the conclusion. The inference, therefore, is invalid, and no matter whether the premises are true or false, we cannot depend upon the truth of the conclusion.

58.3 Telescoped Inferences With Singular Conclusions

Mixed telescoped inferences in support of singular conclusions require a singular and a universal premise. A diagrammatic examination of the following telescoped inference is probably superfluous, since the suppressed premise is obvious. But the appended diagram reveals that the same principles of discovery are applicable:

Professional wrestlers (W) are all good showmen (S), so the Gorgeous Greek (s) is a good showman.

$$W\bar{S} = 0 \supset s \in S$$

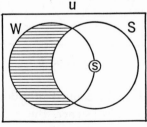

FIGURE 58–4

A singular premise has been suppressed in this inference, and we see on the diagram that if the singular member is located in W, the universal premise will force it into class S. The suppressed premise therefore is "The Gorgeous Greek is a wrestler," and when this premise is entered on the diagram, the inference is seen to be valid:

$$(s \, \epsilon \, W \cdot W\bar{S} = 0) \supset s \, \epsilon \, S$$

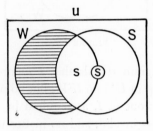

FIGURE 58-5

It is interesting to observe that a slight change in the foregoing argument will render it invalid:

Professional wrestlers are all good showmen, so the Gorgeous Greek is a professional wrestler.

$$W\bar{S} = 0 \supset s \, \epsilon \, W$$

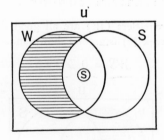

FIGURE 58-6

This inference, stated in the context of ordinary discussion, might easily deceive an incautious listener. But a close inspection of the diagram shows that the given premise contributes nothing toward a proof of the conclusion. Various other premises will, of course, yield the conclusion. For example, $s \in W$ may be deduced from $s \in WS$ or from the conjunction $s \in S \cdot S\overline{W} = 0$. But these premises do not make use of the given premise $W\overline{S} = 0$, and hence the inference may be written off as invalid.

EXERCISES

Symbolize each of the following inferences and test them for validity. Use the diagrammatic method of discovering the suppressed propositions of telescoped inferences.

1. Lake Erie is a fresh-water lake because it is one of the Great Lakes.
2. Prize fighters have tender noses, and that is why Rocky's nose is tender.
3. Some laws are not just, since many are discriminatory.
4. Since Albert Einstein was an outspoken and honest man, he was a much maligned man.
5. Many poor people, because carefree, are happy.
6. She must be on a diet, for she has lost weight.
7. Nothing that lowers the standard of living is welcome, and taxes sometimes do just this.
8. Mexico is not a totalitarian state, because such states do not permit freedom of speech.
9. Anyone who is ill cannot think clearly; hence, no clear-thinking people are ill.
10. That man drinks occasionally, and so is a potential alcoholic.
11. But that other man never touches a drop, and anyone like that is a potential prude.
12. Many intelligent people, because of financial reasons, are not educated.
13. Useful scientific discoveries open new fields of inquiry, whereas scientific baubles never do this. Sputnik, therefore, is not a scientific bauble.

14. Anyone lacking religious convictions will make a bad statesman. John Foster Dulles, therefore, is not a bad statesman.

15. No man knowingly does evil [according to Plato], because no man knowingly seeks his own pain.

59 THE SYMBOLIC EXPANSION TEST

A *decision procedure* in logic is a method of determining the validity of expressions or inferences within a given conceptual system. Hence, the Venn-diagram technique is a decision procedure for certain types of inferences in the logic of classes. The Venn-diagram procedure, however, may only be applied to arguments containing three, or at most (if circles are replaced by overlapping ellipses) four class terms. In this chapter, we shall examine a *symbolic* decision procedure that can apply, if necessary, to inferences comprising any number of class terms. It will be appropriate, as we shall see, to call this new procedure the *symbolic expansion test*.

59.1 Pure Inferences

Suppose we are given a pure compound inference of the following general form:

All *a* are *b* and all *b* are *c*. Therefore, all *a* are *c*.
$$(a\bar{b} = 0 \cdot b\bar{c} = 0) \supset a\bar{c} = 0.$$

An inspection of this argument discloses that three class terms are involved and that one of these terms is missing from each of the premises and from the conclusion. Since we know that the conclusion of a valid inference is necessarily implied in the statement of the premises, it seems that if we could expand each proposition to include the missing term, we could more easily compare premises with conclusion, thus determining whether the one is sufficient to yield the other.

In the following manner, any term whatsoever may be introduced into the symbolic statement of a proposition, without changing the meaning of the proposition. First, we must recognize as a law of the class logic

$$a = a\,(u).$$

This law states simply that any class a is coextensive with the product of the same class and the universe class. In other words, as may easily be seen on a Venn diagram, that which is common to a given class and its universe of discourse is only the given class itself. It follows then, since the product of $a\bar{b}$ and u is identical with $a\bar{b}$, that in the inference above, the first premise, $a\bar{b} = 0$, may be expressed without changing its meaning

$$a\bar{b}\,(u) = 0.$$

The universe class, as we have seen in Chapter 44, is coextensive with the sum of any class and its own complementary class—that is, $u = a + \bar{a}$. Since we wish to introduce the class c into the first premise, and since $c + \bar{c}$ is coextensive with u, we may rewrite the first premise as follows:

$$a\bar{b}\,(c + \bar{c}) = 0.$$

As a final step, we may apply one of the laws of distribution presented in Chapter 45, $a\,(b + c) = ab + ac$, in order to achieve what may be called the *expanded form* of the first premise:

$$a\bar{b}c + a\bar{b}\bar{c} = 0.$$

The meaning of this expanded proposition is precisely the same as that of its original form, $a\bar{b} = 0$, except that the class c is included. We still cannot determine whether the inference is valid, however, until the other premise and conclusion are expanded. A step-by-step expansion of the second premise, introducing the missing term a, is as follows:

(1) $b\bar{c} = 0$ (second premise)

(2) $b\bar{c}\,(u) = 0$ (substituting $b\bar{c}$ for a in $a\,(u) = a$, and using the rule of replacement)

(3) $b\bar{c}\,(a + \bar{a}) = 0$ (since $u = a + \bar{a}$)

(4) $b\bar{c}a + \overline{b\bar{c}a} = 0$ (substituting $b\bar{c}$ for a, a for b, and $\bar{a}$ for c in the law of distribution $a(b + c) = (ab + ac)$

(5) $ab\bar{c} + \bar{a}b\bar{c} = 0$ (using the law of commutation)

This last transformation, utilizing the law of commutation of logical products, $ab = ba$, arranges the variables so as to permit a ready comparison with the first premise.

The conclusion is similarly expanded to include the missing term b:

(1) $a\bar{c} = 0$ (conclusion)

(2) $a\bar{c}\,(u) = 0$ (because $a = a\,(u)$)

(3) $a\bar{c}\,(b + \bar{b}) = 0$ (because $u = b + \bar{b}$)

(4) $a\bar{c}b + \overline{a\bar{c}b} = 0$ (distribution)

(5) $ab\bar{c} + a\overline{b}\bar{c} = 0$ (commutation)

We may, at this point, state the argument in its completely expanded form, and, for convenience in testing a pure universal inference, draw a line through each of the classes mentioned in the conclusion if such class is ascertained from the premises to be empty of membership. The pure universal inference symbolized here, therefore, will be valid only if all the classes in the conclusion are empty —that is, lined out.

$$[(a\bar{b}c + \overline{a\bar{b}c} = 0)\cdot(ab\bar{c} + \bar{a}b\bar{c} = 0)] \supset (a\bar{b}c + a\bar{b}c = 0).$$

We now see that the argument is valid. For the first premise, as indicated by the arrow, empties the class $\overline{abc}$, and the second premise empties the class $ab\bar{c}$. Together, the premises empty the entire class asserted in the conclusion to be identical with the null class. Therefore, we may call the inference valid.

It is not necessary to state all the successive transformations between a proposition and its expanded form each time we use the symbolic expansion test. After the step-by-step derivation of an expanded-form proposition is understood, it becomes apparent that any product ab may directly be expanded to include any other class c simply by adding abc to $ab\bar{c}$.

Consider, for example, the following general form of inference:

All a are b and no c are a. Therefore, no c are b.

The inference is symbolized below and expanded directly, and, for the purpose of comparing propositions, the variables in the second premise and conclusion are rearranged as permitted by the law of commutation.

$$(a\bar{b} = 0 \cdot ca = 0) \supset cb = 0,$$

$$[(a\bar{b}c + a\overline{bc} = 0) \cdot (abc + a\bar{b}c = 0)] \supset (abc + \bar{a}bc = 0).$$

Inspection of this inference discloses that it is invalid. The class abc in the conclusion, to be sure, is indicated as empty in the second premise. But the remaining class in the conclusion, $\bar{a}bc$, is not mentioned in the premises. Since we do not know from the premises whether this class has membership or not, the stated conclusion does not necessarily follow.

59.2 Mixed Inferences

Let us consider a representative inference containing both universal and particular propositions:

All a are b and some c are a. Therefore, some c are b.

Symbolizing and expanding, we get:

$$(a\dot{b} = 0 \cdot ca \neq 0) \supset cb \neq 0,$$

$$[(a\bar{b}c + a\overline{bc} = 0) \cdot (abc + a\bar{b}c \neq 0)] \supset (abc + \bar{a}bc \neq 0).$$

The class $\bar{a}bc$ in the particular premise has been crossed out, showing that it is one of the classes asserted to be empty by the universal premise. Hence, the membership asserted by the particular premise must be in abc. Since this class is also mentioned in the conclusion, it follows that the more inclusive class $abc + \bar{a}bc$ has membership. The conclusion, therefore, is necessarily implied by the premises, and the argument is valid. A decision as to the validity of an argument such as this may be reached, with a little practice, in about the same time it takes to draw a Venn diagram.

The same principles apply in testing a mixed inference containing singular propositions. Take the following example:

No a are b and s is an a. Therefore s is not a b.

Only two classes are involved in this argument, a and b. Since the universal premise already contains mention of these two classes, we need expand only the singular premise and conclusion. The symbolization and expansion, therefore, are as follows:

$$(ab = 0 \cdot s \,\epsilon\, a) \supset s \,\epsilon\, \bar{b},$$

$$[ab = 0 \cdot s \,\epsilon\, (\cancel{ab} + a\bar{b})] \supset s \,\epsilon\, \overrightarrow{(ab + \overline{ab})}.$$

Class a in the singular premise of this inference is expanded to include b, and $\bar{b}$ in the conclusion is expanded to include a. The universal premise tells us that ab is empty, and so we may line it out in the singular premise. Therefore the singular member s must be in $a\bar{b}$. But if s is in $a\bar{b}$, then it is also contained in the more comprehensive class $a\bar{b} + \overline{ab}$. It follows that the conclusion is deducible from the premises, and the inference is valid.

EXERCISES

   A. Use the symbolic-expansion method to test the validity of each of the inferences listed in the exercises at the end of Chapters 55 and 56.

   B. Given the (hypothetical universal) proposition "No good

listeners are poor conversationalists," determine whether each of the following propositions (i) is *equivalent* to the given proposition, (ii) is a *contradictory* of the given proposition, (iii) is *implied by* the given proposition, (iv) *implies* the given proposition, or (v) is *not related* in any of these ways to the given proposition.

1. No poor conversationalists are good listeners.
2. No good listeners are conversationalists.*
3. Some good listeners are poor conversationalists.
4. Some listeners are poor conversationalists.
5. No conversationalists are listeners.
6. No good listeners are both poor and boring conversationalists.
7. No good listeners are poor or boring conversationalists.
8. No good conversationalists are poor listeners.
9. A few poor listeners are good conversationalists.
10. All good listeners are poor conversationalists.
11. Good listeners are the opposite of poor conversationalists.
12. Some good listeners are not poor conversationalists.

60 THE SHORTER SYMBOLIC EXPANSION TEST

For determining the validity of inferences containing more than three variables—inferences, that is, to which the Venn diagram technique cannot be applied—the symbolic expansion test is a little cumbersome. The expansion of a proposition composed of two class terms to include two other terms, for example, is a sum of four products, each of which contains four class terms. However, our application of the symbolic expansion test has thus far been unnecessarily laborious. We have been expanding all the propositions in an argument, whereas ordinarily the expansion of only one proposition is required. Before we examine this shorter version of the expansion test, we must recognize the validity of three simple laws of the class logic:

$$\text{(i)} \quad a = 0 \supset ab = 0,$$

$$\text{(ii)} \quad ab \neq 0 \supset a \neq 0,$$

$$\text{(iii)} \quad s \; \epsilon \; ab \supset s \; \epsilon \; a.$$

The first law states that if any class a is empty, then any part of that class—say ab (or abc or $abcd$)—is also empty. The second and third laws state that if any class ab has membership, particular or singular, then any class which includes ab—for example, the class a (or b)—also possesses membership of the same quantity. The validity of these laws may be easily seen on a Venn diagram.

60.1 Pure Inferences

With Law (i) in mind, it is easy to see that a pure universal inference may be tested by expanding only the *conclusion*. One of the examples of a pure inference used in the last chapter was

All a are b and all b are c. Therefore, all a are c.

We may symbolize this inference in the conventional way, and then expand only the conclusion:

$$(a\bar{b} = 0 \cdot b\bar{c} = 0) \supset a\bar{c} = 0,$$

$$(a\bar{b} = 0 \cdot b\bar{c} = 0) \supset (a\bar{b}\bar{c} + ab\bar{c} = 0).$$

We know that class $ab\bar{c}$ in the conclusion is a part of $b\bar{c}$, said in the second premise to be empty, and that $a\overline{bc}$ in the conclusion is a part of $a\bar{b}$, said to be empty in the first premise. Thus, since we know also that any part of an empty class is empty, we are justified in lining out the two classes in the conclusion and calling the inference valid.

As may be seen by the following inference and symbolization, the shorter expansion test reveals *invalidity* in a similar way.

All *a* are *b* and all *c* are *b*. Therefore, all *c* are *a*.

$$(a\bar{b} = 0 \cdot c\bar{b} = 0) \supset c\bar{a} = 0,$$

$$(a\bar{b} = 0 \cdot \bar{b}c = 0) \supset (\bar{a}bc + \overline{a}bc = 0).$$

The order of variables in both the second premise and expanded conclusion has been rearranged so that a comparison of propositions can more easily be made. We are informed in the second premise that $\bar{b}c$ is empty, and, therefore, we may line out $\overline{abc}$ in the conclusion, since this latter class is a part of $\bar{b}c$. But nowhere in the premises do we find that $\bar{a}bc$, the other class mentioned in the conclusion, is empty. The conclusion, therefore, does not necessarily follow from the premises, and the inference is invalid.

60.2 Mixed Inferences

In the ordinary valid inference of the mixed type, the universal premise empties a part of the class to which the particular or singular premise assigns membership, thus forcing this membership into a class mentioned in the conclusion as having membership. It is, therefore the *particular* or *singular premise* of a mixed inference that must be expanded in order to apply the shorter version of the symbolic expansion test. To illustrate, the following singular inference is symbolized and only its singular premise expanded.

All *a* are *b* and *s* is an *a*. Therefore, *s* is a *b*.

$$(a\bar{b} = 0 \cdot s \,\epsilon\, a) \supset s \,\epsilon\, b,$$

$$[a\bar{b} = 0 \cdot s \,\epsilon\, (ab + a\bar{b})] \supset s \,\epsilon\, b.$$

The class $a\bar{b}$ in the expanded premise has been lined out, as demanded by the universal premise. It follows that the singular member *s* must be in *ab*. If *s* is a member of *ab*, then, by the law mentioned earlier in this chapter ($s \,\epsilon\, ab \supset s \,\epsilon\, a$), it is also a member of any class such as *b* which includes *ab*. The conclusion, therefore, has been validly drawn from the premises.

A similar line of reasoning may be applied in testing a mixed particular inference:

No a are b and some c are a. Therefore, some c are not b.

Once more, we symbolize and then restate the symbolized version, expanding only the premise that asserts membership:

$$(ab = 0 \cdot ca \neq 0) \supset c\bar{b} \neq 0,$$

$$[ab = 0 \cdot (a\bar{b}c + abc \neq 0)] \supset \bar{b}c \neq 0.$$

If ab is empty, then abc, which is a part of ab, is also empty, and we may line it out in the particular premise. This forces the membership into $a\bar{b}c$, which is included in $\bar{b}c$. Thus, if $a\bar{b}c$ has membership, so does $\bar{b}c$, and the inference is valid.

The shorter symbolic expansion test is particularly useful in testing mixed arguments in which a particular conclusion is deduced from two or more universal premises. Take, for example, the inference:

All a are b and no a are c. Therefore, some b are not c.

We have seen previously that a particular conclusion may be deduced from universal premises only if at least one of the premises is existential. If we suppose membership in the class a, the proper symbolization is as follows:

$$(a\bar{b} = 0 \cdot ac = 0 \cdot a \neq 0) \supset b\bar{c} \neq 0.$$

For applying the shorter expansion technique to mixed inferences, the general rule has been that only the premise asserting membership need be expanded. The problem now is to expand $a \neq 0$ so that the *two* missing classes, b and c, are mentioned. However, as the following step-by-step expansion will show, no new principles are required in accomplishing this task:

(1) $a \neq 0$ (particular premise)

(2) $a \, (u) \neq 0$ (because $a = a \, (u)$)

(3) $a \, (b + \bar{b}) \neq 0$ (because $u = b + \bar{b}$)

(4) $ab + a\bar{b} \neq 0$ (distribution)

(5) $ab\,(u) + a\bar{b}\,(u) \neq 0$ (note that *both* products must now be expanded to include c)

(6) $[ab\,(c + \bar{c})] + [a\bar{b}\,(c + \bar{c})] \neq 0$ (because $u = c + \bar{c}$)

(7) $abc + ab\bar{c} + a\bar{b}c + a\overline{bc} \neq 0$ (distribution)

It will be observed that the products conjoined to a in the final expanded form, bc, $b\bar{c}$, $\bar{b}c$, and $\overline{bc}$, exhaust the universe of discourse. A single variable or class abbreviation may, therefore, always be directly expanded to include two other classes in the same way, without going through the time-consuming intermediate steps.

We are now in a position to restate the inference that occasioned this digression, expanding only the particular premise:

$$[a\bar{b} = 0 \cdot ac = 0 \cdot (a\!\!\!/bc + ab\bar{c} + a\!\!\!/\bar{b}c + a\!\!\!/\bar{b}\bar{c} \neq 0)] \supset b\bar{c} \neq 0.$$

The two universal premises empty three of the four classes mentioned in the particular premise. Therefore, only $ab\bar{c}$ can possess the asserted membership, and $b\bar{c}$, said to have membership in the conclusion, is a class which contains $ab\bar{c}$. The inference, consequently, is valid.

EXERCISES

A. Some of the following inferences cannot be tested by means of a Venn diagram. Use the shorter symbolic expansion test to determine the validity of each inference.

1. Some Republicans who are not stockholders are not farmers, because farmers are all landowners, and some Republicans are neither stockholders nor landowners.

2. Any suspect in this case is a person who was both home at the time of the murder and had a motive for the crime. However, only people without a motive were home at the time. Hence, there is no suspect in this case.

3. All bank robbers are criminals and all professionals are clever.

Therefore, all clever bank robbers are professional criminals.

4. All bank robbers are criminals and all professionals are clever. Therefore, all professional bank robbers are clever criminals.

5. Brake troubles are due to either a leaky hydraulic system or worn brake linings. Your brakes are bad, but the pedal doesn't fade to the floor. Only when brakes fade is there a leak in the system, and so you need new linings.

6. This television set has a lighted screen but no picture and no sound. Any set with no sound has a bad audio, tuner, or video tube. But a bad audio tube would not affect the picture, and the absence of sound is not due to a faulty video tube. This set, therefore, has a bad tube in the tuner section.

7. The world must have a beginning in time. For anything that has no beginning in time is something that has endured from eternity. But whatever is eternal is characterized by an infinite temporal series and all infinite temporal series are such that they are never completed in time. The world, however, (to the present moment) is completed in time. And, therefore, the world must have a beginning in time. *Q.E.D.*

8. The world can have no beginning in time. For any world (in general) that has a beginning in time is a world preceded by an empty time (*i.e.,* a time in which the world did not exist). Now every world is such that it requires a cause of its existence (rather than its nonexistence). But no world preceded by an empty time is one that can have a cause of its existence. And since our world is a member of the class of worlds in general, the world can have no beginning in time. *Q.E.D.* (This and the preceding argument are rough paraphrases of a part of Kant's First Antinomy, *Critique of Pure Reason.*)

B. Each of the propositions in List II may be deduced from two or more of the assumptions in List I. Select those premises from List I (or from deductions you have already established) that will yield each proposition in List II, symbolize the resulting inference, and show its validity either by diagrams or symbolic expansions.

List I: Assumptions

1. All events are either self-caused or have prior events as causes.
2. No event is prior to itself.
3. Only something prior to itself is self-caused.
4. All events having prior events as causes are chains of events.
5. All chains of events are themselves events and are finite.
6. Every finite chain of events has a first cause.
7. The world is a chain of events.

List II: Consequences

1. No events are self-caused.
2. All events have prior events as causes.
3. All events are chains of events.
4. An event is the same thing as a chain of events.
5. No chains of events are self-caused.
6. Nothing that is prior to itself is a chain of events.
7. Every chain of events has prior events as causes.
8. A chain of events is identical with something having prior events as causes.
9. Any event is identical with something having prior events as causes.
10. Nothing having prior events as causes is prior to itself.
11. Nothing that is self-caused has prior events as causes.
12. Anything having prior events as causes is finite.
13. All events are finite.
14. Some finite things are not prior to themselves.
15. Some things that are not self-caused are not infinite.
16. All events have a first cause.
17. Anything having prior events as causes has a first cause.
18. All chains of events have a first cause.
19. Some things having a first cause are not self-caused.
20. The world is an event.
21. The world is finite.
22. The world has prior events as causes.
23. The world is not self-caused.

24. The world is not prior to itself.
25. The world has a first cause.

(The list of assumptions is based on, but not entirely in accord with, St. Thomas Aquinas's *Summa Theologica,* Pt. I, Quest. 2, Art. 3)

    C. Supplementing the assumptions in List I (Exercise B) by this one proposition: "All first causes are (themselves) events," deduce from this list at least twenty additional consequences.

61 A LOOK AHEAD

The student, of course, will realize that the developments in modern logic are far more extensive than those presented in this book. Great advances in logical theory have been made during the present century, and applications of this theory have been made in fields ranging from the exact science of physics to the uncomfortably inexact study of jurisprudence. A few of the more dramatic applications, such as to the construction of "thinking machines," have become matters of popular knowledge, and today the name "symbolic logic" seems even to be entering the select class of science-fiction terms.

Whether or not the revolutionary applications of symbolic logic imagined by science-fiction writers will ever become a reality is, of course, an open question. But a few of the developments that show unusual promise of fruitful application should be mentioned here, both to indicate the limits of this textbook, and to suggest the directions in which a further study of logic would lead.

One very interesting development has been the construction of *many-valued logics*. The reader with some training in semantics perhaps felt uneasy about the apparent "two-valued orientation" of the logical systems we have studied. Even though propositions may really be either true or false, he may ask, still, if we limit ourselves to our *knowledge* of their truth or falsity, are we not ordinarily restricted to speaking in terms of probabilities and *degrees* of truth-value? To answer this question, logicians have devised systems ranging from three-valued logics, with "problematical" as a third value, to *n*-valued logics, incorporating any number of additional values. Of particular interest are the so-called *modal logics*, supplementing the two-valued logic with such notions as possibility, impossibility, necessity, consistency, and so on.

Not only do many-valued and modal logics remain to be investigated, but also no techniques have as yet been discussed for incorporating several common types of proposition into logical theory. For example, in the logic of classes we studied the relationship of identity between classes and of singular membership in a class, but we have not mentioned the relationship of identity between names designating singular members, a topic covered in the *logic of identity*. Nor have we looked into the *logic of descriptions*, in which is treated the matter of complex singular names, involving terms that are used to describe other terms. We have not examined propositions asserting relationships *in general* between two or more terms, a task that would require us either to take up the *logic of relations* or at least to extend the logic of propositional functions to include more than one term variable (in which case the "predicate" variable f becomes a relation holding between, say, two term variables x and y).

More striking, perhaps, than the recent developments in the logical treatment of relations, identity, and descriptions are the proposals to extend the apparatus of symbolic logic beyond its usual applications and into the domain of expressive and directive language. Some logicians feel that the nondescriptive functions of language reveal their own patterns of meaning-relationships which, although different from descriptive relationships, are not in any basic sense "illogical." Especially, attempts have been made to ferret out the logical structure of *normative* language, setting up norms or standards of behavior, and identified by the presence of such words as "ought," "good," "right," "beautiful," "just," and "value." Perhaps the greatest obstacle to these attempts is the problem of whether normative language is mainly descriptive, expressive, or directive, or whether it functions characteristically in all three ways at the same time. Whatever is eventually agreed upon, however, it seems apparent that logical features are present in moral, esthetic, juridical, and other types of normative discourse, and that these features may be investigated and systematized by the techniques of modern formal logic.

Not only have new applications of symbolic logic been made, but investigations of logical systems themselves have been prominent during recent decades. In this textbook formal logic is explained in a manner calculated to show the logical structure of ordinary discourse and argumentation. A more rigorous presentation would have demanded that the propositional, functional, and class logics be formulated as *deductive systems,* or more rigorously still, as *logistic* systems. A list of *primitive* (undefined) *symbols* would have been offered, and a set of *definitions* of nonprimitive symbols. Then, by means of carefully stated criteria of *well-formed* (significant) *formulas,* a set of *axioms* or *postulates* would be listed and, by means of our *rules of inference,* the argument forms we have studied would have been deduced as *theorems* within the system. Indeed, it would have been possible in this way to develop a single *uninterpreted* logistic system of which the logics of propositions, functions, and classes (as presented in this book) are three different interpretations. Moreover, using techniques made possible by this rigorous approach, we could determine whether or not our postulate set exhibits *independence* (containing no redundant postulates), whether or not the system is *consistent* (yielding no contradictory theorems), and whether or not it is a *deductively complete* system (capable of yielding as a theorem either any formula that is expressible within the system or the negation of such formula).

And still our study of modern logic would only have begun. We have said nothing about the close relationship between logic and mathematics—for example, how the concept of *number* can be defined by means of concepts taken from the logic of classes, and how the operations, relationships, and principles of pure mathematics can be derived from those of symbolic logic. Nor have we mentioned the antinomies and logical paradoxes that turn up when inquiry is pressed far enough into the construction of deductive systems, although these paradoxes and proposed solutions have been the subject of so extensive a body of literature that their study might be said to constitute a distinct, and rather a fascinating, area of logical inquiry. In pursuing such inquiry, however, we should probably find that a solution of the paradoxes entails a general *theory of signs,* involving a study not only of the formal relationships holding between signs (formal logic or *syntactics*), but also of the relationship of a sign to what it designates (*semantics*), and of the relationship of signs to the people who use or hear them (*pragmatics*).

But the person who is determined to know all about logic will still not be satisfied. He will begin to ask even more fundamental questions—questions peculiar to the *philosophy of logic*. What is the origin and nature of the laws of logic? How do they differ from laws of the empirical sciences? And how is it possible that the laws of logic in the broad sense (thus including the laws of pure mathematics), in view of their universal and necessary character, should so successfully be applied to matters of fact, which are never necessary and the universality of which we presumably could never determine? Precisely what, in other words, is the complex relationship between factually true and logically (or semantically) true propositions—not merely their characteristic features, nor how to distinguish between them, nor how each functions in human discourse, but rather a thorough account of the complex relationship between them? These and related questions in the philosophy of logic, to be sure, have stimulated discussion for at least two hundred years. If the controversial writing in the field is any indication, however, satisfactory answers have still to be offered.

However, the distinction between factual and logical truth suggests what is perhaps the most serious gap in the knowledge of **a** reader whose study of logic has begun with the present textbook. Throughout our examination of formal logic, we have been restricted to the distinction between valid and invalid inferences, and the only pronouncement we could make upon the actual *truth* of any proposition was the hypothetical assertion: *If* the premises of a valid argument are true, then we may rely upon the truth of its conclusion. These premises, of course, may be proved true as conclusions of additional valid arguments. But the additional arguments require new premises, which in turn (if we wish to avoid circular reasoning) require new arguments, *ad infinitum*. Clearly, then, the techniques of formal logic alone can never guarantee the truth of any conclusion. Validity, in other words, although a necessary condition, is not a sufficient condition of such truth. Formal logic must therefore be supplemented by another kind of logic—a logic not of validity, but of truth. This other kind of logic, as mentioned in the Introduction, is called *scientific methodology* or *inductive logic*.

The techniques of inductive logic are now often explained within the broader context of what John Dewey refers to as the method of *reflective inquiry*. When called upon to ascertain the truth of any proposition, we find ourselves in a *problem-situation,* the resolution of which may proceed along a number of different lines. We might accept or reject the truth of the proposition on simple, ungrounded *faith,* or by appealing uncritically to *authority,* or perhaps by resorting to a sophisticated doctrine of *intuition* or *self-evidence*. But the reflective or scientific inquirer after truth, according to Dewey, will try first to gather all the data that he thinks relevant to the problem at issue.

Gathering relevant data, however, is no simple matter, especially when the problem to be resolved is of a refined, scientific nature. The ability to detect what is relevant in the way of data is a talent that depends, not only upon training, but also upon scientific imagination and rare insight into the particular problem. Moreover, after the relevant data have been distinguished, these data must be organized systematically, calling very often for an application of modern techniques of *definition, classification, measurement,* and *statistics.* If the problem concerns the truth of a generalization, highly developed methods of *enumeration* and *sampling* also may be required.

Ordinarily, however, the scientist (or *any* reflective man, Dewey maintains) wants not only to establish the truth of some generalization, but also to arrive at a true *explanation* of the problematical events or objects that occasioned inquiry. During the process of gathering data, suggestions will crystallize into tentative explanations, or *hypotheses,* as they are called—a stage of inquiry so central to induction that the scientific method is sometimes known as the method of hypotheses. Ordinarily, of course, a plurality of hypotheses emerge from a study of the data, and when this happens, the competing hypotheses must be compared and critically evaluated. The preferred hypotheses are those more *adequate* in explaining the phenomena in question, or more *consistent* with prior knowledge in the field, or logically *simpler* (requiring fewer assumptions), or more *fruitful* in explaining problematical events in surrounding areas of inquiry.

But especially important in evaluating hypotheses is the criterion of *verifiability*. For if a hypothesis cannot be formulated in such a way as to permit consequences to be deduced and tested, no really conclusive decision as to its explanatory power can be made. This deduction and verification (or disverification) of consequences, by techniques previously mentioned or by *controlled experiment* or by some other form of *scientific observation,* constitutes the final stage of reflective inquiry and, if successful, will resolve satisfactorily the original problem-situation.

This account of inductive logic, although painfully brief, will perhaps suffice to indicate roughly its relationship to formal logic. Induction, one might say, thoroughly involves deduction. The techniques of deductive inference are inextricably bound up with methods of gathering data, with the formulation of hypotheses, and especially with the deduction and testing of consequences. Something of this intimate connection between induction and deduction is suggested by the study of formal logic, in which it becomes apparent that valid reasoning alone, without true premises, is not sufficient to establish the truth of a conclusion. Even in the process of establishing inductively the truth of premises, however, the principles and techniques of deductive logic must ordinarily be used. Induction and deduction, therefore, are mutually dependent. Deductive inference alone can never reveal any truth that is not already implied when a statement of premises is given, and inductive reasoning, if denied any employment of deduction, is narrowly restricted to the drawing of simple generalizations from the direct observation of factual events. Used in conjunction with each other, however, the methods of deductive and inductive logic constitute a unified and powerful instrument in the search for truth.

Suggestions for Further Reading

Copi, Irving M., *Symbolic Logic*. New York, 1954.
  A clear and simple continuation of the formal logic presented in this book. Especially good on the theory of deductive systems.
Quine, Willard V., *Mathematical Logic*. New York, 1940.
  An advanced, comprehensive treatise for the student who has mastered Copi's text or Quine's more elementary book, *Methods of Logic,* New York, 1950.
Lewis, C. I., *A Survey of Symbolic Logic*. Berkeley, Calif., 1918.
  Excellent early history of symbolic logic.
———— and Langford, C. H., *Symbolic Logic*. New York, 1932.
  Includes a standard system of modal logic.
Russell, Bertrand, *Introduction to Mathematical Philosophy*. London, 1919.
  An unusually clear exposition of the relationship between logic and mathematics.
Morris, Charles, *Signs, Language, and Behavior*. New York, 1946.
  A standard text of semantics and general theory of signs.
Woodger, J. H., *The Technique of Theory Construction,* International Encyclopedia of Unified Science, Vol. 2. Chicago, 1939.
Cohen, Morris, and Nagel, Ernest, *An Introduction to Logic and Scientific Method*. New York, 1934.
  Still a splendid introduction to scientific method.
Dewey, John, *How We Think*. New York, 1910.
  Dewey's method of reflective inquiry.

————— *Logic: The Theory of Inquiry.* New York, 1938.

A study in the philosophy of logic.

Ramsperger, A. G., *Philosophies of Science.* New York, 1942.

An exploration of the problems underlying the use of deductive
and inductive methods in the sciences.

APPENDIX A

SUMMARY OF BASIC LAWS
AND INFERENCES

I. Logic of Propositions

1. *Laws of Association*
   (i) $[p \cdot (q \cdot r)] \equiv [(p \cdot q) \cdot r]$
   (ii) $[p \lor (q \lor r)] \equiv [(p \lor q) \lor r]$
2. *Laws of Commutation*
   (i) $(p \cdot q) \equiv (q \cdot p)$
   (ii) $(p \lor q) \equiv (q \lor p)$
   (iii) $(p \olor q) \equiv (q \olor p)$
   (iv) $(p \equiv q) \equiv (q \equiv p)$
3. *Law of Counterimplication*
   $(p \supset q) \equiv (\sim q \supset \sim p)$
4. *Law of Double Negation*
   $p \equiv \sim\sim p$
5. *DeMorgan's Laws* (*cf.* I.7.(i) below)
   (i) $\sim(p \cdot q) \equiv (\sim p \lor \sim q)$
   (ii) $\sim(p \lor q) \equiv (\sim p \cdot \sim q)$
6. *"Laws of Thought"*
   (i) $p \equiv p$ (Identity)

(ii) $p \vee \sim p$ (Excluded Middle)

(iii) $\sim(p \cdot \sim p)$ (Contradiction)

7. *Useful Transformation Laws*

(i) $(p \supset q) \equiv (\sim p \vee q) \equiv \sim(p \cdot \sim q)$

(ii) $(p \otimes q) \equiv [(p \vee q) \cdot \sim(p \cdot q)]$

(iii) $(p \equiv q) \equiv [(p \supset q) \cdot (q \supset p)]$

(iv) $p \equiv (p \vee p) \equiv (\sim p \supset p)$

(v) $\sim p \equiv (\sim p \vee \sim p) \equiv (p \supset \sim p)$

8. *Implicative Inferences*

(i) $[(p \supset q) \cdot p] \supset q$ (*modus ponens*)

(ii) $[(p \supset q) \cdot \sim q)] \supset \sim p$ (*modus tollens*)

(iii) $[(p \supset q) \cdot p \cdot r] \supset (q \cdot r)$

(iv) $[(p \supset q) \cdot \sim q \cdot r] \supset (\sim p \cdot r)$

(v) $[(p \supset q) \cdot (q \supset r)] \supset (p \supset r)$ (Implicative Series)

9. *Disjunctive Inferences*

(i) $[(p \vee q) \cdot \sim p] \supset q$

(ii) $[(p \otimes q) \cdot \sim p] \supset q$

(iii) $[(p \otimes q) \cdot p] \supset \sim q$

10. *Incompatibility Inference*

$[\sim(p \cdot q) \cdot p] \supset \sim q$

11. *Dilemmatic Inferences*

(i) $[(p \supset q) \cdot (r \supset q) \cdot (p \vee r)] \supset q$ (Simple Constructive)

(ii) $[(p \supset q) \cdot (p \supset r) \cdot (\sim q \vee \sim r)] \supset \sim p$ (Simple Destructive)

(iii) $[(p \supset q) \cdot (r \supset s) \cdot (p \vee r)] \supset (q \vee s)$ (Complex Constructive)

(iv) $[(p \supset q) \cdot (r \supset s) \cdot (\sim q \vee \sim s)] \supset (\sim p \vee \sim r)$ (Complex Destructive)

II. Logic of Propositional Functions

1. *All Laws and Inferences of Logic of Propositions*

2. *Laws of Contradiction*

(i) $\sim(x)(fx \supset gx) \equiv (Ex)(fx \cdot \sim gx)$

(ii) $\sim(Ex)(fx \cdot gx) \equiv (x)(fx \supset \sim gx)$

(iii) $\sim(Ei)\,fx \equiv (Ei)\sim fx$

3. *Law of Application*

$$[(x)\,(fx \supset gx)\cdot(Ex)\,fx] \supset (Ex)\,gx$$

4. *Representative Inferences*

   (i) $[(x)\,(fx \supset gx)\cdot(Ex)\,(hx \cdot fx)] \supset (Ex)\,(hx \cdot gx)$

   (ii) $[(x)\,(fx \supset gx)\cdot(Ei)\,(hx \cdot fx)] \supset (Ei)\,(hx \cdot gx)$

   (iii) $[(x)\,(fx \vee gx)\cdot(Ei)\sim fx] \supset (Ei)\,gx$

   (iv) $[(x)\sim(fx \cdot gx)\cdot(Ei)\,fx] \supset (Ei)\sim gx$

5. *Implicative Series*

$$(x)\,\{[(fx \supset gx)\cdot(gx \supset hx)] \supset (fx \supset hx)\}$$

III. Logic of Classes

1. *Laws of the Universe Class and the Null Class*

   (i) $u = \bar{0}$ (vi) $a + 0 = a$

   (ii) $0 = a\bar{a}$ (vii) $a + u = u$

   (iii) $u = a + \bar{a}$ (viii) $(a = u) \equiv (\bar{a} = 0)$

   (iv) $a\,(0) = 0$ (ix) $(a \neq u) \equiv (\bar{a} \neq 0)$

   (v) $a\,(u) = a$

2. *Laws of Association*

   (i) $a\,(bc) = (ab)\,c$

   (ii) $a + (b + c) = (a + b) + c$

3. *Laws of Commutation*

   (i) $ab = ba$

   (ii) $a + b = b + a$

   (iii) $(a = b) \equiv (b = a)$

   (iv) $(a \neq b) \equiv (b \neq a)$

4. *Laws of Distribution*

   (i) $a\,(b + c) = ab + ac$

   (ii) $a + (bc) = (a + b)\,(a + c)$

5. *Law of Double Negation*

$$a = \bar{\bar{a}}$$

6. *DeMorgan's Laws*

   (i) $-(ab) = \bar{a} + \bar{b}$

   (ii) $-(a + b) = \bar{a}\bar{b}$

7. *Laws of Contradiction*

(i) $\sim(a = 0) \equiv a \neq 0$

(ii) $\sim(a \neq 0) \equiv a = 0$

(iii) $\sim(s \in a) \equiv s \in \bar{a}$

8. *Laws of Contrariety*

(i) $[(a\bar{b} = 0 \cdot a \neq 0)] \supset \sim(ab = 0)$

(ii) $[(ab = 0 \cdot a \neq 0)] \supset \sim(a\bar{b} = 0)$

(iii) $a = 0 \supset \sim(s \in a)$

(iv) $s \in a \supset \sim(a = 0)$

9. *Laws of Subcontrariety*

(i) $[\sim(a\bar{b} \neq 0) \cdot a \neq 0] \supset ab \neq 0$

(ii) $[\sim(ab \neq 0) \cdot a \neq 0] \supset a\bar{b} \neq 0$

10. *Laws of Subalternation*

(i) $(a\bar{b} = 0 \cdot a \neq 0) \supset ab \neq 0$

(ii) $(ab = 0 \cdot a \neq 0) \supset a\bar{b} \neq 0$

11. *Laws Useful in Symbolic Expansion Test*

(i) $a = (ab + a\bar{b}) = (abc + ab\bar{c} + a\bar{b}c + a\bar{b}\bar{c})$

(ii) $a = 0 \supset ab = 0$

(iii) $ab \neq 0 \supset a \neq 0$

(iv) $s \in ab \supset s \in a$

IV. Rules of Derivation

In the following rules, the term *symbolic expression* refers to any symbolized proposition, propositional function, class, or any logically permissable combination of these, including conjunctions, implications, equivalences, products, sums, identities, and so on. *Elementary symbolic expression,* on the other hand, refers only to the symbolization of a single proposition, propositional function, or class. When a symbolic expression is considered as exhibiting validity, invalidity, consistency, or inconsistency, it is called a *formula.* (Thus any of the laws or inferences given above are valid formulas.) With these meanings in mind, and assuming, first, (for the sake of simplicity) that no cross-application between logics is made, and, second, that no greater precision of statement is demanded than has been achieved throughout this text, we may formulate two important rules of derivation in the following way:

1. *Rule of Replacement*

Any symbolic expression can replace a logically *equivalent* or *identical* symbolic expression in a formula without changing the validity, invalidity, consistency, or inconsistency of that formula.

2. *Rule of Substitution*

Any symbolic expression in the logic of propositions or classes can be substituted for an *elementary* symbolic expression in a formula without changing the validity or inconsistency of that formula, provided the same substitution is made for each occurrence of the symbolic expression throughout the formula.

(The logic of propositional functions has not been developed far enough in this text to permit a formulation of its rule of substitution.)

APPENDIX B

ANSWERS TO SELECTED EXERCISES

Part II

Chapter 13.

6. $\sim D/$ this brain will not develop; $\sim P/$ its body does not produce brain cells.

$$[(\sim P \supset \sim D) \cdot \sim D] \supset \sim P$$

19. $J/$ justice is to do good to friends and evil to enemies; $I/$ it is just to injure some one.

$$[(J \supset I) \cdot \sim I] \supset \sim J$$

Chapter 15.

4. $M/$ he had a strong motive; $C/$ he committed the murder.

$$[(C \supset M) \cdot {\sim}C] \supset {\sim}M$$

14. $S/$ a ship can enter safely; $P/$ its pilot knows the bay.

$$[(S \supset P) \cdot P] \supset S$$

Chapter 16.

6. $S/$ sulphur dioxide results from the ignition of certain sulphides; $A/$ sulphur dioxide results from the ignition of certain sulphates.

$$(S \vee A)$$

14. $H/$ the wife were (was) a better housekeeper; $P/$ the husband were (was) more patient; $S/$ the marriage would have been a success.

$$(H \vee P) \supset S$$

30. $L/$ you look; $Y/$ you listen; $H/$ you hear life murmur; $S/$ you see it glisten.

$$(L \vee Y) \supset (H \vee S)$$

Chapter 17.

4. $I/$ I am mixed up; $Y/$ you are mixed up.

$$[(I \vee Y) \cdot {\sim}I] \supset Y$$

Chapter 18.

6. $L/$ the precipitate is lead chloride; $D/$ it dissolves.

$${\sim}(L \cdot {\sim}D)$$

15. $R/$ the car runs; $G/$ it has gas.

$${\sim}(R \cdot {\sim}G)$$

22. *S/* Schopenhauer's theories are true; *N/* Nietszche's theories are true.

$$\sim(S \cdot N)$$

Chapter 19.

8. *A/* Jim is alert at his job; *N/* he stays up all night.

$$[\sim(A \cdot N) \cdot \sim N] \supset A$$

Chapter 20.

5. *C/* conditions are just right; *F/* he flies.

$$(R \vee \sim F) = (\sim R \supset \sim F) = (F \supset R) = \sim(\sim R \cdot F)$$

Chapter 21.

5. *S/* a radio station serves the public; *G/* it is a force for good; *A/* it takes little advertising; *M/* it makes no money.

$$[(S \supset G) \cdot A \cdot M \cdot S] \supset A \cdot M \cdot G$$

12. *B/* he believes that everything makes for the best; *O/* he is an optimist; *P/* he is a pessimist.

$$[(\sim B \supset \sim O) \cdot \sim O \cdot P] \supset \sim B \cdot P$$

Chapter 22.

6. *M/* the minority is willing to accept the majority decision; *R/* the majority respects the rights of the minority; *D/* there can be no democracy.

$$[(\sim M \supset \sim D) \cdot (\sim R \supset \sim M)] \supset (\sim R \supset \sim D)$$

18. *W/* the end of an action is wisely chosen; *C/* the consequences are taken into consideration (judged); *P/*pleasure, only, is taken as an end.

$$[(W \supset C) \cdot (P \supset \sim C)] \supset (P \supset \sim W)$$

Chapter 23.

    4. $F/$ poetry is false; $M/$ poetry is misleading (deceptive); $H/$ poetry is disguised history.

$$[(F \supset M) \cdot (\sim F \supset H)] \supset (M \vee H)$$

$$= (\sim M \supset \sim F) \cdot (\sim F \supset H)] \supset (\sim M \supset H)$$

    5. $E/$ a person enjoys his work; $B/$ he does his best; $R/$ he's the right person for the job.

$$[(E \vee \sim B) \cdot (R \supset B)] \supset \sim(R \cdot \sim E)$$

$$[(R \supset B) \cdot (B \supset E)] \supset (R \supset E)$$

Chapter 24.

    6. $E/$ Podunk Center is east of Metropolis; $W/$ it is west of Metropolis.

$$\sim(E \cdot W), \text{ but not } (E \vee W): \text{ Contraries.}$$

    7. $\sim(E \cdot \sim E) \cdot (E \vee \sim E)$: Contradictories.

    8. $(\sim E \vee \sim W)$, but not $\sim(\sim E \cdot \sim W)$: Subcontraries.

    15. $C/$ he is president of the CIO; $N/$ he is president of the NAM.

$$\sim(C \cdot N), \text{ but not } (C \vee N): \text{ Contraries.}$$

    18. $A/$ he drinks alcoholic beverages; $N/$ he drinks non-alcoholic beverages.

$$(A \vee N), \text{ but not } \sim(A \cdot N): \text{ Subcontraries.}$$

    21. $B/$ he believes that God exists; $\sim B/$ he does not believe that God exists.

$$\sim(B \cdot \sim B) \cdot (B \vee \sim B): \text{ Contradictories.}$$

    22. $B/$ he believes that God exists; $N/$ he believes that God does not exist.

$$\sim(B \cdot N), \text{ but not } (B \vee N): \text{ Contraries.}$$

    25. $C/$ it is colored; $\sim R/$ it is not red.

$(C \mathbf{v} \sim R)$ but not $\sim(C \cdot \sim R)$: Subcontraries.

B. 1 and 3, and 2 and 4 are contradictories.
1 and 2 are contraries.
3 and 4 are subcontraries.

Chapter 25.

1. $K/$ I move my knight; $B/$ my bishop will be captured; $C/$ my knight will be captured.

$$[(K \supset B) \cdot (\sim K \supset C) \cdot (K \mathbf{v} \sim K)] \supset (B \mathbf{v} C)$$

2. $L/$ it makes me grow larger; $G/$ I can get into the garden; $S/$ it makes me grow smaller.

$$[(L \supset G) \cdot (S \supset G) \cdot (L \mathbf{v} S)] \supset G$$

4. $B/$ a person is boastful; $T/$ he talks about himself; $H/$ he is timid.

$$[(B \supset T) \cdot (H \supset \sim T) \cdot (\sim T \mathbf{v} T)] \supset (\sim B \mathbf{v} \sim H)$$

11. $P/$ people proceed as if a depression were going to occur; $D/$ a depression is produced (comes); $\sim P/$ they proceed as as if a depression were not going to occur.

$$[(P \supset D) \cdot (\sim P \supset D) \cdot (P \mathbf{v} \sim P)] \supset D$$

14. $C/$ he is a citizen; $V/$ he votes to change the constitution.

$$[(C \supset \sim V) \cdot (\sim C \supset \sim V) \cdot (C \mathbf{v} \sim C)] \supset \sim V$$

Chapter 27.

A. 2.

p	q	$p \mathbf{v} q$	$\sim(p \mathbf{v} q)$
T	T	T	F
T	F	T	F
F	T	T	F
F	F	F	T

A. 10.

p	q	$p \supset q$	$q \supset p$	$(p \supset q) \equiv (q \supset p)$
T	T	T	T	T
T	F	F	T	F
F	T	T	F	F
F	F	T	T	T

B. 3. *Doubtful* (The first conjunct is true while the second is doubtful. Thus, since a conjunction is true only when all conjuncts are true, the truth-value of this conjunction depends upon the doubtful conjunct.)

B. 9. *Doubtful* (If the antecedent is true, then the truth-value of the implication depends upon the consequent, which in this case is doubtful.)

B. 11. *True* (A true consequent is implied by any antecedent.)

Chapter 28.

D.   ($L/$ It's love; $I/$ It's insanity)

(1) L	I	$\sim L$	$\sim I$	(2) $L \vee I$	(3) $L \cdot I$	(4) $\sim L \vee \sim I$
T	T	F	F	T	T	F
T	F	F	T	T	F	T
F	T	T	F	T	F	T
F	F	T	T	F	F	T

D. 1. A comparison of Columns (2) and (3) reveals that $L \cdot I$ implies $L \vee I$, but that the propositions are not equivalent.

D. 4. The propositions $L \vee I$ and $\sim L \vee \sim I$, as defined in Columns (2) and (4), do not imply each other in either direction, but are consistent.

D. 5. Columns (1) and (2) show that L implies $L \vee I$, but that the reverse implication does not hold.

Chapter 29.

1. ($G/$ Nietzsche was a genius; $M/$ Nietzsche was a madman)

$$[(G \lor M) \cdot M] \supset \sim G$$

$$[(T \lor T) \cdot T] \supset \quad F$$

$$(T \quad \cdot T) \supset \quad F$$

$$T \quad \supset \quad F$$

$$F \quad \text{(Invalid)}$$

2. (S/ Astrology is scientific; T/ Astrology is a superstition)

$$[(S \lor T) \cdot S] \supset \sim T$$

$$[(T \lor T) \cdot T] \supset \quad F$$

$$(F \quad \cdot T) \supset \quad F$$

$$F \supset \quad F$$

$$T \quad \text{(Valid)}$$

Part III

Chapter 35.

2. Dx/x is a person at the door; Kx/x knocks.

$$[(x) \ (Dx \supset Kx) \cdot (Ex)Kx] \supset (Ex) \ Dx$$

7. Ax/x is a person arrested for picketing; Ox/x lives in a city with an anti-picketing ordinance.

$$[(x) \ (Ax \supset Ox) \cdot (Ex)Ax] \supset (Ex)Ox$$

15. Px/x is a pleasure in what destroys society (is destructive of human values); Sx/x should be encouraged.

$$[(x) \ (Px \supset \sim Sx) \cdot (Ex)Px] \supset (Ex) \sim Sx$$

18. Bx/x believes in white supremacy; Vx/x votes for Smith.

$$[(x) \ (\sim Bx \supset \sim Vx) \cdot (Ex)Vx] \supset (Ex)Bx$$

Chapter 36.

4. Ex/x is a man who escapes from prison; Vx/x violates the laws; Sx/S is Socrates.

$$[(x)\ (Ex \supset Vx) \cdot (Ei)Sx \cdot \sim Vx] \supset (Ei)Sx \cdot \sim Ex$$

8. Ix/x is a man with an inquiring mind; Ux/x wants to inquire further at a University; Sx/x is Mr. Smith.

$$[(x)\ (Ix \supset Ux) \cdot (Ei)Sx \cdot \sim Ux] \supset (Ei)Sx \cdot \sim Ix$$

Chapter 37.

1. Tx/x is a student eligible to play on the football team; Sx/x is a student who keeps up in his studies; Ex/x is a student who flunks economics.

$$[(x)\ (Tx \supset Sx) \cdot (Ex \supset \sim Sx)] \supset (Ex \supset \sim Tx)$$

$$[(x)\ (Ex \supset \sim Sx) \cdot (\sim Sx \supset \sim Tx)] \supset (Ex \supset \sim Tx)$$

4. Sx/x is a triangle with equal sides; Ax/x is a triangle with the opposite angles equal; Ix/x is an isoceles triangle.

$$(x)\ [(Sx \supset Ax) \cdot (Ix \supset Sx)] \supset (Ix \supset Ax)$$

14. Sx/x is what seems true to any individual; Tx/x is true; Mx/x is the theory that might is right.

$$[(x)\ (Sx \supset Tx) \cdot (Ei)Mx \cdot Sx] \supset (Ei)Mx \cdot Tx$$

15. Sx/x is the sum of the angles of a Euclidean triangle; Tx/x is equal to two right angles; Px/x is the sum of the angles of a physical triangle.

$$(x)\ [(Sx \supset Tx) \cdot (Px \supset \sim Tx)] \supset (Px \supset \sim Sx)$$

$$= (x)\ [(Px \supset \sim Tx) \cdot (\sim Tx \supset \sim Sx)] \supset (Px \supset \sim Sx)$$

20. Ax/x is art; Bx/x brushes aside conventional generalities; Cx/x is comedy.

$$(x)\ [(Ax \supset Bx) \cdot (Cx \supset \sim Bx)] \supset (Cx \supset \sim Ax)$$

Chapter 38.

3. Rx/x is one who rushes from one activity to another; Tx/x does much thinking; Sx/x is Mr. Smith.

$$[(x) \sim (Rx \cdot Tx) \cdot (Ei)Sx \cdot \sim Rx] \supset (Ei)Sx \cdot Tx$$

$$= [(x) \ (Rx \supset \sim Tx) \cdot (Ei)Sx \cdot \sim Rx] \supset (Ei)Sx \cdot Tx$$

4. Tx/x is one who does a thing; Dx/x has a desire to do it; Mx/x is Mary.

$$[(x) \ (Tx \lor \sim Dx) \cdot (Ei)Mx \cdot Tx] \supset (Ei)Mx \cdot Dx$$

$$= [(x) \ (\sim Tx \supset \sim Dx) \cdot (Ei)Mx \cdot Tx] \supset (Ei)Mx \cdot Dx$$

12. Px/x is a watch which has been pawned; Nx/x is a watch with pawnbroker's numbers scratched on it.

$$[(x) \ (Nx \supset Px) \cdot (Ei)Nx] \supset (Ei)Px$$

18. Px/x is a person who pursues wrong ends in life; Kx/x is a person who knows the right ends; Wx/x is a person who is weak-willed; Sx/x is Mr. Smith.

$$\{(x) \ [Px \supset (\sim Kx \lor Wx)] \cdot (Ei)Sx \cdot Px \cdot \sim Wx\} \supset (Ei)Sx \cdot \sim Kx$$

Suggestion: Solve this exercise in two steps. In the first step, use $(Ei)Sx \cdot Px$ as the second premise.

20. Ax/x is a work of art; Ux/x is unified by a vital principle; Mx/x is a mechanical drawing.

$$(x) \ [(Ax \supset Ux) \cdot (Mx \supset \sim Ux)] \supset (Mx \supset \sim Ax)$$

$$= (x) \ [(Mx \supset \sim Ux) \cdot (\sim Ux \supset \sim Ax)] \supset (Mx \supset \sim Ax)$$

Part IV

Chapter 42.

2. YD; 6. $\bar{D}$; 10. $\bar{D}Y$; 16. $Y + M$

Chapter 43.

2. $L = D$; 3. BD; 5. $s \, \varepsilon \, BD$; 9. $B \neq L$

Chapter 44.

3. $H = 0$; 4. $s \, \varepsilon \, SA$; 11. $\bar{H} \neq 0$; 12. $t \, \varepsilon \, H\bar{S}$

Chapter 47.

7. $C\bar{P} = 0$; 8. $JC = 0$; 11. $R\bar{P} = 0$; 15. $M\bar{R} = 0$

Chapter 48.

4. $s \, \varepsilon \, NS$ (compound singular affirmative);
5. $LT \neq 0$ (compound particular affirmative—$L/$ biologists; $T/$ botanists);
6. $Z\bar{M} \neq 0$ (compound particular negative);
7. $A\bar{P} = 0$ (compound universal affirmative).

Chapter 49.

3. $s \, \varepsilon \, S$ (simple singular affirmative);
4. $S\bar{T} \neq 0$ (compound particular negative);
5. $CT \neq 0 \cdot C\bar{T} \neq 0$ (conjunctive particular);
10. $\overline{FM} = 0 \cdot FM = 0$ (exceptive—conjunctive universal);
11. $B\bar{U} = 0 \cdot U\bar{B} = 0$ (or: $B = U$; coextensive class—conjunctive universal).

Chapter 51.

B. 2. *Invalid.* (The cross for membership in a must be entered on the line between $a\bar{b}$ and ab on a Venn diagram, showing that such membership may be in either class or in both classes.)

7. *Valid.* (If $a\bar{b}$ is empty, then the membership in a must necessarily be located in ab.)

C. 1. $(b = 0) \supset (ab = 0)$. *Valid.*
3. $(a\bar{b} = 0) \supset (b\bar{a} = 0)$. *Invalid.*
5. $[(a\bar{b} = 0) \cdot (b\bar{a} = 0)] \supset (b\bar{a} = 0)$. *Valid.*

Chapter 52.

3. $(D\overline{\overline{H}} \neq 0) \supset (DH \neq 0)$. *Valid.*
5. $(s \, \varepsilon \, \overline{\overline{G}}) \supset (s \, \varepsilon \, G)$. *Valid.*

Chapter 53.

B. 1. *Deducible*, because the inference $(H\bar{A} = 0) \supset (\overline{\overline{AH}} = 0)$ is valid.

Chapter 54.

A. 2. *True*, because the inference $[(FH = 0) \cdot (F \neq 0)] \supset (F\bar{H} \neq 0)$ is valid.

B. 2. *Subalternate*.

C. 2. *Doubtful*, because $\sim(FH = 0) \equiv (FH \neq 0)$ is valid, while $(FH \neq 0) \supset (F\bar{H} \neq 0)$ is invalid. Or, more directly, $(F\bar{H} \neq 0) \supset (FH = 0)$ is invalid.

D. 2. Patent tautology.

E. 2. $F\bar{H} \neq 0$ is deducible from, but not equivalent to, $FH = 0 \cdot F \neq 0$.

Chapter 55.

2. $(F\bar{E} = 0 \cdot AF = 0) \supset AE = 0$. *Invalid*.

3. $(E\bar{F} = 0 \cdot AF = 0) \supset AE = 0$. *Valid*.

Chapter 56.

3. $A/$ associates with communists; $C/$ communists; $F/$ FBI men $(A\bar{C} = 0 \cdot FA \neq 0) \supset FC \neq 0$. *Valid*.

4. $M/$ men; $D/$ degraded; $N/$ noble; $(M\bar{D} = 0 \cdot M\bar{N} = 0 \cdot M \neq 0) \supset DN \neq 0$. *Valid*.

Chapter 59.

B. 2. $GLC = 0$ implies, but is not implied by, $GLPC = 0$, as may easily be seen in the expanded inference: $(GLPC + GL\bar{P}C = 0) \supset GLPC = 0$.

INDEX

INDEX

Abbreviations: class 256; propositional 74f.; singular 257. *See also* Variables

Accent, fallacy of 51f.

Ad hominem 33f.; constructive 33; destructive 33f.

Affirmative propositions 284ff.; existential 304ff.; particular 292ff.; singular 292, 295ff.; universal 286ff. *See also* Obversion

Ambiguity, fallacies of 49ff. *See also* Equivocation

Amphiboly 52f.

Antecedent 81f.; denying the 90, 220

Application, law of 218f., 377

Argument, *see* Inference

Aristotle 4, 21, 144, 198, 255

Associative laws 279, 375, 377

Authority, fallacies of 38ff.; misplaced 42f.; misrepresented 44f.

Axioms 370

Begging the question 55ff.

Bentham, Jeremy 45f.

Circular reasoning, fallacy of 58ff.

Class: abbreviations 256; complementary 257f.; identity 265f.; logic 255ff.; membership 257, 267; nonidentity 266ff.; products 259ff.; sum 262ff.; variables 256. *See also* Universe class, Null class

Coextensive-class propositions 265f., 300f.

Commutative laws 78, 104f., 278f., 311, 320, 375, 377. *See also* Conversion

Complex question, fallacy of 55f.

Complexity of propositions 282f. *See also* Compound, Conjunctive, and Simple propositions

Composition, fallacy of 50; converse fallacy of 51

Compound inferences 311

Compound propositions 282f.

Conclusion 3f., 14, 67, 70ff., 310; irrelevant 36; suppressed 344f.; terms indicating 91, 314. *See also* Inference

Condition 81f.; necessary 36, 83, 95; sufficient 36, 82

Conjunction 76f.; negation of 113; truth-table definition 161, 169

Conjunctive class, *see* Class product

Conjunctive propositions: in class logic 282f.; coextensive class 300f.; exceptive 301ff.; mixed 304ff.; particular 298ff.; pure 298ff.

Connotation, *see* Intension

Consequent 81f.; affirming the 90, 220

Consistency, Inconsistency 160; of deductive systems 370; truth-table test for 172ff.

Constructive dilemma 149f.

Contingency 277, 282

Contradiction, Contradictory 212ff., 324ff.; laws of 144, 376ff.
Contraposition 320ff.
Contrariety, Contrary 144f., 214, 324, 326f.; laws of 378
Converse fallacy 46; of authority 46f.; of composition 51
Conversion, Converse 320ff.
Counterimplication 83f., 123; laws of 375
Crowd, appeal to 34f.

Decision procedure 160, 168, 176f., 356. *See also* Symbolic expansion, Truth-table, Validity, Venn diagram
Deductive logic 4ff., 185, 373f.; and truth-tables 160
Deductive systems 370f.
Definition 16, 18, 370; Aristotelian 21f., 24, 29, 271; circular 25f.; extraneous 28f.; fallacies of 24ff.; figurative 27f.; genetic 20f.; incongruous 24f.; negative 20f.; nominal 19f.; obscure 27f.; operational 22f.; ostensive 18f.; question-begging 56ff; synonymous 19
DeMorgan's laws 105, 114, 124, 183, 279f., 375, 377
Denial, *see* Negation
Denotation, *see* Extension
Derivation, rules of 378f.
Descriptive language 8ff., 369f.
Destructive dilemma 150f.
Dewey, John 372f.
Dilemma 148ff., 376; constructive 149f.; destructive 150f.; and implicative series 152
Directive language 8ff., 369f.

Disguised conclusion, fallacy of 56
Disjunction 100ff., 209; in implicative series 139f.; inferences based on 107ff., 235, 376; negation of 105; truth-table definition of 162, 169; weak and strong 102f.
Disjunctive class, *see* Class sum
Distributive laws 280, 377
Division, fallacy of 51
Dogmatic authority 39ff.
Double negation laws 76, 278, 316ff., 320ff. *See also* Contraposition, Obversion

Emotive language 8ff., 369f.
Enthymeme, *see* Telescoped inference
Equivalence 95f., 122ff.; in class logic 311f., testing for by truthtable method 171; truth-table definition of 165f. *See also* Inference, reciprocal
Equivalents 123ff., 311ff.; counterimplication 123; disjunction 123f.; incompatibility 124; table of 124ff.
Equivocation, fallacy of simple 49f. *See also* Ambiguity
Exceptive propositions 301ff.
Excluded middle, law of 144, 376
Exclusive propositions 208f., 289f.
Existential propositions 201f., 304ff.; affirmative 304ff.; in inferences 217ff., 327ff., 340ff., 364f. *See also* Hypothetical propositions
Expressive language, *see* Emotive language
Extension 14f.; inverse ratio of intension and 16

Fallacies, informal 5, 30ff. *See also* Ambiguity, Authority, Definition, Presumption, Relevance

False cause 35f.

Fixed authority 46

Force, appeal to 31

Formal logic, *see* Deductive logic

Functions of language 7ff., 369f. *See also* Descriptive, Directive, and Emotive language

Galileo 212f.

Generality of propositions 194f., 243

Genetic fallacy 21

Half-truth, fallacy of 52

Hasty generalization, *see* Subalternation

Holmes, Sherlock 68f., 217f., 224

Hypotheses 373

Hypothetical propositions 200f., 205, 305ff. *See also* Existential propositions

Hypothetical syllogism, *see* Implicative series

Identity: of classes 265f.; law of 375

Ignorance, appeal to 32f.

Implication 80ff.; disjunctive equivalent of 123f.; incompatibility equivalent of 123f.; and inference 86f.; inferences based on 87; material 20, 83f.; mutual 163; truth-table definition of 162ff., 169.; in universal propositions 200f.

Implication-in-reverse 94ff; inferences based on 97ff., 234; in quantified proposition 207f.

Implicative series 133ff., 229f., 376f.; containing disjunction 139f.; containing incompatibility 140. *See also* Dilemma

Incompatibility 113ff.; implicative equivalent of 124; in implicative series 140; inferences based on 118ff., 235 f., 376; in quantified propositions 210

Inductive logic 4f., 185, 372ff.

Inference 3ff., 14, 86, 310; detecting form of 91, 314; equivalence of valid forms of 126f.; and implication 86f.; logical form of 67; pure and mixed 331ff.; reciprocal 311ff., 323; simple and compound 310f. *See also* Deductive logic, Laws of logic, Validity

Informal fallacies, *see* Fallacies, informal

Intension 14f.; inverse ratio of extension and 16; personal and social 15f.

Invalidity, Invalid 41f., 86, 89f., 130, 219f.

Irrelevant conclusion 36

James, William 116

Language, *see* Functions of, Meaning, Normative, Semantics

Laws of logic 371, 375ff.; of class logic 276ff.; equivalence of 126f. *See also* Associative, Commutative, DeMorgan's, Distributive, Double negation, Validity

Laws of thought 375f. *See also* Contradiction, Excluded middle, Identity

Logic 3ff.; of classes 255ff.; of descriptions 369; of identity 369; philosophy of 371; of relations 369; study of 4ff.; symbolic 7, 255, 368. *See also* Deductive, Inductive, Many-valued, Modal logics

Logical form 67ff.

Logistic system 370

Many-valued logics 163, 369

Mathematics 6, 371; symbolism of logic and 262

Meaning 5; kinds of 12ff.; propositional 13ff. *See also* Extension, Functions of language, Intension, Semantics

Membership: class 257, 267; singular 268f. *See also* Class nonidentity, Particular propositions

Mill, J. S. 101f.

Misplaced authority 42f.

Misrepresented authority 44f.

Mixed inference 331ff.

Modal logics 369

Modus ponens (*tollens*) 87f., 219, 376; basic to many inferences 127; shorter truth-table test of 180f.; truth-table test of 168ff.

Mutual implication, *see* Equivalence

Necessary condition 36, 83, 95

Negation 75; of contradictory 144; of conjunction 113; of disjunction 105; law of double 76; truth-table definition of 160f., 169

Negative propositions 284f.; Particular 294.; Singular 292, 296f.; Universal 288f. *See also* Obversion

Normative language 370

Null class 273ff.; interchangeability with universe class 274f., 283; laws of 377

Obversion 316ff.; of universal propositions 316f.; of particular propositions 317f. *See also* Double negation laws

Only if, *see* Implication-in-reverse

"Only" propositions, *see* Exclusive propositions

Opposition 323ff. *See also* Contradiction, Contrariety, Subcontrariety

Parentheses 87n.

Particular propositions 201f., 205f., 210, 283f., 292ff.; affirmative 292ff.; contradictories of 214, 324f.; negative 294f.; obversion of 317f.; subcontrariety of 327f.

Patent tautology 317

Petitio principii, see Circular reasoning

Pity, appeal to 31f.

Plato 7, 108f.

Possibility 115f.

Postulate 370

Pragmatics 371

Predicate 255

Premise 3f., 14, 67, 86, 310; suppressed 155, 238f., 344ff.; terms indicating 91, 314. *See also* Inference

Presumption, fallacies of 55ff.
Primitive symbol 370
Principia Mathematica 6, 83
Propositional functions 198ff.; laws of 376f.
Propositional variables 74f.
Propositions 13, 74; in class logic 265ff.; classification of 282ff., 307f.; contingent 277, 282; generality of 197f., 243; laws of 376. *See also* Affirmative, Complexity, Compound, Conjunctive, Exclusive, Functions of language (descriptive), Meaning, Negative, Particular, Quality, Quantity, Singular, Universal
Psychology 5
Pure inferences 331ff.

Quality of propositions 284; change of 316ff. *See also* Affirmative, Negative propositions, Obversion
Quantification 197ff., 243; improper 220. *See also* Propositional functions
Quantifier 200; particular 202; singular 202f.; universal 201
Quantity 283f. *See also* Particular, Singular, and Universal propositions
Question-begging definition, fallacy of 56ff.

Reasoning 3. *See also* Deductive, Inductive logic, Inference
Reductio ad absurdum 151
Reflective inquiry, *see* Inductive logic

Relevance, fallacies of 30ff.
Replacement, rule of 280, 378f.
Rhetoric 5f.
Rules of derivation 378f.
Russell, Bertrand 6, 20

Scientific methodology, *see* Inductive logic
Semantics 5, 7ff., 371; general 8. *See also* Functions of language, Meaning
Shorter truth-table method 176ff.; limitations of 182f.
Simple inferences 310f.
Simple propositions 282f.
Singular propositions 202f., 218, 283f., 292, 295ff.; contradictory of 214ff., 326; obversion of 318f.
Socrates 7, 108f.
Special pleading, fallacy of 52
Specific variables 74f. *See also* Abbreviations
Standard form propositions 282
Strong disjunction 102f., 162, 169
Subalternation, Subaltern 328; laws of 378
Subcontrariety, Subcontrary 145f., 324, 327f.; laws of 378
Subject 255
Substitution, rule of 378f.
Sufficient condition 32, 82
Superalternation, Superaltern 329
Suppressed premise, *see* Telescoped inference
Sweeping authority, fallacy of 38f.
Syllogism 255, 332
Symbolic expansion 357ff.; laws useful in 378; shorter test 361ff.; test for validity 356ff.
Syntactics 371

Telescoped inference 155ff., 238f., 344ff.; invalid 348; pure and mixed 350

Terms 14ff.; privative 26f. *See also* Definition, Extension, Intension, Predicate, Subject

Term variable 198f.

Theorems 370

Transformation laws 376

Transitivity 133

Truth-function 160. *See also* Truth-table

Truth-table 160ff.; definitions 160ff.; method 168ff.

Truth-value 160; inferences to opposite 324ff. *See also* Many-valued logics, Truth-function, Truth-table

Universal propositions 200f., 204f., 220, 229ff., 283f., 286ff.; affirmative 286ff.; contradictories of 212ff., 324f.; contrariety of 326ff.; exclusive 289f., negative 288f., obversion of 316f.

Universe class 270ff.; interchangeability with null class 274f., 283; laws of 377

Universe of discourse 257, 270ff. *See also* Universe class

Unless 81

Validity, Valid 69ff., 86f., 160, 311; testing: by symbolic expansions 356ff.; by truth-tables 168ff.; by Venn diagrams 312f.; and truth 67ff., 276, 344, 371f. *See also* Decision procedure, Deductive logic, Inference

Variables: class 256; propositional 74f.; singular 257; term 198f.; values of 74f., 256

Venerable authority, fallacy of 45f.

Venn diagram 258; limitations of 264; test for validity 312f.

Weak disjunction 102f., 162, 169

Whitehead, A. N. 6